HANDBOOK OF MOISTURE DETERMINATION AND CONTROL

PRINCIPLES, TECHNIQUES, APPLICATIONS

VOLUME 2

HANDBOOK OF MOISTURE DETERMINATION AND CONTROL

PRINCIPLES, TECHNIQUES, APPLICATIONS

IN FOUR VOLUMES

by A. Pande
Shriram Institute for Industrial Research
Delhi, India

VOLUME 2

MARCEL DEKKER, INC.   New York

COPYRIGHT © 1975 by MARCEL DEKKER, INC. ALL RIGHTS RESERVED

Neither this book nor any part may be reproduced or transmitted in any form or by any means, electronic or mechanical, including photocopying, microfilming, and recording, or by any information storage and retrieval system, without permission in writing from the publisher.

MARCEL DEKKER, INC.

270 Madison Avenue, New York, New York 10016

LIBRARY OF CONGRESS CATALOG CARD NUMBER: 73-86820

ISBN: 0-8247-6185-5

Current printing (last digit):
10 9 8 7 6 5 4 3 2 1

PRINTED IN THE UNITED STATES OF AMERICA

Dedicated to the Memory of

Sir Shri Ram

Industrialist, Philanthropist, Educationist

and Founder of the

Shriram Institute for Industrial Research, Delhi

GENERAL PREFACE

The question of moisture determination and control is an important one in many scientific and industrial disciplines. The available information, however, is scattered through the literature in divers scientific journals. This monograph represents an attempt to create a basic source book to bring these various contributions together as a unit. It also includes for the first time many unpublished results obtained by the author and his associates during the course of their investigations. Many scientific disciplines (for instance chemistry, physics, statistics, and electronics) are covered and are synthesized in the techniques of moisture determination and control.

The four-volume monograph discusses the phenomena of moisture sorption, total versus 'free water' and 'bound water' effects, equilibrium relative humidity-moisture content relationship and describes most of the physicochemical methods and techniques with the latest developments in moisture determination and control in various materials such as food stuffs, cereals, grains, textiles, bagasse, pulp, paper and paper products, coal, coke, chemicals (even in the ppm range) and biological materials.

The monograph is broadly divided into two groups, i.e., methods and techniques and their applications. A certain amount of overlapping could not be avoided as specific applications had to be described to illustrate the effectiveness of a particular method or technique. These methods and techniques were developed independently by research workers in their own fields, often unaware of similar work in other fields. All of these have been compiled for the sake of completeness of the state of the art.

It is believed the value of the monograph has been enhanced to a large extent due to the indexing and bibliography provided in Volume 4 to facilitate the location and extraction of information. The latest pertinent references to the original publications and illustrations have been provided for further study of this fascinating field. It is earnestly hoped that the book will serve the purpose for which it has been compiled.

Any suggestion for the improvement of the monograph would be highly appreciated.

A. Pande

Shriram Institute
Delhi (INDIA)
September, 1974.

PREFACE TO VOLUME 2

This volume, consisting of four chapters (V through VIII), covers physical methods of moisture determination and control. Chapter V first describes the basic electrical properties of water such as conductivity, dielectric constant, and dielectric loss, upon which a number of electrical and electronic moisture meters are based. After discussing the electrical properties in some detail, various types of electric and electronic moisture meters are described, their merits and deficiencies are compared, and important applications of these instruments are described. In addition to the usual electric or electronic moisture meters (known as resistance- or capacitance-type moisture meters), the microwave moisture meter (recently developed and applied to a few materials) is treated at some length. Novel methods and techniques of moisture measurement using sonic and ultrasonic devices are cited and typical examples in scientific and technological fields are critically examined. Electrolytical moisture meters which are capable of measuring moisture content in the ppm range are also described and references are provided for further study. Some of the research work done by the author and his associates which have not been published heretofore are included in this chapter.

Chapter VI covers infrared spectroscopic and mass spectrometric methods of moisture determination and control. First, a general theory of infrared absorption is described. This is followed by the techniques of instrumentation. As there is a considerable body of literature available on the instrumentation of infrared spectoscopy, only a brief description of the basic outline of the double-beam infrared spectrometer is provided; however, copious references are given for further study. Typical examples of the applications of infrared spectroscopy for moisture determination in the near, medium, and far infrared regions are given and some of the applications of this technique for the continuous monitoring of moisture in chemical processings are discussed and critically evaluated.

Concluding this section, there is a short discussion of attenuated total reflection technique together with some suggested applications. Trace water analyzers for process steam utilizing infrared technique are described and the future possibilities of this technique are discussed. A novel application of infrared spectroscopy for measuring the quality of steam is described in which the measurement of the water content of steam gives an estimate of the quality of steam, i.e., its energy potential. A brief description of the measurement of moisture in the upper atmosphere (stratosphere) is provided, wherein these instruments are flown in balloons up to heights of 15 to 20 kilometers. Finally another important and novel application of infrared spectroscopy for the analysis of heavy water in a mixture of heavy and light water is described.

The second part of this chapter describes the mass spectrometric method of moisture measurement. First a short description of the double-beam focusing mass spectrometer is provided, after which an ion resonance mass spectrometer is described. Important applications of mass spectroscopy for the estimation of trace quantities of water in a mixture of organic chemicals are discussed and a table is provided showing the applications of this technique in a number of organic chemicals. References to the latest literature are provided for further study.

Chapter VII describes nuclear methods and techniques of moisture determination and control. The chapter begins with a discussion of the theory of NMR spectroscopy. This is followed by a description of the NMR broad and high resolution spectrometer, as well as a brief description of commercial NMR instruments and analyzers. The instrumentation section contains a short description of the interpretation of NMR spectra. Specific applications of this NMR method and technique for the measurement of moisture content of materials such as grains and chemicals are discussed. A novel, continuous method of moisture determination, known as the continuous process analyzer, is described. This NMR technique has also been applied to the continuous monitoring of light water in a mixture of light and heavy water. A detailed description of this technique is provided and examples of the trace determinations in the field of heavy water analysis are cited.

Some of the applications of NMR for the study of the absorption phenomona of moisture using spin-echo technique are briefly mentioned. Finally, the advantages and disadvantages of this technique and the present status of the method are examined.

In the second part of this chapter neutron scattering methods and techniques are covered, beginning with the basic principle of this method, and followed by details of instrumentation. Two types of neutron moisture meters, i.e., surface type as well as depth type and portable neutron moisture meters for field operations are described. Procedures for the calibration of the neutron scattering analyzer for use in the field are discussed and a correlation with the laboratory data has been attempted.

The application of this technique for the determination of moisture in soils and similar materials follows. A specific application of this technique for well logging (for which purpose this technique was specifically developed) is described in some detail. This method has also been used for measuring traces of light water in heavy water. A brief description of this application and its comparison with the NMR method follow. Finally the merits and shortcomings of this method for moisture determination and control are weighed.

Chapter VIII details the methods and techniques of automatic control of moisture in industrial processings. As there are a number of books and papers published on this subject, only brief descriptions of the fundamentals of automatic control and basic units of the automatic control system are provided. Other modes of control such as pneumatic, electric, and hydraulic are noted. The control of the speed of an electric motor (on which the well-known Ward-Leonard control system is based) is briefly described and thyratron-controlled dc and ac motor control systems are discussed. Some of the unpublished work of the author dealing with the control of the speed of a motor in a dryer is included in this chapter.

After describing the phenomena of automatic control and the devices employed for achieving this control, the applications of these devices in textile, paper, and wood shaving processing, and in the production of lumber, timber and veneer are detailed. Some of the important applications of the automatic control of moisture in the food industry as well as in cottonseed processing are discussed. Finally the economics of the automatic control of moisture is discussed. The evaluation of the savings in steam consumption in an industry is given as a specific example.

The author gratefully acknowledges the cooperation received from scientists working in this field who provided him with the reprints of their publications which have been included in this monograph. The author is specially thankful to editors and publishers of the following journals and books who gave permission for the reproduction of illustrations from their publications. These are J. Colloid Sci.; J.S.I.R. India; Text. Res. J.; J. Text. Inst.; Anal. Chem.; J. Polymer Sci.; Electronic Eng.; Can. J. Res.; J. Opt. Soc.; J. Sci. Instrum.; Carnegie Institute Washington Publication; Ind. Eng. Chem.; J. Appl. Phys.; Brit. J. Appl. Phys.; J. Phys. Chem.; Soil Sci. of America; Melliand Textilber.; Textile Manufacture and Reinhold Publishing Corporation.

The author is thankful to manufacturers of moisture measuring and controlling instruments and equipments who provided technical literature with illustrations. These are Associated Electrical Industries, U.K.; Consolidated Electrodynamics Corporation, U.S.A.; Schlumberger Corporation, U.S.A.; Japan Electron Optics Laboratory

PREFACE TO VOLUME 2   xi

(JEOL); Tata Institute of Fundamental Research; Nuclear Enterprises U.K.; George Kent Ltd., England; Honeywell Inc., U.S.A.; Bradford Dryers Association U.K.; Electronova S.A. Switzerland; USDA Forest Products Laboratory, Madison, Wisconsin, U.S.A.

The author gratefully acknowledges the help given by Dr. C. S. Pande during the preparation of Chapters V, VI, VII, and VIII which are physics and electronics oriented.

The author is thankful to Dr. Charat Ram for giving permission to publish this monograph and to dedicate it to Sir Shri Ram, founder of the Institute. The author is thankful to Dr. John Mitchell, Jr., Manager, Research and Development Division, E. I. du Pont de Nemours & Co., who kindly reviewed the manuscript and made very useful suggestions. Thanks are due to Mr. Ashok K. Sadhu for giving help in the literature survey of this Volume. Thanks are also due to Mr. P. M. Goel who typed the entire manuscript so skillfully.

Finally the author is very grateful to the publisher and his editorial staff who gave unflinching cooperation during the publication of this monograph.

A. Pande

Shriram Institute
Delhi (INDIA)
November, 1974

CONTENTS

GENERAL PREFACE	v
PREFACE TO VOLUME 2	vii
CONTENTS OF OTHER VOLUMES	xv
CHAPTER V. ELECTRICAL AND ELECTRONIC METHODS	267
1 Electrical Techniques	267
2 Sonic and Ultrasonic Techniques	316
3 Microwave Method	320
4 Electrolytic Method	334
5 Conclusion	340
References	341
CHAPTER VI. SPECTROSCOPIC METHODS AND TECHNIQUES	345
1 Infrared Spectroscopy	345
2 Mass-Spectrometric Method of Moisture Measurement	393
References	403
CHAPTER VII. NUCLEAR METHODS AND TECHNIQUES	409
1 Nuclear Magnetic Resonance Method of Moisture Determination	409
2 Neutron-Scattering Method of Moisture Measurement	472
3 Conclusion	495
References	497

CHAPTER VIII. AUTOMATIC CONTROL OF MOISTURE		505
1	Introduction	505
2	Fundamentals of Automatic Control	506
3	Automatic Control System	509
4	Applications of Automatic Control of Moisture	532
5	Economics of Automatic Control of Moisture	578
	References	583

Cumulative Indexes will appear at the end of Volume 4.

CONTENTS OF OTHER VOLUMES

VOLUME 1

Chapter I   Water, Its Properties and Interaction with Hygroscopic Materials
Chapter II   Gravimetric Methods and Techniques
Chapter III   Azeotropic Distillation and Chromatographic Methods and Techniques
Chapter IV   Karl Fischer Method and Its Applications

VOLUME 3

Chapter IX   Moisture in Textiles
Chapter X   Moisture in Bagasse, Wood, and Paper
Chapter XI   Moisture in Foods and Allied Agricultural Products
Chapter XII   Moisture in Soils, Sands, Concrete, Silica, and Silicates

VOLUME 4

Chapter XIII Moisture in Coals and Similar Materials
Chapter XIV   Moisture in Chemicals and Their End Products
Chapter XV   Moisture in Biological and Biochemical Materials

Chapter V

ELECTRICAL AND ELECTRONIC METHODS

1 ELECTRICAL TECHNIQUES

1.1 Introduction

Methods of moisture measurement can be broadly classified into two groups: direct (chemical) and indirect (physical) methods. In direct methods, moisture is normally removed from the material by oven drying, desiccation, distillation, and other physicochemical techniques, and its quantity found by weighing or by observing changes in the pressure or temperature. Techniques based on these principles, which are usually employed in the laboratory, have a high degree of accuracy and in most cases (with proper precautions in sampling) can be made to yield absolute values. In indirect methods, moisture is not removed from the material, but parameters of the wet solid which depend on the quantity of water or number of constituent hydrogen atoms present are measured instead. Since each parameter can be used in different ways, a variety of instruments have been devised. The readings obtained are purely arbitrary and they have to be calibrated against moisture values found by one or more of the direct methods.

These two categories of techniques have their own advantages and disadvantages. It is possible to get very accurate and even absolute values by employing one or more direct methods. The time required for these methods, however, is usually considerable and operations are mostly manual. Indirect methods, though dependent in accuracy on the results of direct measurements against which they are calibrated, are quicker than direct methods. Further, only the indirect methods offer the possibility of continuous measurement and automatic control of moisture content in industrial processes. Once a particular instrument has been calibrated at a certain setting, very little attention and time are required to measure or control the moisture content of the material. The increase in instrumentation has been one of the striking advances made in chemical technology over the past decade or so, and today the determination of moisture is more often achieved by instrumental methods than by direct chemical analysis.

There have been tremendous developments in methods for estimating moisture content through the application of modern physical techniques such as electronic resonance spectroscopy, neutron scattering, etc. Electrical and electronic methods are described in this section. Two electrical properties of water, i.e., conductivity and dielectric behavior, have figured largely in the development of electrical or electronic instrumentation and techniques.

1.2 dc Conductivity or Resistance Moisture Meters

1.2.1 <u>Theory</u>. It has been observed by a number of investigators that there is a definite relationship between the moisture content of hygroscopic materials and their dc conductivity or dc resistance. Kujirai and Akhari [1] studied the change of resistance of sheets of paper and cloth with changing humidity conditions and found that resistance fell with increasing humidity, the logarithm of the re-

1 ELECTRICAL TECHNIQUES

sistance being practically a linear function of the humidity. They also studied the effect of the duration of application of the voltage and found that at medium and high humidities, resistance rise was gradual and continued to rise for 5 min after the current was switched on, whereas if the relative humidity was below 30%, the resistance was not dependent on the time factor. Murphy and Walker [2] obtained similar results. They showed that the logarithm of longitudinal resistance varied linearly with moisture (content) of the cotton yarns. Similar results were obtained in the case of wood by Hasselbatt [3] and Stamm [4] who found that the logarithm of the resistance is approximately proportional to the percentage of moisture content below the saturation point. In the case of wood, resistance increases approximately 1.8-fold for a decrease of 1% in absolute moisture content. At a given moisture content, the ordinary resistance law governing solid conductors, that is, $R \propto (L/A)$ where R, L, and A are resistance, length, and area of the conductor, respectively, appears to hold approximately for many hygroscopic materials. Such factors as density of wood, species of wood, direction of current flow relative to grain structure, variation of the specimen beyond the electrodes, and similar geometrical factors are relatively unimportant compared to the enormous change of resistance with change in moisture content. A plot of the logarithm of specific resistance vs moisture content results in approximately straight lines for different wood and textile materials as shown in Fig. 5.1. A similar plot is given in Fig. 5.2 for lint cotton, seed cotton, and cottonseed. In the case of jute [5] for a change in the regain from 10 to 35%, the resistance of the fiber changes from 10^{11} to 10^6 ohms, i.e., in the ratio of 10^5:1 as shown in Fig. 5.3.

The relation between the degree of sorption of water vapor by polymers and their electrical resistance has recently been investigated by Kawasaki [6] who gives the following relationship between conduction current and moisture content when the latter is low:

$$\log \frac{i}{i_0} = KM \qquad (5.1)$$

270   V. ELECTRICAL AND ELECTRONIC METHODS

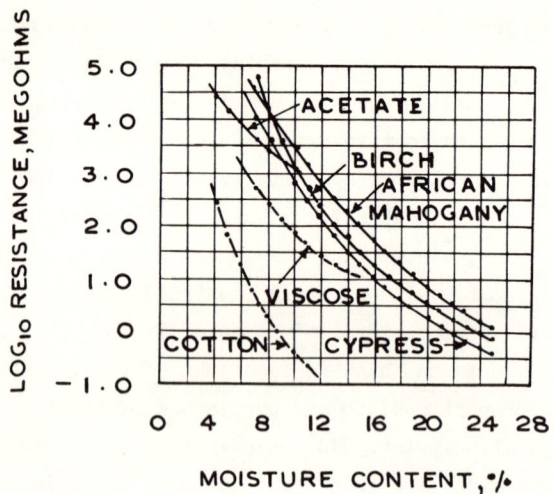

FIG. 5.1. Variation of resistance with moisture content of various materials.

where i and i_0 are the currents through the sorbed and desorbed samples, respectively, M is the moisture content, and K is a constant. This is shown graphically in Fig. 5.4.

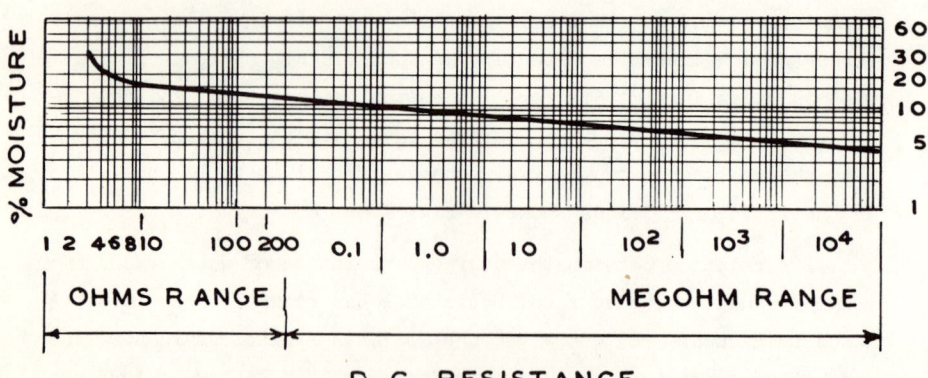

FIG. 5.2. Relation between resistance and water content of lint cotton, seed cotton, and cottonseed.

1 ELECTRICAL TECHNIQUES

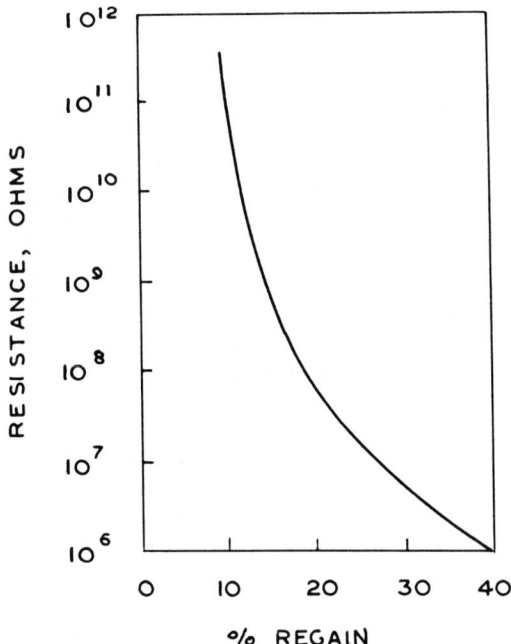

FIG. 5.3. Relation between dc resistance of jute and its moisture content.

However, if the moisture content is high, the relation between conduction current and moisture content is given better by the relation

$$\frac{i}{i_o} = 1 + K_1 M \qquad (5.2)$$

where K_1 is another constant.

The conduction current increases linearly with moisture content up to a critical point which depends on the material. This critical value of moisture content is 25% for polyvinyl alcohol film and about 15% for gel cellophane film. The deviation from the original logarithmic relationship may be due to the change in the nature of the sorbed water, viz., from localized water to mobile water.

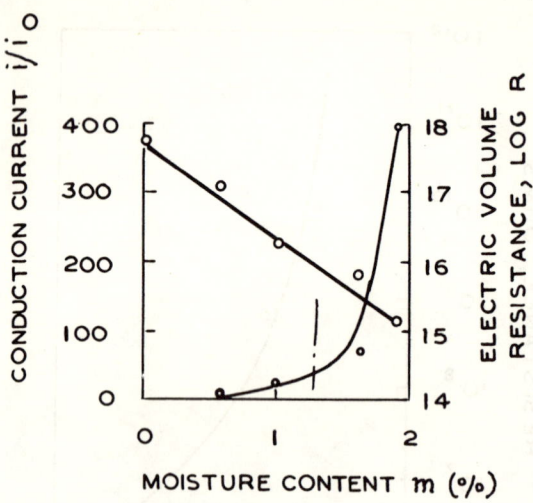

FIG. 5.4. Relation between conduction current, resistance, and moisture content of polymethyl methacrylate.

The conductivity or resistance of a hygroscopic material is not only affected by water content, but also by the presence of naturally occurring electrolytes in the material. In the case of conduction of electricity through raw cotton, this has been verified by a few investigators [7-9]. If these electrolytes are removed by washing, the conductivity of cotton is very greatly reduced. The electrical conductivity of cellulose in the presence of salts and moisture has been investigated very exhaustively by Sullivan [7], who used cellophane instead of cotton sheet for his experiments. His experiments showed that at a given humidity the conductivity of the sheet increases with increasing salt content and is to some extent dependent on the amount of salt present. For a given salt content, the conductivity is an exponential function of the conditioning humidity over a wide range. For salt content of 1% and above, the conductivity of the cellulose is almost entirely determined by the moisture content, but for salt content much below 1%, the latter also becomes an important factor. The conductivity behavior of salt-impregnated cotton yarns is qualitatively the same as that of sheet cellulose. The above-mentioned

1 ELECTRICAL TECHNIQUES

workers have shown that the dc conductivity of a textile material is almost entirely due to absorbed moisture and the electrolytic material which it dissolves from the natural constituents of textiles. For a given sample of impregnated cellulose, the conductance may change a millionfold when the moisture content changes only tenfold. As the passage of an electric current through salt-impregnated sheet is due largely to the migration of salt ions, such local changes may seriously affect the conductances if the measuring current is passed for a considerable time. It is therefore essential that the measurements be made as quickly as possible. This is of great importance, because ac and dc conductivities are of the same order only when dc measurements are made with a period of electrification short enough to avoid the error due to polarization (increase of resistance with time of application of the impressed measuring voltage).

Sinijelnikoff and Walther [10] have shown that the true dc conductivity of a dielectric is equal to its ac conductivity, the apparent discrepancy between them being due to an error in the dc measurements caused by a back emf of polarization, which makes the apparent resistance much larger than the true resistance. However, it has been shown by Murphy and Walker [11] that there is a wide discrepancy between the ac and dc conductivities of cotton at humidities below 80%, though at humidities higher than this, the two conductivities are equal. The relation between the dc and ac conductivities of cotton is shown in Fig. 5.5. It is evident from these graphs that at humidities above 80% most ac and dc conductivities are equal, while below this the two values are quite divergent. The dc conductivity is less than 1% of ac conductivity at humidities below 25% for samples of normal electrolyte content, and at humidities below 45% for samples of low electrolyte content. Further, the rate of increase of ac conductivity of cotton with frequency becomes smaller, the higher the humidity, being practically independent of frequency at very high humidities. The ac conductivities of moisture-absorbing and other dielectrics are in general much greater than their dc conductivities, and the energy losses in such a dielectric

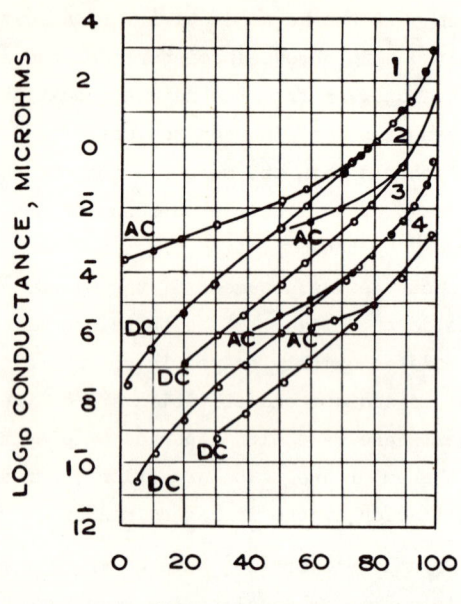

FIG. 5.5. Relation between dc and ac conductivity of cotton at different relative humidities.

for a high-frequency current are therefore considerably greater than for direct current.

Sullivan [7] has also studied the effect of temperature change on the conductance of cellulose impregnated with sodium nitrate and copper sulfate and having a wide range of moisture content. Sullivan finds that with moisture contents above 50 parts per 100 of cellulose, the temperature coefficient is 2 to 4% °C^{-1}. As the moisture content is lowered, the temperature coefficient rises with increasing rapidity, reaching a value of about 11% °C^{-1} at a moisture content of 10 parts per 100 of cellulose. He also finds that the temperature coefficient does not change very rapidly with moisture content.

1.2.2 Design Features. Based on the principle of dc resistance variation, a large number of dc conductivity or resistance-type moisture meters have been developed. Geary [12] in a recent paper

1 ELECTRICAL TECHNIQUES

has given data about 12 types of electrical moisture meters manufactured in England. Three basic units are common to all these instruments: (1) An electrode system, (2) an electronic unit, and (3) an indicating meter or recorder.

For measurement of moisture, the sample is held between two electrode elements and the current flowing through the sample is measured by the electronic unit and indicated on the meter.

1. The electrode system: The electrode system varies with the type of sample to be examined. For resistance measurements, the electrode should always have two points (separated by a fixed distance and proper insulation) between which the sample can be grabbed. For a large number of wood products, bales of cotton and jute, and soils, the electrode system consists of a half-dozen or so sharp points or tapering needles of 1/4 to 1/3 in. in length connected together in groups of three, embedded in suitable insulation, and mounted on a handle so that these needles may be driven directly into the sample to a depth of 1/4 in. or so. These needle points are usually about 1 in. apart. Figure 5.6 shows one such electrode system for wood and timber described by Rehman et al. [13]. For the continuous measurement of moisture in textile or paper processings, the electrode system consists of two suitable rollers separated and insulated from each other so that they make good contacts with the sheet of the material and the resistance between them is measured continuously. Typical electrodes for use with moving sheets of textiles or paper are shown in Figs. 5.7 and 5.8. The latter has provision for adjustment of the gap between the parallel plates.

Fluffy materials like cotton, wool, and seed cotton obviously need to be packed by uniform compression to a constant density to give reproducible results. It has been found by Jones [14] that, on compressing the samples within the field of measurement by applying a force normal to the face of the electrodes until a certain degree of compression is reached, the measured resistance of the samples becomes practically independent of the initial degree of

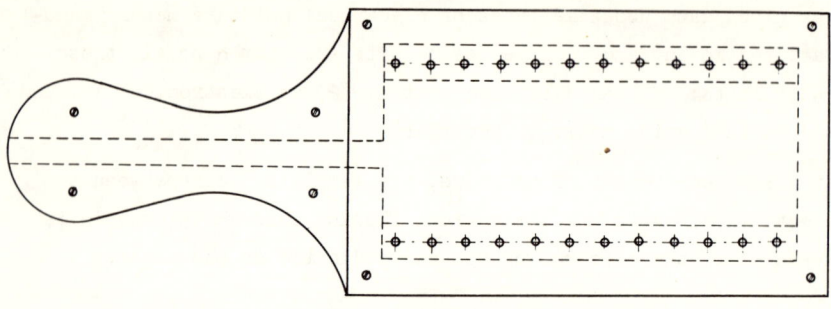

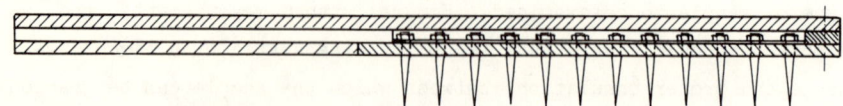

FIG. 5.6. Schematic diagram of needle-type electrode.

packing and is not appreciably altered by any further increase in the force applied to the electrodes. A pressure of about 20 psi was found adequate to produce the desired state of compression. Reddick et al. [15] have also made a systematic study of this effect, in the case of lint cotton, cottonseed, and seed cotton, and found that a surface force of 40 psi gives the best results. A graph

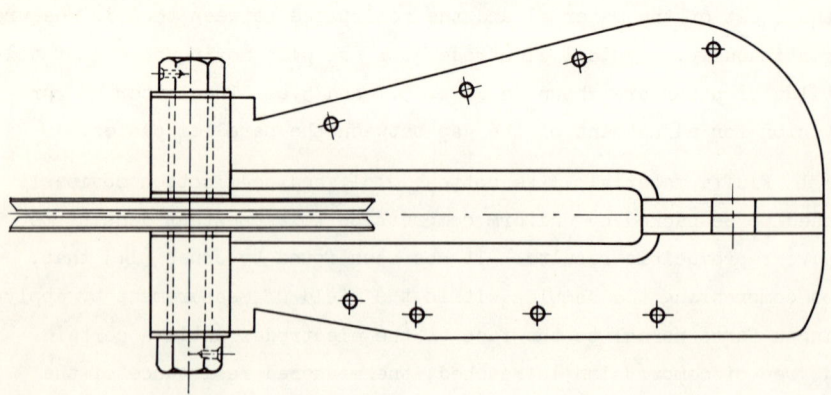

FIG. 5.7. Electrode for sheet materials.

1 ELECTRICAL TECHNIQUES

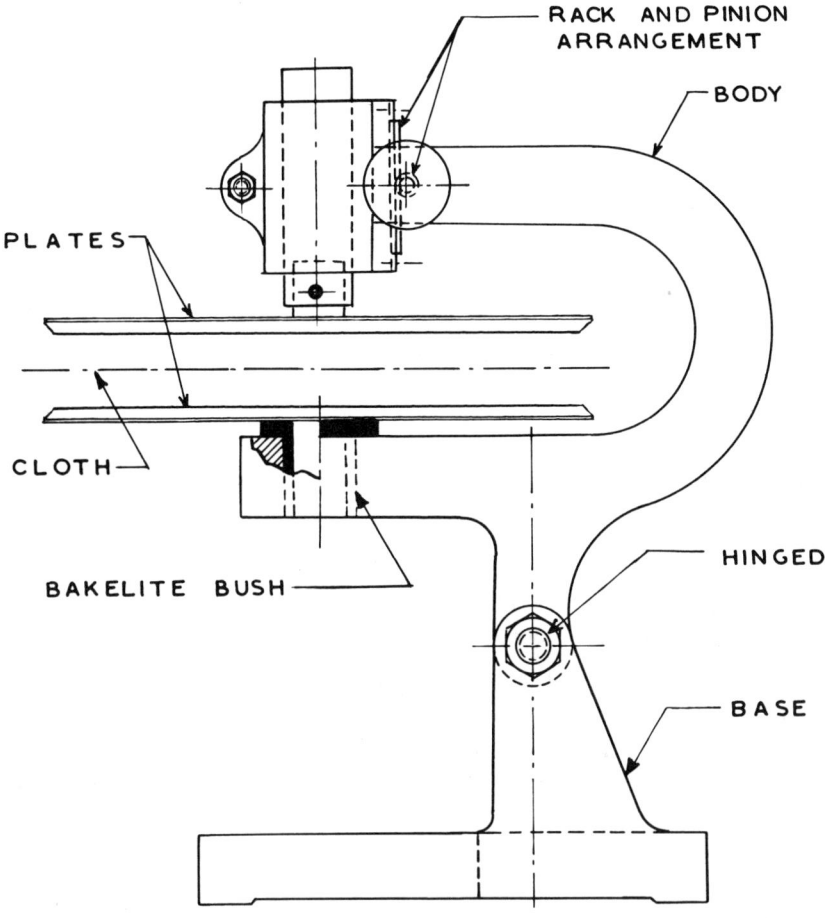

FIG. 5.8. Electrode system for sheet materials with provision for adjustment of the parallel plates.

showing the variation of moisture content readings with applied pressure is shown in Fig. 5.9. The required compressive force was maintained by hydraulic power because it afforded excellent control besides being inexpensive.

2. *The electronic unit:* Some of these instruments employ a basic Wheatstone bridge circuit for measuring the high resistances involved, which are of the order of thousands of megohms at low

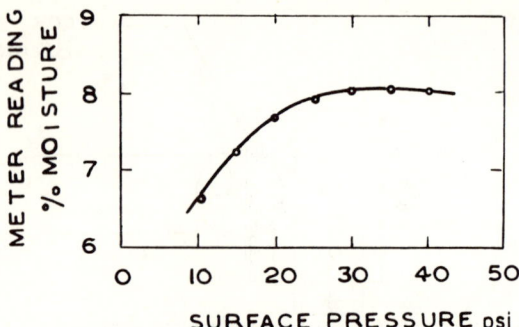

FIG. 5.9. Effect of sample pressure on meter readings.

moisture content and thousands (even hundreds) of ohms at high moisture content, e.g., for a moisture variation of 5 to 15%, a typical resistance change occurs from 1000 megohms to 0.17 Mohms. The bridge detector is usually a sensitive high-impedance electronic voltmeter or ammeter. It is required to measure a wide range of resistances, depending on moisture content of the samples. The value of the resistance to be measured depends on the following factors: (1) Moisture content of the sample, (2) type of material, and (3) dimensions and distance apart of the electrodes. The main contribution, however, to the increase or decrease of resistance is from the variation of moisture content.

Some investigators and manufacturers have utilized variations in the plate current of a triode with change in grid bias by using the resistance offered by the sample containing moisture as part of the grid-bias resistor. It is well known that for a given range of the grid-bias voltage, the plate current of a triode varies almost linearly if the plate voltage is kept constant, as is shown by the characteristic curve of a triode. Also, from the principle of voltage measurement across a high resistance, it follows that the measuring device should also have a high internal resistance and this condition is satisfied by choosing a suitable electronic tube with a high resistance between grid and filament. The principle has been utilized by Jones [14] in developing the Shirley moisture meter

1 ELECTRICAL TECHNIQUES 279

which is one of the most accurate electrical moisture meters for textiles and similar hygroscopic materials. The basic circuit diagram of this meter is given in Fig. 5.10 and the practical circuit is shown in Fig. 5.11.

A suitable direct potential is maintained across the potential divider ABCDE, which consists of the fixed resistances R_7, R_8, R_9, and the variable resistance R_{10}. The positive end of the divider is at A and this is connected through a fixed resistance R_{11} and a variable resistance R_{12} to the anode of the triode whose filament is indirectly heated and connected to C as shown in Fig. 5.10. The grid of tube PM-202 is connected to D through a 100-Mohm resistance R_1, and to L_1 through a 300-Mohm resistance R_2. The total value of R_1 and R_2 should be about 400 Mohms. The sample under test is connected between the highly insulated leads L_1 and L_2, the latter being connected to E, the negative point of the circuit. A mean voltage of about 50 V dc is maintained between the two terminals of the electrode. A milliammeter M_1 is connected between B and F. The circuit works as follows: X, the resistance X across the electrodes, is infinite when there is no sample and the grid potential attains

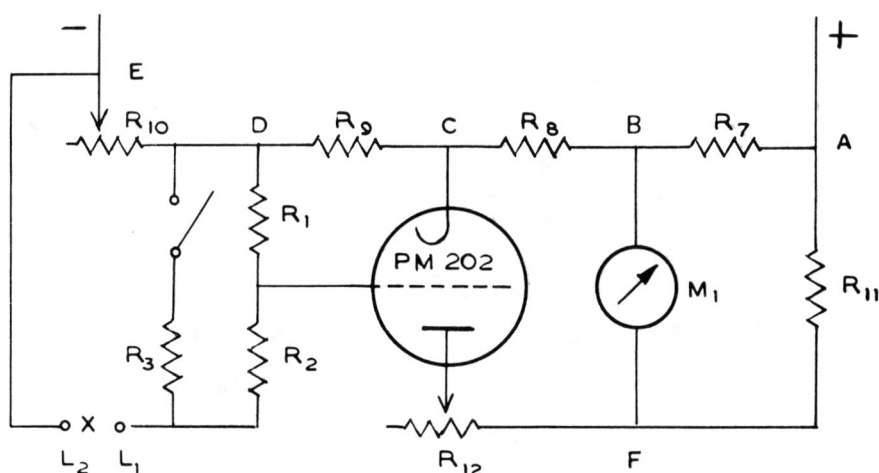

FIG. 5.10. Basic circuit diagram of the Shirley moisture meter.

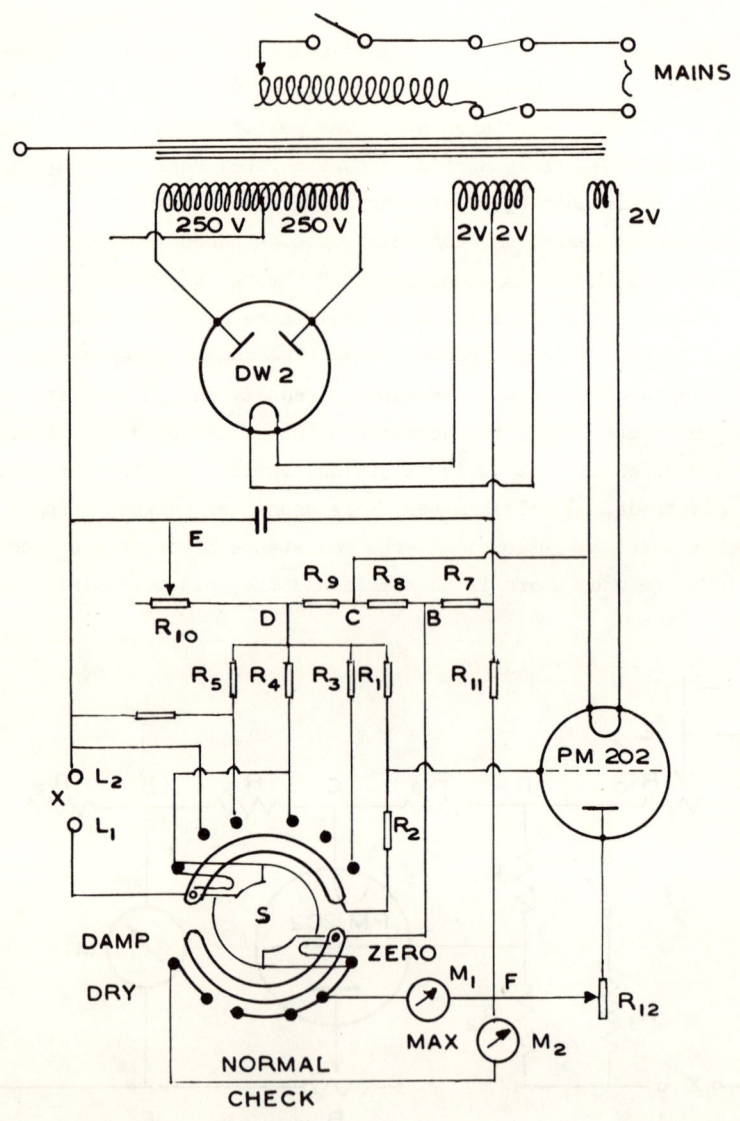

FIG. 5.11. Practical circuit diagram of the Shirley moisture meter.

1 ELECTRICAL TECHNIQUES

its minimum negative value, the potential existing at the point D, and the anode current will have a maximum value, say I_1. On the other hand, if X is nearly zero, the grid will attain its maximum negative potential and the plate current will have a minimum value, say I_2. It has been found experimentally that for any finite value of X, the plate current I and the resistance R are related by the following equation:

$$\frac{X}{R} = \frac{I - I_2}{I_1 - I} \qquad (5.3)$$

where R is the value of X for which $I = 1/2(I_1 + I_2)$.

Equation (5.3) gives in general a hyperbolic form of curve for the grid potential-plate current variation. For the type of triode selected in which the curvature of the characteristic curve is comparatively small over the limited range, this relationship holds quite accurately. It also holds good for other types of triodes as well.

A similar moisture meter for measuring moisture content in jute bales has been developed by Banerjee and Sen [16] who use a battery instead of main supply for making the instrument portable and applicable for field operations. The electrodes consist of a pair of stout steel rods each circular in cross section and gradually tapering to a pointed end. The total length of the electrode is 18.5 in. The circuit diagram and calibration curves of this meter for three ranges of the instrument are shown in Figs. 5.12 and 5.13. It was found that these curves hold equally well for measuring the moisture content of loose jute as well as that of jute bales. The tube V_1 is a miniature-type pentode amplifier capable of working with low supply voltages. With the range selector switch any one of R_1, R_2, or R_3 may be connected between the grid and the filament, i.e., input, of the tube V_1. The resistor R_5 is used to reduce the filament current for diminishing the electron emission of V_1 and hence increasing the internal resistance of the tube. When the

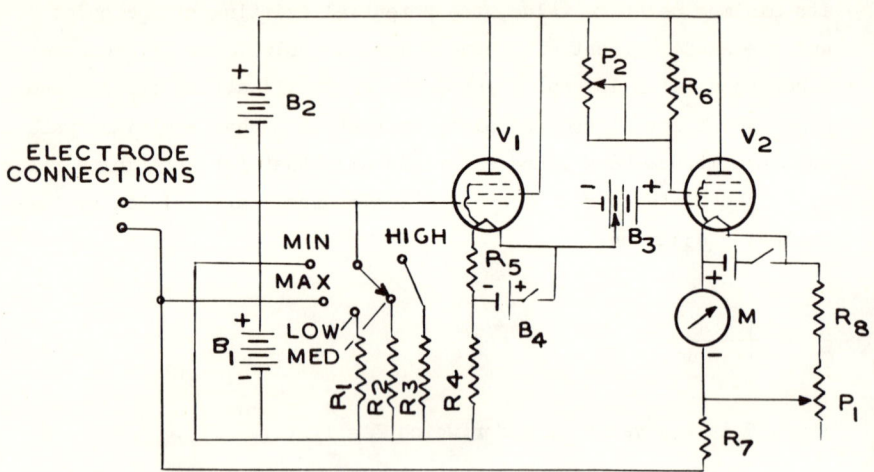

FIG. 5.12. Circuit diagram of the moisture meter for jute.

positive terminal of the voltage source B_1 (Fig. 5.12) is connected to the control grid of V_1, increased current flows through the resistance R_4 which works as the load resistance for V_1. The tube V_1, therefore, functions as a cathode follower, whose main purpose is to

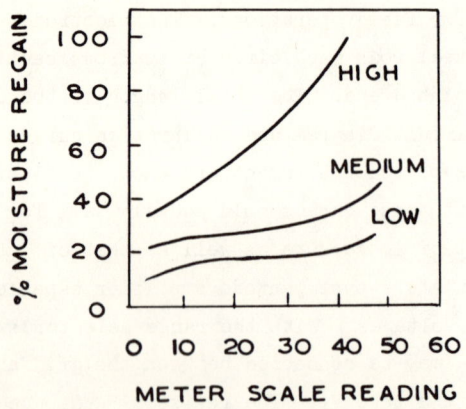

FIG. 5.13. Calibration curves for the three ranges of the moisture meter for jute.

1 ELECTRICAL TECHNIQUES 283

isolate the next tube V_2 from the effect of the varying resistance at the input of V_1 and to present to its input a constant resistance R_4 for all conditions of measurement. The accuracy of this instrument is the same as that of other instruments of its kind, viz., ±0.5% in the low and medium ranges. The applications of this instrument for measurement of the moisture content of loose jute and jute bales are described in Chap. IX.

A number of moisture meters which originally employed tubes have been transistorized; the circuit of one such moisture meter [17] is shown in Fig. 5.14. The circuit is based on the principle of variation of collector current of a transistor in accordance with the change, in the voltage of the emitter of the transistor. As is well known the transistor can be made to have a characteristic curve similar to that of a tube in circuits involving low resistances or impedances and can, therefore, be used for amplifying small current changes flowing through a high resistance.

The electrode terminals E in series with a suitable high resistance R and a battery of suitable polarity and voltage are connected between the common point of the circuit and the base of the transistor T_1. A second transistor T_2 is connected with T_1 such that the emitter and collector of the latter are connected with the collector of the former. The bases of the two transistors (T_1 and T_2) are shortened in order to produce increased amplification of the emitter current of T_1, thus an amplification factor of 2 is obtained. The emitter and collector are biased as usual. Clearly there is virtually infinite resistance between the electrode terminals E when they are not connected to a sample. In this case, the positive bias on the base of pnp transistor T_1 has its minimum value and hence the current indicated in the microammeter M has its maximum value. The magnitude of this current is adjusted so as to be equal to the full-scale reading of the meter by means of the potentiometer control P_2.

When the electrode terminals are inserted into the sample whose moisture content is to be measured, the resistance between the terminals is less, the higher the moisture content, with the result

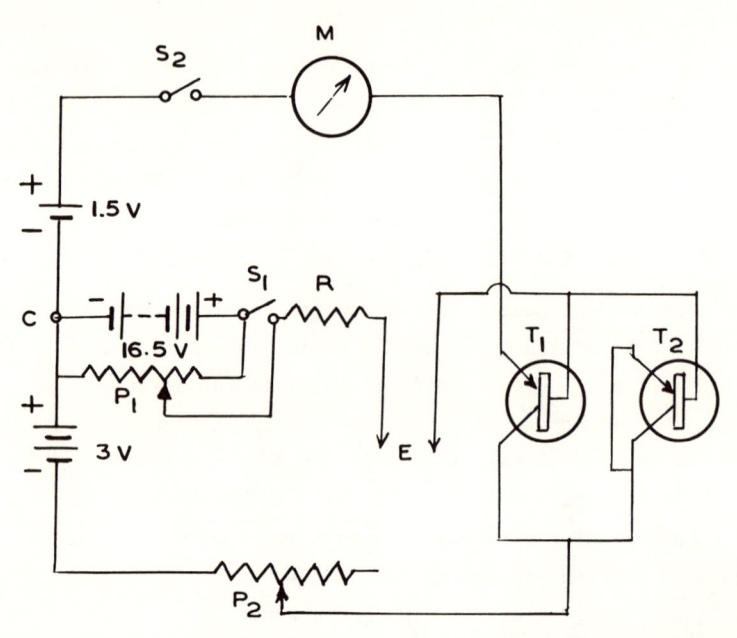

FIG. 5.14. Circuit diagram of a dc conductivity-type transistorized moisture meter.

that the base of T_1 becomes more and more positively biased with respect to the emitter, and the emitter current flowing through the meter decreases accordingly. When the electrode terminals are short-circuited, minimum scale reading of the meter M is obtained by the proper adjustment of the control potentiometer P_1. The meter readings are calibrated beforehand against materials of known moisture content, so that the moisture content of any sample of the same material can be determined directly from the scale readings of the meter. The relationship between logarithm of the resistance and the regain was found [17] by testing samples whose regains were later determined by standard oven-drying methods at 110°C. The battery voltages to emitters and collectors of the transistors T_1 and T_2 are applied through the switches S_1 and S_2 (Fig. 5.14).

3. Indicating meter or recorder: After a linear relationship between the moisture content of the sample and the plate current of

1 ELECTRICAL TECHNIQUES

the tube or the collector current of the transistor is established, it is required to get a direct calibration of the meter scale by known values of moisture content. In order to get samples of different moisture content, they are conditioned for 24 to 48 hr in desiccators containing saturated solutions of salts which give standard relative humidities [18] at 20°C. A wide range of relative humidities (in desiccators and other closed spaces) can also be obtained by using dilute sulfuric acid.

The moisture regains of such conditioned samples are determined by carefully weighing the samples on a very accurate chemical balance before and after they have been dried to a constant weight in a standard oven having air circulation arrangement at 105 to 110°C. The precautions necessary to get correct oven-dry values of moisture content have been described in Chap. II. Corresponding readings for the same samples as observed on the meter of the moisture meter are obtained and plotted against the oven-dry values in Fig. 5.15 from which calibrated values of the meter scale are obtained. Once this calibrated scale has been substituted for the current scale, moisture content values of the unknown sample can be read off directly. A pen recorder can be used to give a continuous record of variation of moisture content, e.g., in a processing operation.

Subsequent meters can be calibrated by inserting them in series with a suitably calibrated moisture meter. Hence the instrument can be calibrated once for all using a typical electronic tube or valve and the calibration will not subsequently be affected to any appreciable extent except through aging of the tube, which causes poor electron emission.

1.2.3 Accuracy. If properly calibrated, the conductivity moisture meter gives an accuracy of ±0.5% moisture content. However, inventors and manufacturers claim an accuracy of ±0.1 to ±0.5%, depending on the range of moisture content covered and the type of sample tested. Independent scientific investigations by Toner and co-workers [19] have shown that for textile materials conductivity meters give

286   V.   ELECTRICAL AND ELECTRONIC METHODS

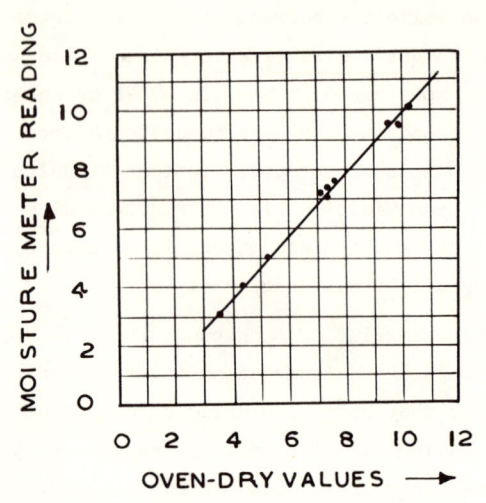

FIG. 5.15. Relationship between current readings of the moisture meter and the oven-dry values of moisture content.

a standard deviation of ±0.07% moisture content as compared to ±0.12% for oven-dry values. It was also found that electrical meters are better than oven-drying methods of moisture measurement from the precision point of view. The fundamental calibration curves were found to shift under the influence of temperature, nature of material, and presence of impurities. Similar findings have been reported by a committee formed by the American Association of Textile Chemists and Colorists [20] to examine the performance, accuracy, and industrial usefulness of various types of electrical and electronic moisture meters developed and manufactured in the United States. It was found that the dye treatments have the effect of giving higher readings (about 1%) on the meters as compared with results obtained with untreated fabrics. The resin treatments, on the other hand, give lower meter readings by about 2%.

On grains the accuracy of resistance-type moisture meters has been found [21] to be ±0.25% or better. In the case of wood and other similar hygroscopic materials, however, there is a possibility of error due to dc polarization. This has been largely minimized by

1 ELECTRICAL TECHNIQUES

using large electrodes. To eliminate completely the errors due to the polarization effect, electrodes of stainless steel have been used. For optimum results from the conductivity moisture meters, the following factors should be taken into consideration.

1. <u>Moisture distribution:</u> Moisture must obviously be well distributed throughout the sample, since conductivity meters will measure the path of least resistance and a single wet spot in the sample can vitiate the test. In using needle-type electrodes which make contact on only one side of the sample, surface moisture on the material should be avoided and a number of measurements should be made at different portions of the sample.

2. <u>Range of measurement:</u> While the relationship between electrical resistance and moisture content is generally sound for the hygroscopic range of the material (usually 30 to 90% relative humidity) the accuracy will be less and some error is likely to be introduced at very low or very high moisture contents. Accurate measurements of ±0.5% can be made in the range of 3 to 30% moisture content on a dry weight basis for most materials.

3. <u>Temperature:</u> Most meters are calibrated for samples having a temperature of 20 to 25°C. The electrical resistance of a hygroscopic material is an inverse function of its temperature, and the rate of change of resistance increases with moisture content. Readings of a resistance-type moisture meter should, therefore, be corrected if the temperature of the sample being tested is different from the meter calibration temperature. The temperature coefficient correction is roughly 1% for a temperature difference of 5°C. For more accurate measurements, however, temperature correction charts should be prepared.

4. <u>Sampling:</u> It is fundamental to any testing procedure that the larger the sample, the more representative is the result. The sample should be as nearly representative of the average of the

material conditions as possible. Two or three tests should be made to obtain the average of the uncontrolled variables. According to Reddick et al. [15] samples of about 35 g of lint cotton or 100 g of seed cotton and cottonseed are adequate for giving correct and reproducible results for these materials.

5. Packing density: In the case of fluffy materials, constant and uniform pressure (about 40 psi) should be applied to get repeatable and dependable results. With certain granular materials, e.g., various types of grains and coals, packing density does not appreciably affect the measured values.

6. Purity of the sample: The presence of small amounts of impurities in the sample in the form of an electrolyte should be avoided. A salt (20:1 liquor ratio) or presence of an acid will drastically affect conductivity of the sample as a whole and may cause departure from the original calibration.

7. Method of measurement: Moisture content of grab samples must be measured as rapidly as possible. However, due regard should be paid to the standardization and balancing of the instrument before taking observations, as conditions that require the measurements to be made rapidly may lead to inaccuracy due to incorrect balancing, reading, location on points, poor contact, and dependence on a single measurement. As much care as possible should be exercised in all the measurements to get reliable results and to this effect the needle electrodes of resistance-type meters should be driven their full extent (~ 5/16 in.) into materials like wood, plaster, cotton, jute bales, etc.

1.2.4 Merits and Demerits. There is a considerable change in resistance or conductivity for a comparatively small change in moisture regain. For many materials, an almost linear relationship holds between the regain and the logarithm of the resistance over the hygro-

1 ELECTRICAL TECHNIQUES

scopic range, in which accurate moisture measurements can therefore be made.

For textile materials, the regain-resistance relationship is not, except at very low regain values, affected to any extent by the hygroscopic history of the material. Hence an average logarithm versus resistance-regain relationship can be assumed without consideration of the fact of whether the material approached its equilibrium moisture conditions by absorption or desorption.

If the material is a natural product, resistance-regain relationship is negligibly affected by the origin of the materials. Similarly, in the case of manufactured products, the method of production has negligible effect on the resistance-regain relationship of the material.

Resistance is a property which can be measured by simple, robust, and reliable apparatus and is most suited for certain types of materials. Whitten and Holaday [22] have, however, found that resistance method is not practical for cottonseed and similar materials.

Moisture measurement is instantaneous after the sample has been presented to terminals of the electrodes. Hence continuous measurement and control of moisture can be made in an industrial process.

Moisture measurements are affected by the degree and efficiency of the contact between electrodes and sample. It is not always possible or practicable to obtain uniform standard contact (due to unevenness of the surface of the sample) and accuracy of measurement is of doubtful nature in such cases. Electrical resistance detectors are, therefore, prone to error due to varying surface characteristics of the material over which the detector elements are supposed to make contact.

The reading of the meter is also very much affected by the presence of electrolytes, and it is not possible to control these in mill-operating conditions as the apparent moisture content may vary with the quality of water used in processing the material. This is quite a serious drawback in this type of meter.

1.3 ac Conductivity or Radiofrequency Power Loss-Type Moisture Meter

These instruments use the ac conductivity and high-frequency power absorption properties of hygroscopic materials. The sample is employed to change the impedance of a condenser (forming part of a circuit) by placing it between the plates of the condenser or by placing concentric ring electrodes in contact with the material. One such instrument developed commercially is known as the Moisture Register. This instrument is designed to test loose or compressible materials such as scoured wool, bulk cotton, synthetic fibers, cakes of rayon, orlon, nylon, dacron, etc. A controlled pressure is applied to the electrodes, and the entire electrode face is movable and mounted on a 20-lb pressure spring. When the correct pressure is applied (indicated by the glow of a lamp) accurate readings are obtained. This meter, however, gives moisture content values slightly higher (0.84%) than standard oven-dry values, especially when salts and other impurities are present in the sample. In all other respects, this type of moisture meter is similar to the resistance-type moisture meter.

This instrument uses a nickel cadmium battery which is rechargeable and gives accurate results even though the penetration of the electrodes in materials such as lumber and veneer is of the order of 1 in. only.

1.4 Dielectric or Capacitance Moisture Meters

1.4.1 Theory. It has been observed by a number of research workers that the variation of the dielectric constant of hygroscopic materials with moisture content is approximately linear over a limited but useful range of 0 to 35% moisture content corresponding to a change in relative humidity of 30 to 90% at 20°C. The dielectric constant of water is 81, whereas the dielectric constant of most organic materials of vegetable origin, such as textile fibers, paper, wood, grains, cereals, etc., is quite low, ranging from 2.2 to 4.0 in a "bone-dry" condition. The presence of a very small quantity of water in the material, therefore, causes a considerable change in the dielectric constant of the combined system.

Though the water absorbed by hygroscopic materials does not form a mixture in the true sense, the free water as well as the water mechanically held within the pores of porous materials can be treated as forming a mixture with the solid material, and the composite dielectric constant of such a mixture can be theoretically estimated by the use of Debye's relation for the dielectric constant of mixtures.

Under ideal conditions, the dielectric constant (E_m) of this mixture is given by the following relationship:

$$E_m = E_1 S_1 + E_2 S_2 \tag{5.4}$$

where S_1 and S_2 are the volume-filling factors of each component into another to form the mixture, and E_1 and E_2 are the dielectric constants of the individual substance. Theoretically it has been estimated that the presence of 1% of water in any substance will lead to an increase in the dielectric constant of the mixture of approximately 0.8 unit. Curves showing variation of dielectric constant of a mixture with moisture content are given in Fig. 5.16. Most of the systems encountered in practice do not behave ideally and hence separate calibration curves are necessary for every system to be analyzed. The effect of addition of water on the dielectric properties of p-dioxane at different temperatures as observed by Wolfe [23] is shown in Fig. 5.17.

There are fairly wide deviations between theory and experimental results which appear to be due partly to decrease in the accuracy of the experimental measurement as the dielectric constant of the mixture increases with increase of the amount of water content, and partly to the nature of the molecular association in the

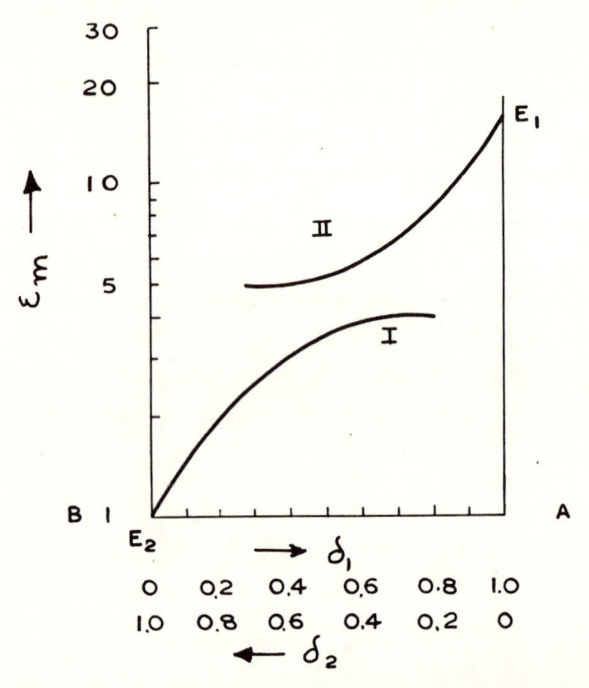

FIG. 5.16. Variation of dielectric constant of a mixture with moisture content: effective dc ε_m of mixtures of A in B (curve I) and of B in A (curve II).

solution. Another explanation of this discrepancy is based on the fact that the moisture content of the system consists of both bound and free water molecules and that the bound water molecules, which are chemisorbed or electrostatically held in the ordered or the crystalline region of the sample, are unable to follow the electric-field variations, especially at higher frequencies. Rowen and Hope [24] have derived the following theoretical relationship, based on this hypothesis, between the dielectric change ΔE at microwave frequencies and the fraction of free water:

$$E = 52 \, \alpha \, V_w \tag{5.5}$$

1 ELECTRICAL TECHNIQUES

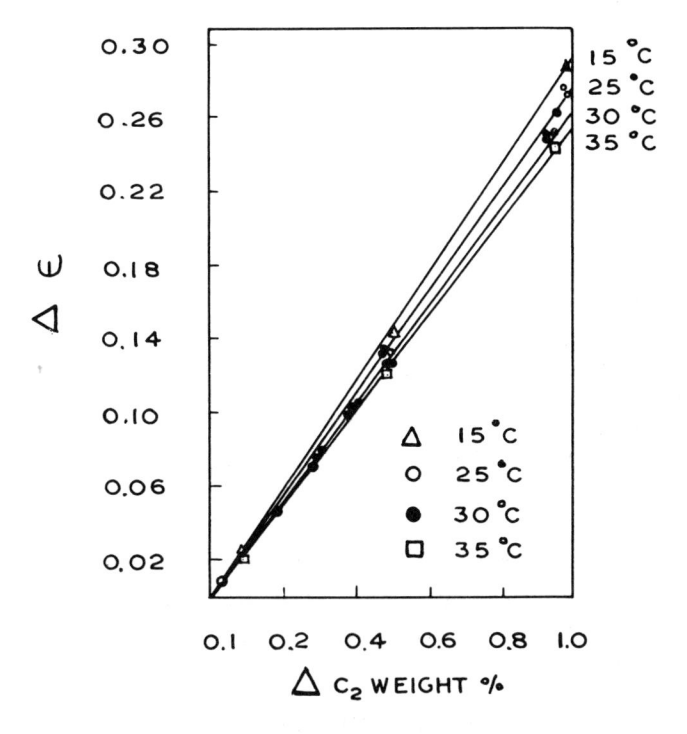

FIG. 5.17. Effect of addition of water on the dielectric properties of p-dioxane at different temperatures.

where V_w represents the volume fraction of sorbed water, and α is the parameter which gives the fraction of water that is free or unbound.

A plot of the change in dielectric constant with the change in amount of water sorbed shows a linear relationship (Fig. 5.18) for a number of polymers at microwave frequencies. However, it should be emphasized that no "mixture law" proposed so far gives an accurate description of the dielectric behavior of a heterogeneous mixture, and for each individual case it is still necessary to determine the particular parameters experimentally. Besides this there is a variation of dielectric constant and dielectric loss with temperature (Fig. 5.19). In general the change in the dielectric constant of any material with increase in moisture content can be used for the measurement of moisture content. The dielectric constant E is

294 V. ELECTRICAL AND ELECTRONIC METHODS

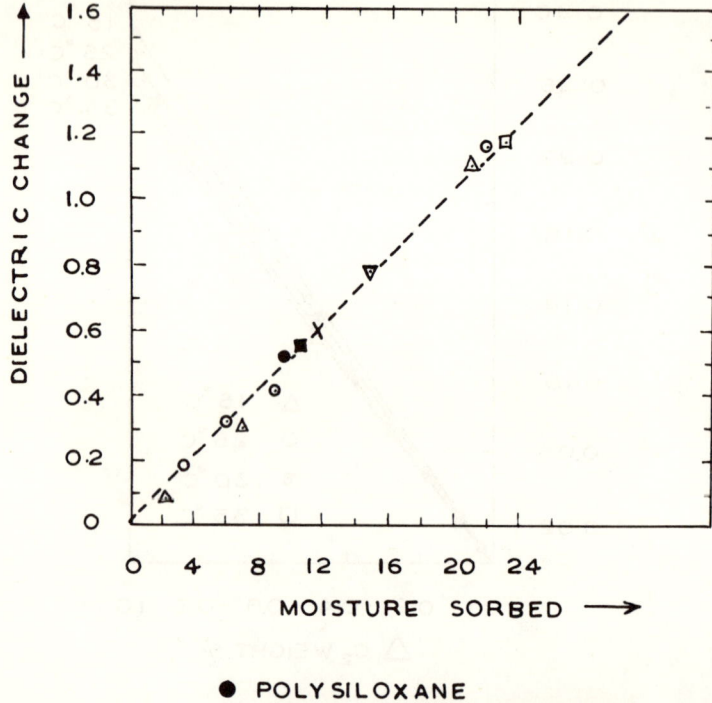

FIG. 5.18. Comparison between the theoretical and experimental values of dielectric constants at microwave frequencies as a function of absorbed moisture.

related with the capacity of a parallel plate condenser as follows:

$$C = 0.225E \left(\frac{A}{D}\right) \tag{5.6}$$

where C is capacitance in microfarads, E is dielectric constant, A is area of the plates, and D is spacing between the plates.

1 ELECTRICAL TECHNIQUES 295

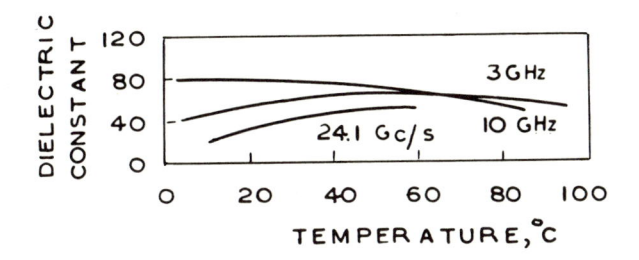

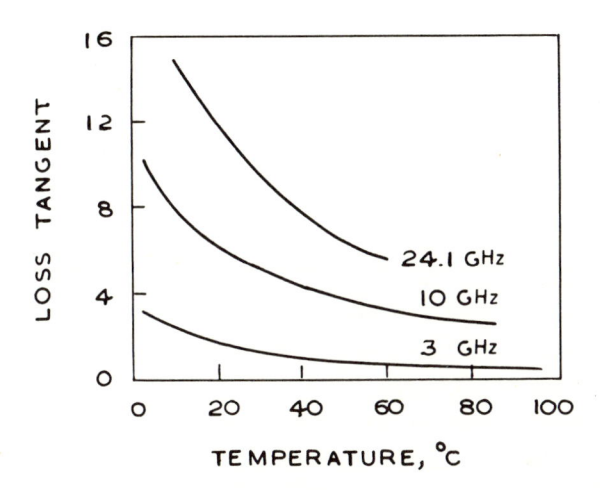

FIG. 5.19. Variation of dielectric constant and loss factor with temperature at different frequencies.

The capacity for a simple concentric cylindrical condenser is given as:

$$C_1 = 0.614E \frac{L}{\log (b/a)} \qquad (5.7)$$

where L is length of the cylinder, b is inner radius of the outer cylinder, and a is outer radius of the inner cylinder.

The capacity change for a small change in moisture content varies appreciably with the microstructure of the material. In the case of liquids, where part of the water content may form an emulsion, the capacity change is generally independent of the size of the water droplets so long as the moisture content remains within certain limits.

1.4.2 Design Features. These moisture meters have three constituent units, that is, (1) an electrode system, (2) an electronic circuit, and (3) an indicator or recorder. The sample is positioned so as to form a dielectric between the electrodes, which are usually flat, parallel plates or concentric cylinders. The capacity change introduced into the electrode system due to a sample of given material of unknown moisture content is converted by the electronic unit into a corresponding current or voltage change read off on the indicating device which is usually a calibrated milliammeter or microammeter. These three units will now be described in some detail.

1. Electrode system: The geometry of the electrode system depends on the nature of the sample and type of measurement to be made. Plate-type electrodes are found to be most suitable for sheet materials and are mostly used for continuous measurements. One such sampling electrode is shown in Fig. 5.7 in which air is used to insulate the sample from direct contact with the electrodes. The total capacitance of the sampling assembly (when the sample is introduced in it) comprises that of two separate condensers. One condenser is formed by the air gap between electrodes and the sample, whereas the other is formed by the sample and the electrodes. One of the problems in the design of a parallel plate electrode is the prevention of "fringing" which causes error in estimation of the capacity of the condenser from its parameters. There are theoretical formulas to calculate the contribution of the fringing effect, and they can be minimized experimentally by introducing a guard ring in the plane of one of the plates and around it, but insulated from it. The guard ring should be maintained at ground potential and its associated electrode should be kept at a low potential with respect to ground, while the opposite electrode is kept at a higher potential. By this arrangement, the fringing is confined to the guard ring only and the

1 ELECTRICAL TECHNIQUES

opposite electrode keeps the electrostatic lines of force straight between the upper and lower measuring electrodes. For liquids, grains, and granular materials, the concentric cylindrical sampling electrode (Fig. 5.20) can be used. This is also known as a "dielectric cell."

Some fluffy materials such as cotton and raw wool, and other materials such as sand, sawdust, etc., require the application of a uniform pressure for maintaining constant uniform-packed density. An electrode system designed by the author for applying a known

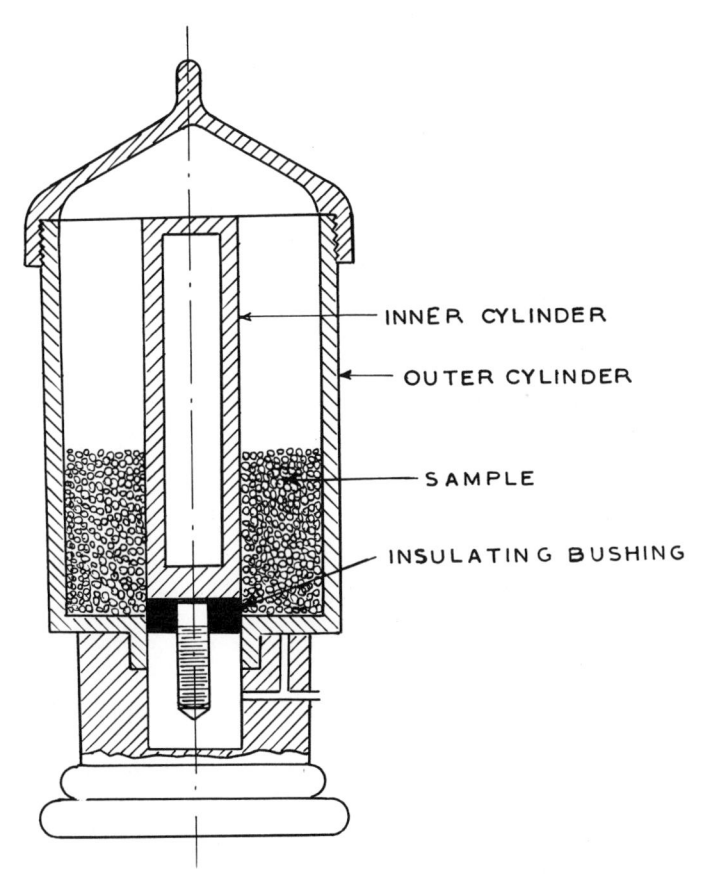

FIG. 5.20. Schematic diagram of a cylindrical electrode for granular materials.

pressure to such materials is shown in Fig. 5.21. However, it is found that in capacitative-type moisture meters most materials require very small pressures to give standard moisture content values.

For measuring moisture content in bales of cotton and jute, needle-type electrodes are made of sufficient length to reach the inner layers of the material. The electrodes are a pair of stout steel rods each circular in cross section and gradually tapering to a pointed end. The total length of an electrode is about 18 in., and there is a binding screw on each for making electrical connections to the meter. Three readings for each bale are taken by introducing the electrode successively into the positions marked A_1-B_1, A_2-B_2, A_3-B_3 (Fig. 5.22). Gentle hammering on the electrodes is necessary to ensure adequate contact with fibers. The average of the three readings with the electrodes in the position marked as in the diagram has been found from many preliminary trials to give representative value of the moisture regain of the whole bale.

2. <u>Electronic circuitry</u>: Three electronic techniques are used for measuring the small capacitance changes obtained in the electrode system: (1) use of bridge circuits, (2) resonance circuit, and (3) beat frequency methods. These circuits have their individual advantages and disadvantages.

Bridge Circuits. The Fielden Drimeter [25] is typical of a moisture meter using a bridge circuit. The circuit diagram of the Fielden Drimeter is shown in Fig. 5.23. The essential parts of the circuit are:

 1. A screened radiofrequency oscillator (A) oscillating at 500 KHz.

 2. An audiooscillator (B) oscillating at 400 Hz and modulating the RF oscillator

 3. A screened radiofrequency transformer (F) coupled to the RF generator in the primary and to two condensers (G and H connected in series) in the secondary

 4. A tuned radiofrequency stage having two tubes

1 ELECTRICAL TECHNIQUES

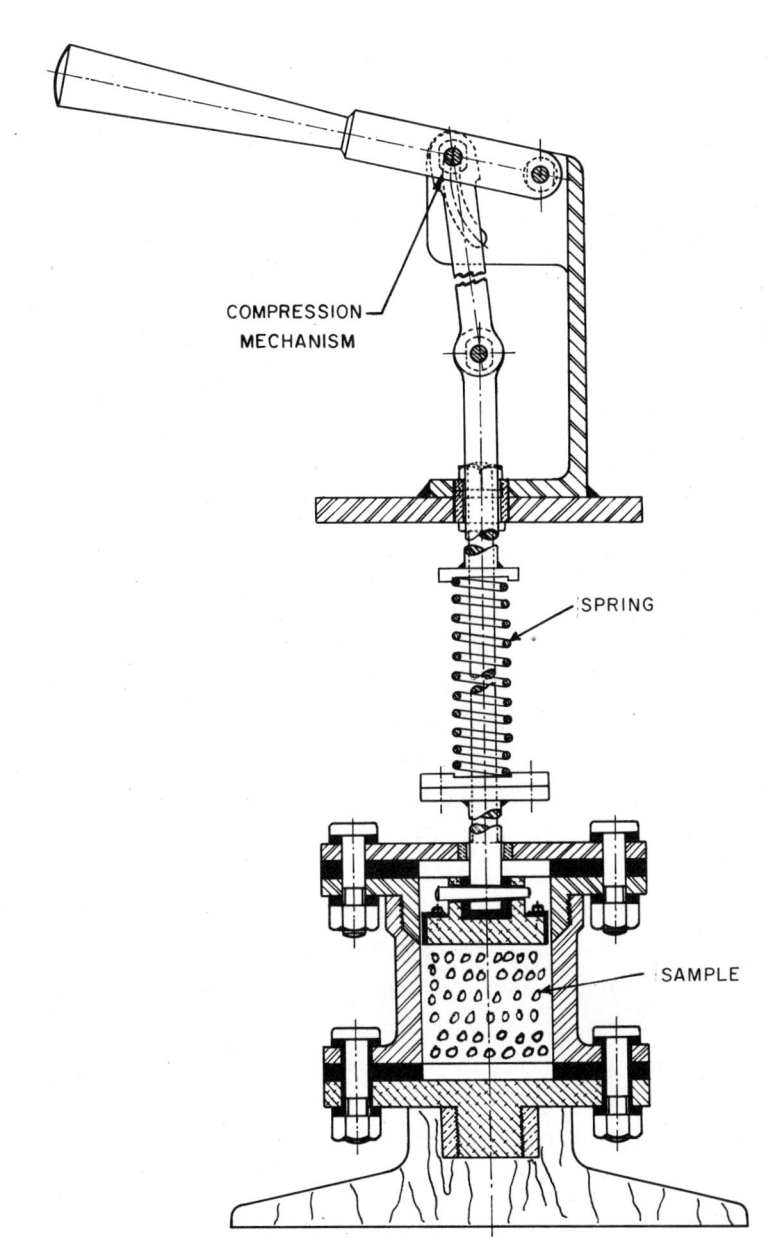

FIG. 5.21. Schematic diagram of electrode for fluffy materials (cotton, wool, and sawdust).

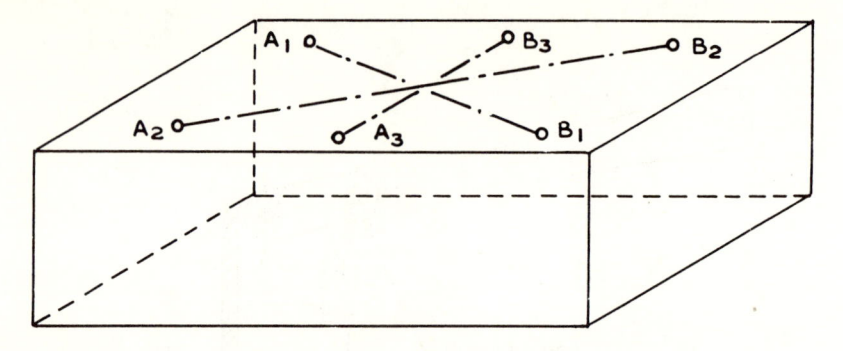

FIG. 5.22. Positions of needle-type electrode marked on a jute bale for representative sampling.

5. A demodulator (M)
6. A low-frequency amplifier (N)
7. A rectifier network (O) with a variable resistance (R)
8. Associated power supplies comprising a transformer, a rectifier, and a smoothing electrolytic condenser

The radiofrequency voltage from the modulated oscillator is fed to the primary of the screened radiofrequency transformer F, the secondary terminals of which are connected to the two condensers G and H, the former being variable and the latter containing the sample. To begin with when there is no sample in the condenser H, the value of the condenser G is adjusted to the same capacity, so that no high-frequency current flows through the system. The sample is then introduced between the plates of condenser H, which changes its capacity. The resulting capacity difference between the two condensers develops a radiofrequency voltage which is amplified by the radiofrequency-tuned two-stage amplifier. This radiofrequency voltage is demodulated by the demodulator tube M and amplified by the audioamplifier tube N (Fig. 5.23). This detected audio signal is connected to the four-terminal rectifier network O which rectifies it to a direct current which actuates an indicating meter Q or a recorder.

1   ELECTRICAL TECHNIQUES   301

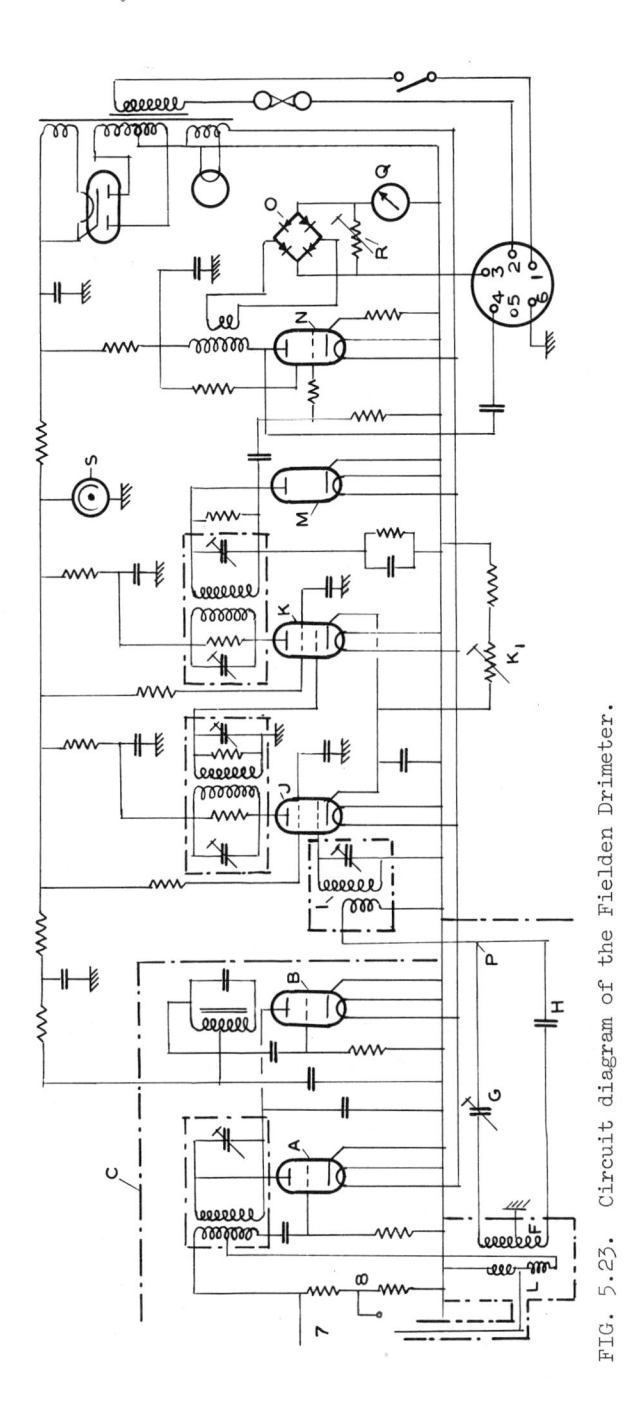

FIG. 5.23. Circuit diagram of the Fielden Drimeter.

The use of high frequency in this method gives the advantage that impedance of the test condenser is reduced to such a value that stability and accuracy can be obtained and very small increments in capacity caused by small changes in moisture content can therefore be measured. Further, the use of a radiofrequency-tuned amplifier renders the apparatus free from instability due to stray electrostatic fields. It is possible to obtain reliable readings of moisture content in increments of 0.5% or less, down to complete dryness, with an accuracy of ±1% in the range dry to 20% moisture. This instrument has been used quite successfully as a control device on sizing machines in the textile industry. However, the rectification ratio of such a rectifier bridge or network is likely to be very low unless a polarizing voltage is applied to the two opposite junctions of the bridge [26]. As no such polarizing voltages are used and as small voltage changes are involved in the measurement of moisture content, the detection is very likely to be nonlinear, especially near the null point. Hence the response of the apparatus is likely to be rather poor to the small changes of moisture content encountered in industrial processes. This has been found to be the case when it was used for measuring the moisture content of paper [27].

Resonance Circuits. This method utilizes the well-known characteristics of the variation of voltage or current in a series or parallel resonant circuit, near its resonance frequency. As shown in Fig. 5.24, over a limited portion of the resonance curve, the voltage or current will vary approximately linearly with the unknown value of the capacitance which is now forming a part of the resonant circuit and whose capacity varies with change in moisture content of the sample. The SRI electronic moisture meter developed by Pande [28] is a typical example of a moisture meter based on the utilization of the "off-resonance" principle.

A block diagram of the electronic layout of the SRI moisture meter is given in Fig. 5.25, which shows the crystal oscillator A, modulator oscillator B, detector amplifier system D, electrode

1 ELECTRICAL TECHNIQUES   303

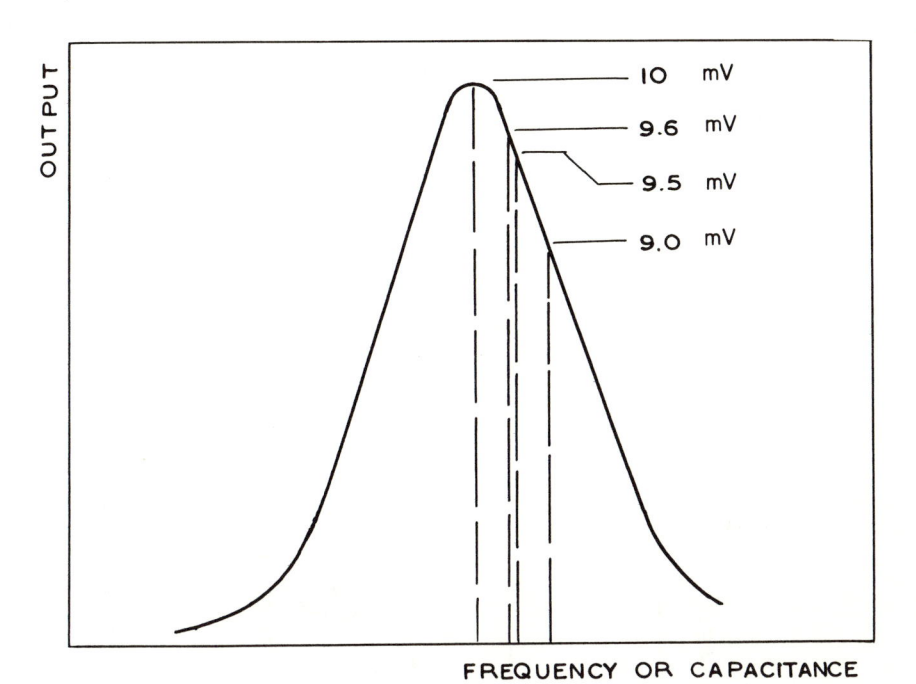

FIG. 5.24. Relation between voltage and frequency in a resonant circuit in millivolts.

system E, linear amplifiers J and K, and calibrated meter M. The electrode system E consists of two parallel plates whose distance apart can be minutely adjusted by a rack-and-pinion arrangement and measured by conventional feeler gauges. However, as a result of operational studies in a textile mill, it was found that this distance could be kept constant in almost all cases to 7/64 in. without affecting the sensitivity of the moisture meter.

Figure 5.26 shows the circuit diagram of the SRI electronic moisture meter which consists of the crystal oscillator A and tube V_1 oscillating at a frequency of 5.40 Hz and modulated by the phase shift oscillator B (tube V_3) at constant frequency of 800 Hz. This modulated radiofrequency signal is fed to grid g of the detector system as well as the high-Q parallel resonant circuit consisting of a condenser C and low-loss coil L and the plates of the electrode system E. Initially this high-Q circuit is in complete resonance

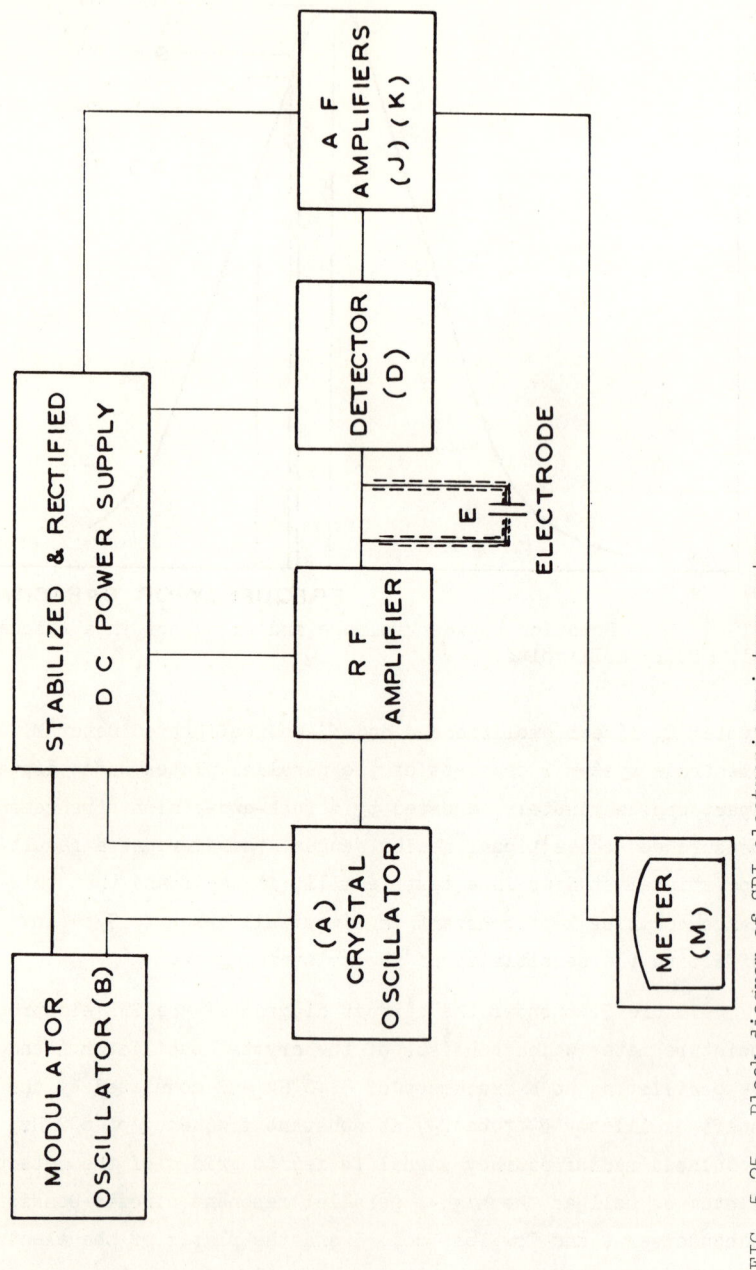

FIG. 5.25. Block diagram of SRI electronic moisture meter.

1 ELECTRICAL TECHNIQUES 305

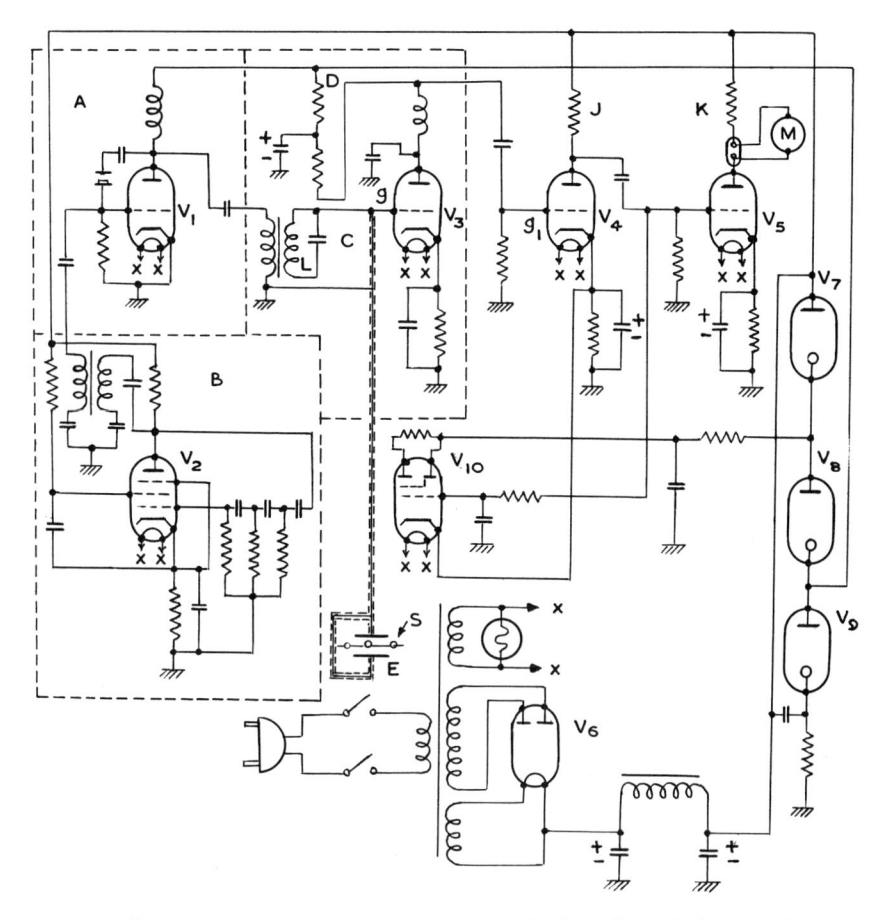

FIG. 5.26. Circuit diagram of the SRI electronic moisture meter.

with the frequency of the crystal oscillator as visually indicated by the null detector V_{10}. The signal is demodulated and amplified by the detector-amplifier system D (V_3). This detected and amplified signal is connected to the grid g_1 of another linear amplifier tube (V_4). The output from tube V_4 is fed to the grid of the next tube V_5, the plate current of which varies in accordance with the change in capacitance of the electrode system E. The plate current fluctuations of V_5 are shown by the meter M connected in its plate circuit. The high voltage to the tubes V_1, V_2, V_3, V_4, V_5 is supplied by a stabilized power supply comprising thyratron tubes V_7, V_8, and V_9.

The apparatus works as follows: When a sample containing some moisture is introduced between the two plates of the electrode system E, a different current is indicated on the meter M because the resonant frequency of the circuit is changed by the presence of moisture in the sample. The current varies linearly with the moisture content of the sample, and the meter M is calibrated by conventional vacuum oven-dry methods to give a direct reading in terms of percentage of moisture content. As it is not necessary for the sample to touch the electrodes, this system is found to be most useful in continuous industrial processes. Both the radiofrequency oscillators A and audiooscillators B are completely shielded and earthed to avoid extraneous effects. By modifying the shape of the plates of the electrode system a "dielectric cell" (Fig. 5.20) is designed which is used for measuring the moisture content of materials in bulk, e.g., cotton, grains, soils, sand, coal, and clays. The moisture meter calibration remains steady and results are not affected by changes in temperature, humidity, or power-supply fluctuations. This is due to a "floating-zero" adjustment of the moisture meter. However, since aging of components such as tubes and condensers affects the calibration, they should be tested periodically and changed if necessary.

After a linear relationship between moisture content and output current has been established, accurate calibration of meter readings in terms of moisture content is necessary. There are two independent methods of calibration, i.e., the Karl Fischer method and the vacuum oven-drying method. The Karl Fischer method is rather complicated and requires very great precaution to keep the hygroscopic chemicals free from moisture. It is, therefore, more convenient to use the conditioned oven-drying method. The preparation of samples having known moisture content at room temperature has been described earlier. The bone-dry sample is prepared by heating it at 105 to 110°C in an oven having automatic temperature control and an air-circulation arrangement for repeated periods of 5 hr until no change in weight is observed. This weight is used for obtaining the dry reading on the meter. In all cases two exactly similar samples are prepared, one for the moisture meter reading and the other for checking by the oven-drying method. The two sets of samples are kept exactly similar so that sample variation is kept to a minimum.

This moisture meter was tested for a period of 2 years on a sizing machine and was found to give very satisfactory results. Values of moisture content as indicated by the meter showed excellent agreement with those obtained under mill conditions on an oven-dry basis [29]. The SRI moisture meter was also used for measuring the moisture content of materials in bulk by using the dielectric cell (Fig. 5.20). In the case of grain an excellent agreement between the meter readings and oven-dry values is obtained [30] as shown in Table 5.1.

TABLE 5.1

Comparative Values of Moisture Content of Grains as Determined by the Electronic Meter in the Dielectric Cell and Standard Oven-Dry Method

Sample no.	Electronic meter reading (%)	Oven-dry values (%)
1	12.15	12.05
2	12.90	12.98
3	13.20	13.15
4	13.65	13.70
5	13.80	13.88
6	13.98	14.05
7	14.45	14.55
8	14.90	14.78
9	15.80	15.88
10	16.80	16.75

For fluffy materials such as wool or cotton, the sample holder (Fig. 5.21) was found to give reliable results. The SRI moisture meter has also been used successfully to measure the moisture contents of coal, soils, and sands with an accuracy of ±0.2%. Details of these measurements are given in chapters dealing with the applications of electronic techniques to such materials.

Beat Frequency Oscillation Method for Moisture Measurement. Anderson et al. [21] have developed an electronic moisture meter for measuring the moisture content of different varieties of grains by utilizing the phenomenon of beats obtained by mixing two radiofrequency oscillations. In this system, two oscillators, one having a fixed, preferably a crystal-controlled frequency, and the other having a variable frequency, are used (Fig. 5.27). The test condenser and a calibrated condenser are connected to the variable oscillator. Initially both the oscillators have the same frequency, i.e., show a zero beat, as indicated by the null detector which can be either a headphone or a meter. A similar circuit (Fig. 5.28) has been used by Rasmussen and Anderson [31] in a moisture meter devised for estimating the moisture content of various types of grains. The circuit shows a crystal oscillator for operation at 7.3 MHz. Three condensers, C_1, C_2, and C_3, are connected in its plate circuit. The condenser C_3 forms a dielectric cell for the material to be tested and C_2 is a calibrated condenser.

Before the sample is placed in the dielectric cell C_3, the oscillator tube is made to oscillate, which is indicated by a change in the shadow angle of the indicator section of the same tube. When the sample is placed in the dielectric cell, its capacity changes and oscillation ceases. The change in the capacity of C_3 is compensated by adjusting the capacitance of C_2 (which is calibrated) until oscillation just starts again. Each dial division of C_2 represents 0.144 pF. The change in the reading of C_2 gives the value of the change in capacity of C_3 caused by the moisture content of the sample. This meter has been calibrated with 159 samples of

1 ELECTRICAL TECHNIQUES 309

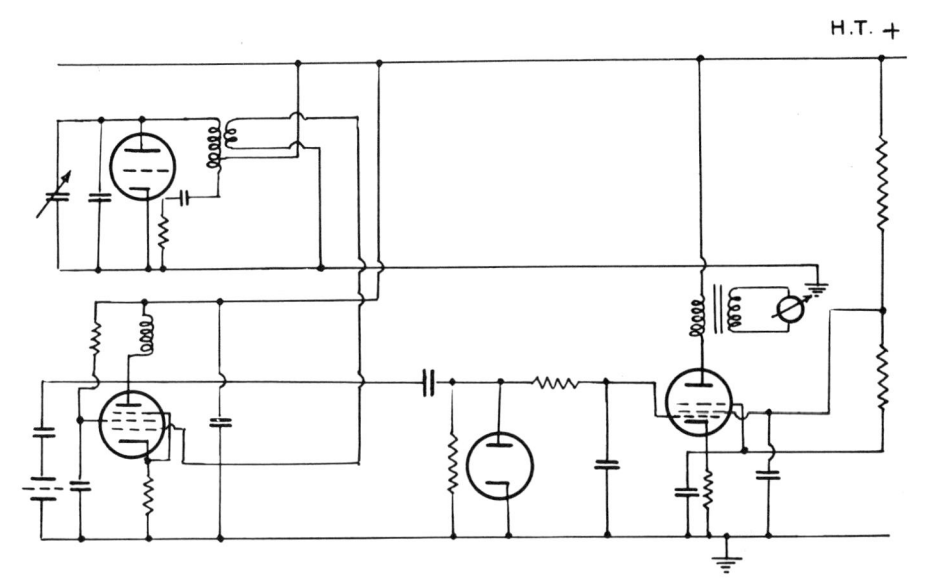

FIG. 5.27. Circuit diagram of an electronic moisture meter using a beat-frequency oscillator circuit.

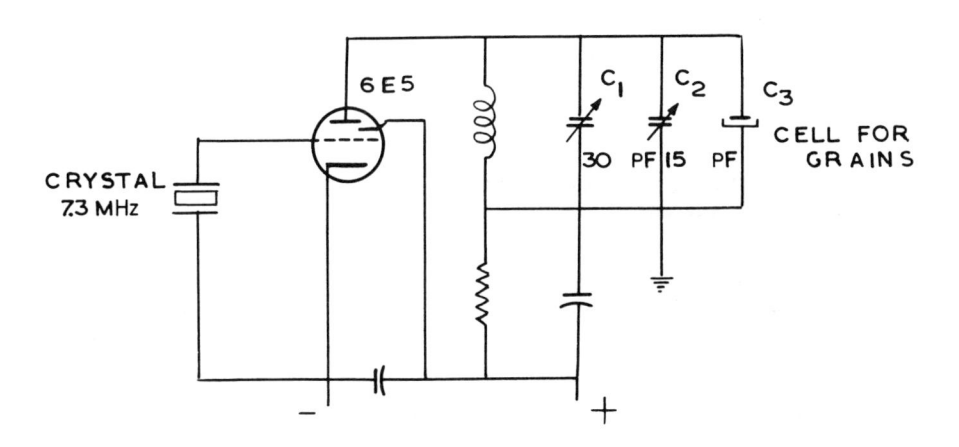

FIG. 5.28. Circuit diagram of the Rasmussen and Anderson moisture meter.

Canadian wheat by the standard ovendrying method, and the standard error of estimate was found to be 0.36% over the range 10 to 17% moisture content. Such a meter, however, cannot be used for continuous measurement as it requires a two-step operation.

The author has recently developed a transistorized moisture meter whose details have been published elsewhere [32]. This transistorized moisture meter is again of the capacitance type and is based on the "off-resonance" principle already discussed. The total capacity of the electrode system is less than 100 pF. This transistorized moisture meter has been used for measuring the moisture content of samples of coal (of moisture content below 5%) received from various mines in India and gave consistently repeatable and accurate results (Table 5.2).

TABLE 5.2

Comparison of Transistorized
Moisture Meter Readings with Oven-Dry Values
for Samples of Different Varieties of Indian Coal

Sample no.	Type of sample	Transistorized moisture meter readings (%)	Oven-dry values (%)
1	Coal with rock phosphate (60 mesh)	9.50	9.40
2	Coal with bauxite (60 mesh)	1.40	1.50
3	Coal (Upper Kurja sample) (60 mesh)	4.90	5.00
4	Coal (Birla Cotton Mills) (60 mesh)	6.10	6.00

The simple LC parallel resonant circuit and its modifications, which are mostly used in the case of vacuum tube circuits, are not suitable for application as coupling networks for high-frequency amplifiers using transistors. The parallel resonant network, while offering a high impedance in a transistor circuit, presents a low impedance at frequencies removed from resonance so that oscillations are likely to occur. Series resonant circuits are accordingly employed in a transistor tuning circuit. The series resonant circuit has its minimum value of impedance at resonance and it is then equal to the coil resistance. It is thus seen that a series-coupled network should have a comparatively high resistance, to ensure stability, while the overall Q of the circuit should permit the required selectivity. It is due to these considerations that a series resonant circuit has been used in the transistorized model of the SRI moisture meter, whereas a parallel-tuned circuit was employed in the mains model.

The electronic (transistor) circuit (Fig. 5.29) consists of the following units:

1. A crystal controlled rf oscillator
2. A Wien bridge phase shift audiooscillator
3. A series-tuned network with an electrode system
4. A crystal detector and a demodulating circuit
5. Low-frequency amplifiers
6. A calibrated meter
7. A highly stabilized zener-controlled battery supply

The functioning of this electronic unit is briefly as follows: The crystal-controlled oscillator produces a constant radiofrequency of 13.30 MHz and is modulated by a phase-shift audiooscillator operating at 800 Hz. The modulating frequency and amplitude are kept rigidly constant and undeviated by incorporating a Wien bridge circuit [33-34]. The modulated radiofrequency signal of the crystal-controlled oscillator (RFO) modulated by the audiofrequency oscillator (AFO) is fed to a high-Q, series-tuned resonant circuit which consists of a tuning coil, a negative temperature coefficient condenser, and the electrode condenser E containing the sample S whose moisture content is to be measured (Fig. 5.29). The coupling condenser C_3 is 10 pF. To begin with the tuned circuit is in complete resonance with the crystal-controlled oscillator at 13.30 MHz and a steady signal voltage is obtained in the output of the tuned circuit.

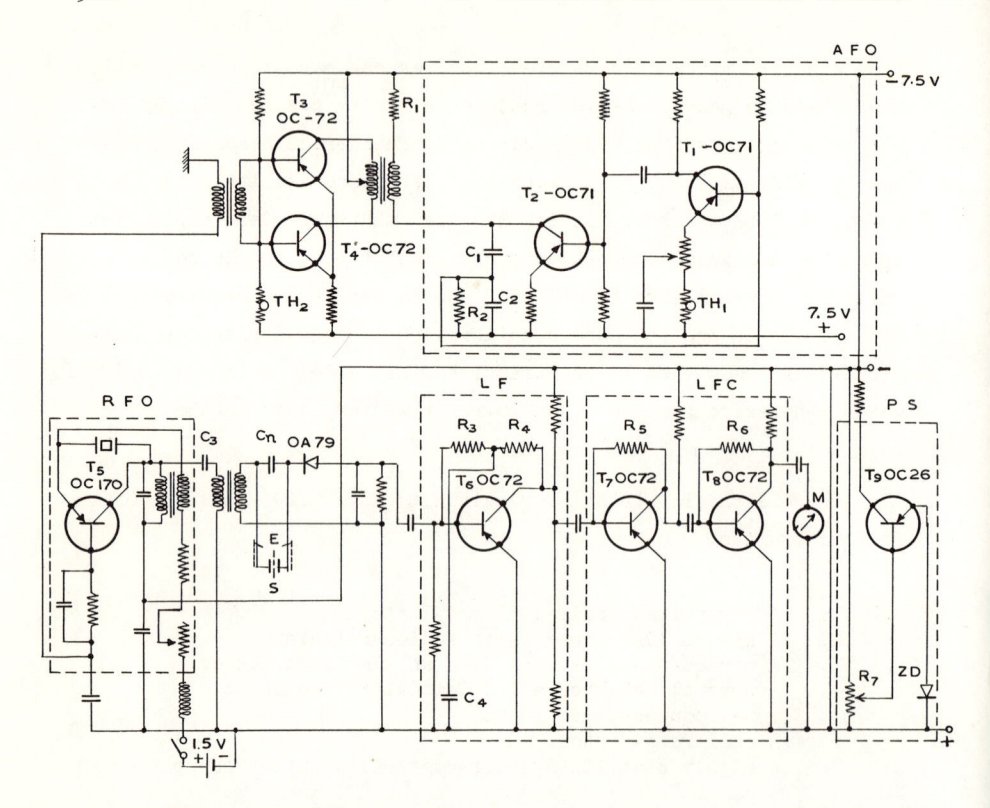

FIG. 5.29. Circuit diagram of SRI transistorized moisture meter.

This signal is detected by a crystal detector OA 79, operating in the linear part of its characteristic. This rectified signal is amplified by transistor amplifiers LF and LFC and indicated by the calibrated meter M connected in the collector circuit of the output transistor. This is the balanced or null position of the electronic circuit. Whenever there is a change in the moisture content of the sample S forming the dielectric of the electrode condenser E, the resonance conditions are altered and an off-resonance condition is obtained resulting in change of the power (signal) output of the series resonant circuit, causing a corresponding change in the rectified voltage and the collector current which is shown by the meter.

The battery voltage has been regulated by using a Zener diode (ZD) as is well known the Zener reference diode establishes a fixed

1 ELECTRICAL TECHNIQUES   313

voltage. In the regulator circuit the Zener diode is used in combination with a transistor. This combination acts to maintain a constant output voltage.

    3. <u>Indicating meter or recorder:</u> Finally the output of the current is connected to a microampere meter or milliampere meter or recorder which indicates the moisture content of the sample into corresponding current variations. As described earlier this current is calibrated in terms of moisture content.

1.4.3 Performance Characteristics. The range of moisture contents over which electronic measurements are absolutely precise depends on the nature of the sample but is always limited to the hygroscopic range, the most satisfactory results being obtained on materials in equilibrium with atmospheres of relative humidities of 30 to 90%. When the material is drier than this, the moisture is so tightly bound that it has a relatively small effect on the electrical properties, while when the material is very damp, the electrical characteristics are strongly influenced by factors other than the moisture content. Electronic meters in general show about 0.5% higher values than those obtained by oven-drying methods, but capacity-type meters are accurate up to ±0.2% in the range 5 to 20% (Table 5.3). For highest accuracy, however, the meter should be calibrated for each type of material in the same state as that in which the moisture content is to be measured. In order to get the best results from capacitance moisture meters, the following factors should be taken into consideration.

    1. <u>Moisture distribution:</u> Moisture should be well distributed throughout the sample being tested and the moisture content should preferably be under 40%, depending on the nature of the sample.

    2. <u>Presence of electrolytes:</u> Small concentrations of electrolytes do not introduce appreciable error in the moisture measurement; excessive concentration of additives in the form of electrolytes,

TABLE 5.3

Comparison of Moisture Measurement Values as Obtained
by a Dielectric Moisture Meter (Kappa Moisture Meter) and
a Standard Oven-Drying Method (Spencer Oven) for Raw Sugar

Sample No.	Spencer Oven Moisture, %	Spencer Oven Dilution Indicator	Kappa Moisture, %	Kappa Dilution Indicator	Polarization Range
1	1.13	68	1.16	71	97.2°
2	1.38	51	1.36	50	95.5°
3	1.02	40	1.02	40	96.4°
4	0.77	32	0.82	35	96.8°
5	1.01	44	1.02	45	96.7°
6	0.92	66	0.98	69	97.6°
7	1.07	58	1.02	54	97.1°
8	0.93	53	0.90	50	97.3°

however, are likely to lead to erroneous results by introducing dielectric losses which give a higher indicator reading. Separate calibrations may be required for such samples.

3. Packing factor: For uniform results, the sample in the dielectric cell should be packed to a constant density. It is usually best to pack a known weight of the sample into a fixed volume to get the same packing factor every time. In the case of sheet materials and parallel plate electrodes, the sheet should be kept taut so that a constant mass of sheet is included between the plates forming the condenser. However, the packing density is not so important a factor in the case of capacity meters as in the conductivity meters.

4. Temperature effect: A temperature correction is necessary if the temperature at which measurements are made differs widely from the temperature at which the moisture meter has been calibrated,

1 ELECTRICAL TECHNIQUES

as the dielectric constant of water is very sensitive to temperature changes. For accurate measurements temperature corrections should be applied.

1.4.4 Merits and Demerits.

1. The calibration of such a meter is not appreciably affected by the majority of additive agents encountered in processed products; whereas the addition of acid salts in a product may have no appreciable effect on its dielectric constant, its conductivity may be affected considerably.

2. A comparatively large change in dielectric constant occurs for small changes in moisture content of most materials, hence very good sensitivity can be obtained.

3. It is not necessary that the material be in contact with the electrodes. In the continuous measurement systems which are most convenient in industrial operations, the usual practice is for the material to contact one electrode only.

4. The electrode system can be modified in different ways to meet the requirements for sampling a large range of materials, including liquids, and thus its applicability has been made almost universal.

5. In the case of capacitative-type moisture meters, it has been reported that dyes ranging in pH from 2.7 to 6.7 give no calibration difficulty.

6. When the moisture meter is exposed to abnormal temperature and tension variations, its calibration is affected, but it should be noted that such variations seldom occur under operating conditions.

7. It is possible to use the capacitance-type moisture meter as a monitoring device as well as a measuring instrument as is the case with the SRI meter.

2 SONIC AND ULTRASONIC TECHNIQUES

The degree of absorption of sound energy is dependent on the medium through which it is transmitted. For many sheet materials such as paper, textiles, etc., sound absorption also depends on the quantity of water present in the sample. This principle has been applied [35] to the measurement of the moisture content of such materials. An audiofrequency sound of a fixed frequency is generated by a phase-shift RC audiogenerator and fed to a loudspeaker as shown in Fig. 5.30. This generator is placed on one side of the web, and a receiver or microphone placed on the other side picks up the transmitted sound; the output of the microphone after passing through a sufficient number of stages of electronic amplification gives an adequate voltmeter reading. The resultant amplifier signal can also be utilized for electrical control of the web-forming process by automatic adjustments when the moisture content departs from a desired value.

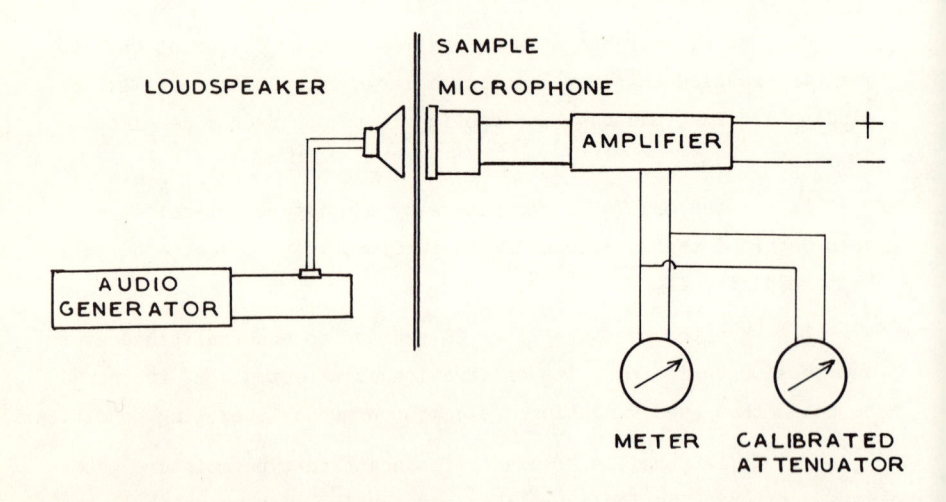

FIG. 5.30. Diagram of a sonic moisture meter for a web of paper or sheet of textile.

2 SONIC AND ULTRASONIC TECHNIQUES

Another property related to the change in moisture content of the material is the sonic or acoustic velocity. Considerable improvements in the design of a sonic analyzer based on this principle have been made recently by Martin and Mounfield [36] whose apparatus is shown in Fig. 5.31. In the figure, T is a sound transmitter in which a diaphragm is caused to vibrate at the impressed frequency

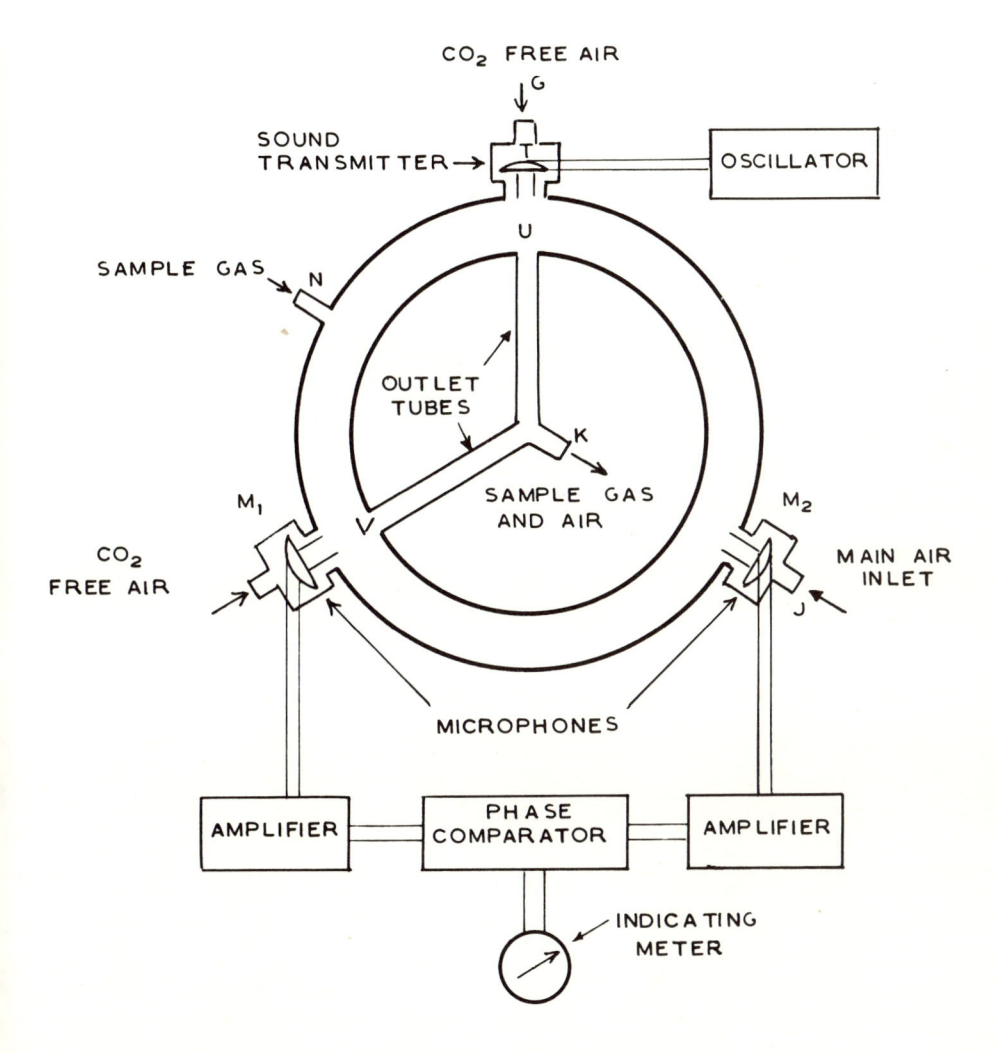

FIG. 5.31. Schematic diagram of a sonic moisture meter for gases.

within an annulus of circular cross section. A convenient form of transmitter T is of the type used in hearing aids and may be electromagnetic or piezoelectric in action; M_1 and M_2 are two microphones approximately equidistant from each other and from T. The amplified output from microphone M_1 (or M_2) provides the signal which initiates the flow of direct current through the indicating meter while the signal from M_2 (or M_1) shuts off the flow of current. The meter indication thus depends directly on the phase difference existing between the signals from M_1 and M_2, and therefore on the composition of the gas contained in the tube. Sample gas is fed into the tube at N, approximately halfway between T and M_1, while a datum gas, such as dry CO_2 free of air, is fed in at G approximately halfway between T and M_1. Outlet tubes U and V are fitted at points opposite T and M_1. By careful control of the gas flow into N and G, the mixing of the two gases in the spaces between T and M_1 and T and M_2 can be kept to a minimum. Standing waves are greatly reduced since no reflecting surfaces exist, except slight discontinuities at the inlet and outlet points, and also where T, M_1, and M_2 are connected to the circular tube. In this apparatus the relative phase lag of the voltage at the microphone with respect to that at the source gives a measure of the moisture content of the gas. In order to avoid ambiguity the phase shift is not allowed to exceed 2π or 360°C. In order to measure the phase change an electronic circuit is employed in which direct current is caused to flow at a certain point on the ac wave which is the source of sound, while the aforesaid current is switched off at a suitable point on the ac wave derived from the amplified output from the microphone, or vice versa. This interrupted direct current is passed through a meter. Owing to the high interruption frequency, and the high inertia of the measuring instrument, a steady deflection is obtained which changes as the value of the relative phase lag varies.

Utilizing the same principle of sound absorption, ultrasonic waves have been used for measurement of moisture content. Due to their high frequency (short wavelength), these waves have special properties of reflection, refraction, and absorption. They can be beamed and focused in a desired manner, and consequently a number of technical and industrial applications have been made, which are fully described in the literature [37-39]. In such devices the audio generator is replaced by an ultrasonic generator comprising a radiofrequency oscillator and a piezoelectric transducer, viz., a quartz or ceramic crystal, the microphone being replaced by a piezoelectric quartz receiver having the same resonant frequency as the generator. The ultrasonic waves, after passing through the web of material, are picked up by the piezoelectric transducer and amplified by a suitable amplifier whose output is connected to a meter or a recorder.

It has also been observed that ultrasonic velocity is dependent on the medium through which the sound passes and that the presence of water in a solid medium may influence it. Based on this principle, ultrasonic velocity measurements have been used for determining bound water in aqueous solutions of electrolytes and nonelectrolytes [40]. The usual method of determining ultrasonic velocity in a liquid is based on the Debye-Sears [41] method, which is based on the phenomenon of diffraction of light waves by a liquid column. When vibrations are produced in a liquid column by a vibrating crystal refraction and compression waves are set up in it and the liquid behaves like a diffraction grating, producing a diffraction pattern of the slit through which light waves are passing. By measuring the distance d between the fringes, together with the frequency of the radiofrequency crystal oscillator, by a wave meter, the velocity of the ultrasonic waves is determined by the following equation:

$$2d \sin \theta = n\lambda \qquad (5.8)$$

where θ is the angle of the diffracted ray and λ is its wavelength, and n is the order of diffraction.

The determination of bound water in aqueous solutions of electrolytes and nonelectrolytes has been made by Pasynskii [42] from ultrasonic velocity measurements based on this technique. In the case of sugars, i.e., nonelectrolytes, Shiio et al. [43] have derived equations relating volumes of the solutions, the solvent, and the solute with adiabatic compressibilities, which in turn were calculated from ultrasonic measurements by the well-known relationship:

$$V = \left(\frac{C_a}{\rho}\right)^{1/2} \tag{5.9}$$

where V is the ultrasonic velocity, ρ is the density of the substance, and C_a is the adiabatic compressibility.

These authors measured ultrasonic velocities in aqueous solutions of glucose, maltose, and dextrin at 20°C by a different method. They used an interferometer and used an X-cut crystal having a resonant frequency of 1 MHz. The amount of bound water was found to be 0.43, 0.23, and 0.40 g for glucose, maltose, and dextrin, respectively. For glucose, the results indicated that 1 mole of water was bound to each free OH group. For maltose, however, the lower result indicated a decrease in free OH groups due to intermolecular hydrogen bonding.

3 MICROWAVE METHOD

3.1 Introduction

It has long been recognized that attenuation due to rain affects radar performance, but the idea of using the absorption of microwave energy in a material as an index of its water content was not recognized until 1956 when Watson [44] measured the relationship between the attenuation produced by various building materials and their water content, and established the fact that this method could be used for studying the structure as well as the moisture content of these materials. Electromagnetic waves, including microwaves, had been applied [45] earlier for detecting the presence of water mole-

3 MICROWAVE METHOD

cules in crystals and solids. However, the experimental techniques involved in the microwave technology are different from those employed in the case of ordinary radiofrequency waves. Since detailed descriptions of microwave theory and experimental techniques are readily available in the literature [46-48] only a brief description of the principles and techniques involved in the measurement of moisture content of certain materials is given here.

3.2 Theory

The electric dipole relaxation of water in the centimeter wave band has been widely employed by Hasted [49] as a nondestructive test for water. Among the most valuable developments is the apparatus originally developed by Watson [44]. This consists of 10-cm wavelength transmitting and receiving horn antennas, which are placed on either side of a wall, or similar slab-shaped specimen, the dampness of which is indicated by the absorption. The principle of measuring losses at microwave frequencies, on which the method depends, is based on the fact that at centimeter wavelengths the loss tangent and dielectric constant of water are very high compared with those of most materials in which water is absorbed. The loss of energy in a dielectric can be accounted for by considering the dielectric constant as a complex quantity of the form

$$\epsilon = \epsilon' - j\epsilon'' \tag{5.10}$$

where ϵ' is the real part of the dielectric, and ϵ'' is the imaginary part of the dielectric. The loss tangent is defined as

$$\tan \delta = \epsilon'' = \frac{\text{loss current}}{\text{charging current}} \tag{5.11}$$

and ϵ'' is the loss factor of the material. At normal temperatures in the frequency range 1 to 30 GHz, the dielectric constant of water is between 40 and 80 and the loss tangent ranges from 0.15 to 1.2.

Most dry materials have a dielectric constant ranging from 1 to 5 and a loss tangent between 0.001 and 0.05, unless some conducting material is present. Differences of the above order mean that the loss due to the water is at least ten times greater than the loss in the material when no water is present.

Based on quantum-mechanical considerations, it is possible to calculate the relaxation frequency of the water molecule in the microwave region as many liquids, solutions, and solids have absorption peaks and associated regions of anomalous dispersion caused by orientation of the molecular dipoles in the electromagnetic radiation field. The frequencies of the absorption peaks are given by the following relation:

$$f = \frac{1}{2\pi\tau} \qquad (5.12)$$

where f is the frequency of electromagnetic radiation, and τ is the relaxation time of its molecular dipole. The relaxation time τ is given theoretically by the following equation due to Debye [48].

$$\tau = \frac{V 3\eta}{KT} \qquad (5.13)$$

where η is the macroscopic viscosity of the liquid, V is the volume of a molecule of the liquid, K is the Boltzmann constant, and T is the temperature (absolute scale). Water at room temperature has a viscosity of about 0.01 P and the radius of its molecule is 2 Å. Hence the relaxation time is given as 0.25×10^{-10} sec.

This value of the relaxation time of water corresponds to a wavelength of 1 cm. Though there is a wide divergence between the theoretical and experimental values of the microwave frequency of maximum dielectric absorption, Debye's theory [48] gives an idea of the order of frequency involved for investigating relative absorption by water molecules. It has recently been found by Garg and Smyth [50] that water shows two relaxation times when in a mixture with different fractions of dioxane. In the water-dioxane mixtures, the dioxane molecules alter the environments of some of the molecules and thereby introduce a second relaxation time. In the case of water, it has been observed that the absorption band corresponds to a frequency of 2450 MHz, which falls in the microwave region of the radiofrequency spectrum. It has been reported [51] that there is a linear relationship between the moisture content of granular materials and the absorption of microwaves having frequencies of 2450 MHz (S band) and 10,680 MHz (X band). Microwave absorption depends mainly on the moisture content and is not affected by the nature of the granular solid material, thus making available a unique method for its determination.

3.3 Design Features of the Microwave Moisture Meter

The microwave moisture meter has been developed jointly by Associated Electrical Industries (AEI) and the Building Research Station (UK), and the details of the apparatus have been recently described by Taylor [52-53]. The AEI moisture meter is designed to measure attenuations rapidly and accurately at one or two frequencies (in X band or S band). The equipment as a whole consists of the following:

1. A constant source of microwave radiation of 2450 and 10,680 MHz modulated by a square wave of 3 kHz
2. Waveguide terminating in a horn and associated components
3. A microwave detector
4. A microwave attenuator and amplifier
5. An indicating meter

The experimental arrangement is shown schematically in Fig. 5.32. This is the usual tranmitter-receiver combination, the specimen forming the absorbing medium. The most commonly used source of microwave radiation is the reflex klystron oscillator which works on the well-known principle of velocity modulation and electron

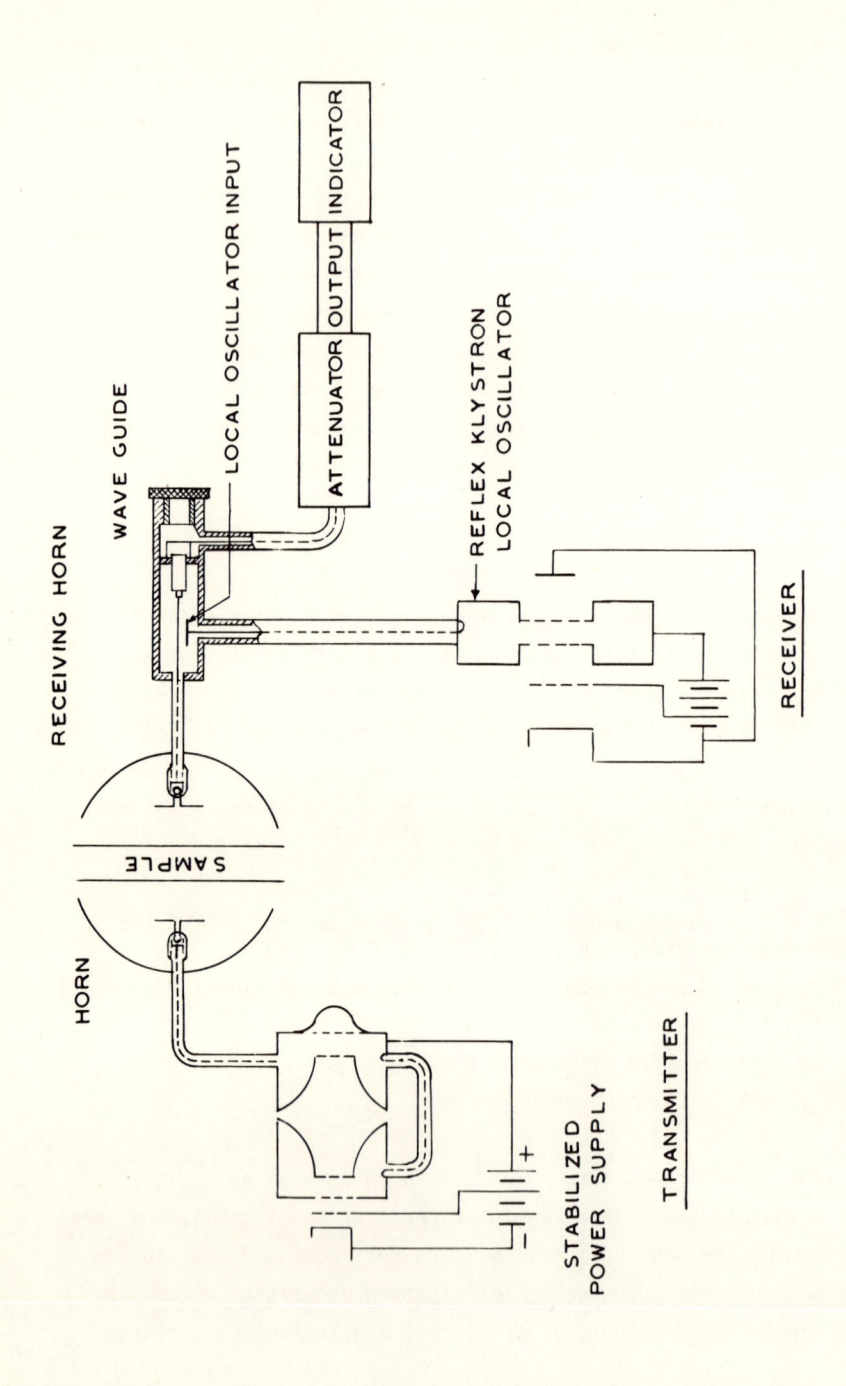

FIG. 5.32. Schematic diagram of a microwave moisture meter.

3 MICROWAVE METHOD 325

bunching [54]. With careful oscillator design, using high-Q circuits and a highly regulated power supply, it is possible to achieve a frequency stability of an order sufficient for this purpose. By using an external high-Q cavity, Pound [55] has been able to control the frequency of microwave oscillators oscillating at 10,000 MHz to within a few kilocycles per second. This oscillator gives a modulated power output of 0.5 W and is coupled to a radiating horn by a quarter-wavelength waveguide system (Fig. 5.32). The receiver consists of the receiving horn which is coupled to a 70-dB variable attenuator followed by crystal mixer, local oscillator, limiter, discriminator, and final amplifier. The transmitter and receiver units of the AEI moisture meter are fully transistorized with the exception of the klystron oscillators. A photograph of the complete AEI apparatus, i.e., the X-band moisture meter, is shown in Fig. 5.33.

FIG. 5.33. Microwave moisture meter developed by AEI (UK).

3.4 Procedure for Moisture Measurement

To measure moisture in solids or liquids, the transmitter and receiver are set up with transmitting and receiving horns facing each other in a horizontal plane. The distance between the horns is set to be the same as the thickness of the material being measured and the attenuator is adjusted to give a midscale reading on the meter. The material is then placed in the gap and the attenuator is reset to give the same reading on the meter. The difference between the two attenuator readings gives the attenuation due to the material. For measurements on powders or granular materials, a constant weight is used in a cell. Because of the variations in packing density which may be experienced, it has been found necessary to measure the attenuation through the cell in a vertical direction. Under these conditions, as a given weight of the material packs down in the cell, the sample thickness changes but the amount of water per unit area remains constant. However, as the packing density increases, so does the dielectric constant and the reflection from the two air-material interfaces, thus increasing the measured attenuation. It has been found by Taylor [52] that if proper leveling of samples of granular materials and cereals is done by a plunger, the packing effect is negligible.

In all measurements, the cross-sectional area of the sample must be larger than the horn aperture so as to minimize leakage of energy around the material. For assessing granular materials at 2.45 GHz with a $5\frac{1}{4}$ x $7\frac{3}{4}$ in. horn aperture, a simple and convenient cell consists of a Perspex box with a cross section of 13 x 11 in. and a height adjusted to suit the material. At 10.688 GHz with 3 x 3 in. horns a Perspex tube has been used to enclose a sample of about 5-in. diameter circular cross section. For most materials these cell dimensions prove to be adequate. The sample is leveled, and ideally the horns should be in contact with the material or be held in a constant relationship close to the surface. It is found, however, that with many materials a fixed horn spacing can be used with a constant cell height. In some cases the cell may consist of

3 MICROWAVE METHOD

a waveguide directly coupled between transmitter and receiver. The small cross-sectional area used enables the amount of material to be minimized when only small samples are available, while if the water content is low, it permits a greater thickness to be examined without requiring an excessive amount of material. The water content of each material must first be determined by one of the conventional methods available and a calibration chart prepared showing percentage water plotted against decibel attenuation. This chart can subsequently be used in conjunction with the instrument to ascertain the water contents of samples of that material. Calibration charts of the AEI moisture meter for wheat and foundry sand are shown in Figs. 5.34 and 5.35, respectively.

3.5 Application of the Microwave Moisture Meter

Though the moisture meter was originally developed for measuring the moisture content of soils, sand, and other similar building materials and structures, it has found wide applications in the measurement of the moisture contents of such diverse materials as

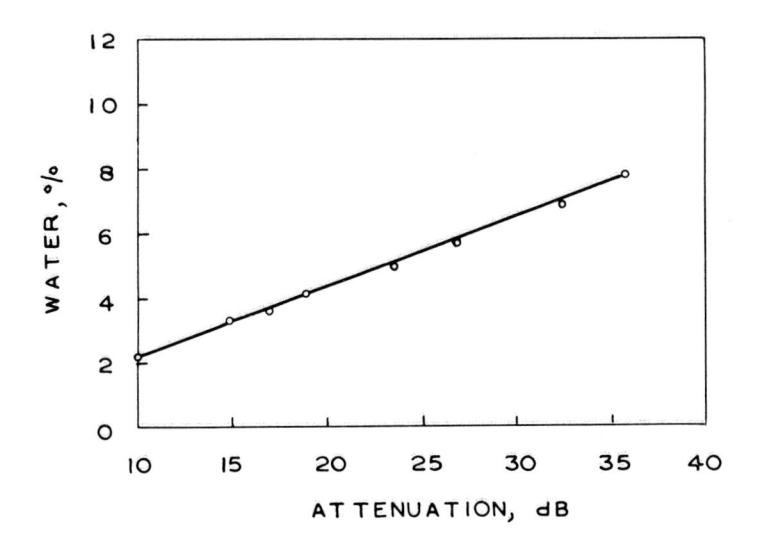

FIG. 5.34. Calibration curves of the AEI moisture meter for wheat.

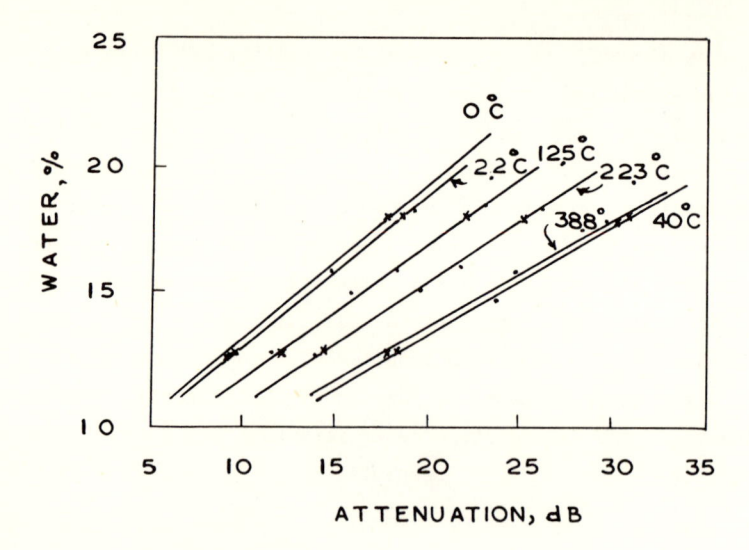

FIG. 5.35. Calibration curves of the AEI moisture meter for foundry sand at different temperatures.

wood, pulp, animal feed, nylon tow, cereals, coal, marzipan, etc. This moisture meter has been used for determination of the moisture content of proteins by Vogelhut [56] and of plain cakes by Ince and Turner [57]. Lagutin et al. [58] found that the microwave method was most suited for the measurement of moisture content of building materials such as cement, sand, and clays, etc. Data obtained by applying this moisture meter to different materials and the special sampling techniques adopted for them have been described in the chapters dealing with the applications of the meter in the respective fields.

This moisture meter can also be adopted for the measurement of small quantities of water of the order of a few ppm. At water contents below 100 ppm, the attenuation due to the water is small compared with the basic dry attenuation. It is therefore necessary to use microwave bridge techniques in which the sample of wet material is compared with a sample of dry material, so that only the difference caused by the water is observed. For very small samples in the region where the water losses predominate, the samples could be

3 MICROWAVE METHOD

introduced into a resonant cavity and the change in Q factor measured and related to the water content. For gases, where the attenuation effects are very small, a resonant cavity could again be used and the changes in resonant frequency measured. This change would be caused by the change in dielectric constant of the gas due to the addition of water vapor. In performing this measurement it would be necessary to use a reference cavity filled with dry gas, so that the effects of frequency drift and transmitter output variations could be overcome.

The instrument described so far has a limited potential for continuous indication of water content. Since the detector response is a good approximation to a square law, a 2:1 change of output meter reading represents a 3-dB attenuation, while a deflection from full-scale to one-eighth scale on the meter represents 9 dB. With a fixed attenuator setting it should be possible to see the variation of water content on the meter over a limited range, depending on the sample thickness used. It would be necessary to check the zero setting occasionally, and to do this requires either no material between the horns or a system of a waveguide, switches, and a reference attenuator. Measurements made in this way take no account of temperature changes in the sample, but these could be allowed for by using a sealed sample of the material in a waveguide as the reference attenuator.

3.6 Factors Affecting the Accuracy of Measurement

In a measurement based on the difference of two attenuator readings the accuracy depends only on the attenuator. This is accurate up to 0.1 dB as it can be read to 0.1 dB. Thus if the sample is thick enough to give a change of attenuation of at least 3 dB for 1% change of water content, the error introduced by the instrument itself will not exceed 0.07%. The readings obtained from the moisture meter are affected in a number of ways by the form of the sample. The various factors involved have been discussed by Taylor [52] as follows:

3.6.1 Leakage. If the cross-sectional area of the sample is much larger than that of the horn aperture, there is no leakage of microwave energy. However, in case the size of the sample or the cell is limited and is smaller than the aperture of horn, leakage of energy takes place. It is possible to detect this by moving a hand around the edge of the sample and observing the effect on the output meter. If the sample has less than 35 to 40 dB attenuation, the effects of leakage are generally small; above this some form of screening is necessary for one of the moisture meter units, to ensure that all the energy arriving at the receiver comes through the sample. There are materials whose reflection coefficients are very high and these will require either a screen or microwave-absorbing material around the horn, even though the attenuation is below 40 dB.

3.6.2 Formation of Standing Waves. At each air-material interface, there is an impedance mismatch and consequent reflection of microwave energy. In the case of a sample of low attenuation, the reflected wave from the output interface can either add to or subtract from the wave reflected from the input interface and cause variations in the measured attenuation. If the minimum attenuation through the sample is kept above 7 dB the reflection from the output interface is absorbed in the sample and the interaction can be neglected. The loss of power due to reflection increases the apparent attenuation of the material; this is, however, accounted for in the calibration.

3.6.3 Particle Size. In a granular material attenuation of microwave energy can be regarded as due to two causes, the dielectric losses in the water and the scattering of the beam at the particle surfaces in the material. This scattered energy will be absorbed, but the degree of scattering, and hence the losses, will depend on the particle size. To avoid unpredictable variations in loss due to scatter, the particle size should be small compared with the wavelength, preferably less than one-fourth of the wavelength used. It is important to remember that the wavelength in a material depends on its dielectric constant; for example, the wavelength in

3 MICROWAVE METHOD

lean meat with a dielectric constant of 40 is 2 cm at 2.450 GHz so that the maximum permissible particle size in this case is about 0.5 cm. The magnitude of variation of losses due to scattering can be checked by shaking and thus rearranging a given sample.

3.6.4 **Polarization**. The radiation from the moisture meter is polarized in one plane. It has been observed that many materials show different attentuations when the sample is rotated in the beam from the horns. An extreme case is wood, in which water can be regarded as being held in tubular pores separated by cellulose. Another is nylon thread, in which the water is carried by thin filaments which tend to align themselves when baled under pressure. It is necessary to ensure that such materials are always measured with a fixed alignment between the horns and the material.

3.6.5 **Soluble Salt Content**. It is known that at low frequencies water shows an increase in loss when it contains dissolved salts, due to its increased conductivity. This implies that some variations of loss may occur with samples of different salt contents. This effect has not yet been fully investigated but measurements on meat indicate [52] an increase in loss of 6 dB in 40 dB at 2.450 GHz, due to the addition of 1.5% common salt. At higher frequencies these effects become much smaller and at 10.6680 GHz the same salt addition to meat changes the attenuation by less than 1 dB in 40. An addition of salt to a sample of coal at 10.6680 GHz does not change the attenuation.

3.6.6 **Temperature**. The loss factor of pure water decreases with increasing temperature. Measurements made of the energy loss due to water absorbed in various materials at different temperatures indicate that the behavior is different from that of water alone. Each type of material, therefore, requires an individual calibration for a particular temperature for precise measurements.

3.6.7 Bonded Water. Some of the water present in many materials is bound in a manner which restricts the molecular dipole movement and consequently reduces the loss factor. This may be water of crystallization, which is held tightly in the crystal lattice and will therefore have a low loss factor. In materials such as grains and timber there are more complicated bonds holding water to protein or cellulose. In margarine, which is an emulsion of water and oils, it has been suggested that the size of the water particles is such that the thickness of the surface tension layer around each droplet represents a significant part of the total water content. The surface tension forces may be sufficient to reduce the mobility of the water molecule and so reduce the attenuation. Coal is a material with a network of fine tunnels extending through it, and is said to have a surface area of 100 m^2/cm^3. When the whole of this area has a layer of water one or two molecules thick adsorbed upon it, the coal contains approximately 10 to 12% water in which the dipole movement is restricted. With materials of this kind, the time taken for water to penetrate the structure can be as long as 24 hr, and care must be taken to ensure that the moisture content has been stabilized before measurements are made.

3.6.8 Volatile Materials. The conventional methods of water content measurement consist of weighing, drying, and reweighing a sample. Many organic materials contain volatile substances which may be driven off during the drying, and any such loss of material other than water represents an error when calibrating the microwave instrument. It also means that in some materials the relationship between attenuation and water content may not be the same for drying out as for rewetting, because of the changed composition. In such cases, it is necessary to calibrate the instrument with samples having moisture content values determined by the azeotropic or the Karl Fischer method described in Chaps. III and IV.

3.6.9 Frequency. The loss factor of pure water varies with frequency so that for a given material and water content, the measured attenuation is a function of frequency as well as of sample thickness. For reasons given earlier, it is preferable for the working range of attenuation to lie between 7 and 40 dB. For maximum sensitivity in terms of decibels for 1% water, the attenuation should be as high as possible. Within practical limits the choice of sample thickness and frequency is based on these considerations, with due regard to other factors such as sensitivity to dissolved salts which may depend on frequency.

3.7 Performance Characteristics of the Microwave Moisture Meter

Despite the complexity of the loss mechanism in microwave moisture measurement the results show that it is possible to obtain calibrations which in many cases are linear with moisture content in the region of interest. The accuracies found by AEI and other workers lie between ±2 and ±3% of the actual amount of water present. Ince and Turner [57] made a comparative measurement of the moisture content of plain cakes by using microwave absorption technique and the Brabender oven-drying procedure between the range of 16 to 20% moisture content. They tested 21 samples of plain cakes by these two methods in the temperature range of 21 to 31°C. None of the microwave results differed from the oven result by more than 0.6% of moisture, while 75% showed a difference of less than 0.3%. The mean deviation from the oven result was ±0.15%. Since the Brabender determination contributes to the errors, the microwave method could be more accurate than these results suggest, particularly when account is taken of the fact that the errors due to sampling will be less for this method because of the much larger samples handled. Each material has its associated microwave, handling, and calibration problems, such that each requires individual attention, particularly with regard to calibration. The choice of the correct wavelength, sample thickness, and method of sampling can only be made on this basis.

4 ELECTROLYTIC METHOD

4.1 Introduction

This is one of the best techniques available for measuring the moisture content of gases at concentrations (by volume) of less than 1 ppm up to 100 ppm. Many liquids can also be analyzed by this technique after vaporization. Other methods which are applicable at higher concentrations (including those based on ac conductivity measurement) are generally unsuccessful when water concentrations to be measured are under a few thousand parts per million. In the presence of water, a few parts-per-million concentration often profoundly affects the entire course of a chemical reaction and it is often essential to carry out accurate monitoring and control of moisture content at such levels throughout the course of a process, whether it is a small-scale laboratory reaction or a full-scale operation. The temperature of such water measurement problems has led to the development of a completely new analytical instrument based on the principles of absorption of water in a suitable hygroscopic material followed by electrolysis of water to oxygen and hydrogen, the electrolysis current serving as a direct measure of water content as reported by Keidel [59]. The technique is particularly useful for continuous determinations of moisture, though it can be used in batch analysis as well.

4.2 Principle

In accordance with Faraday's law of electrolysis, 0.5 g/mole of water (9.01 g) requires 96,500 C of electricity for its electrolytic decomposition. The electrolysis current is proportional to the number of moles of water absorbed per unit time. It is necessary, therefore, to regulate the sample flow at some arbitrary predetermined value. Usually a flow rate of 100 ml/min at normal temperature and pressure is generally maintained for ideal gaseous samples. Under these conditions, the electrolysis current is 13.2 µA/ppm water by volume. This current, which is readily measurable, corresponds to a water flow of 7.4 × 10⁻⁸ g/min, which is almost impossible to detect by any gravimetric method. Analysis for water content is accomplished in a special cell which combines absorption with electrolysis. Water vapor in the gas flowing through the cell is absorbed by a hygroscopic electrolyte. Simultaneously, the absorbed water is quantitatively electrolyzed by using platinum electrodes and applying a dc voltage greater than the decomposition potential of water. The electrolyte used is hydrated phosphorus pentoxide. Phosphorus pentoxide is a strong desiccant that becomes electrically conducting when wet.

4.3 The Electrolytic Water Analyzer

The analyzer comprises a flow controller, an electrolytic cell having platinum electrodes (connected to a 45-V battery) and containing hydrated phosphorus pentoxide, and a micrometer (Fig. 5.36). In one practical design, the absorbing material is in the form of a thin, viscous film in contact with two spirally wound 5-mil platinum electrode wires on the inside of an inert Teflon fluorocarbon resin tube through which the vapor (to be sampled) passes. The sample gas which enters the electrolytic cell through the flow controller at the rate of 100 cm³/min has its water content absorbed by the hydrated phosphorus pentoxide and quantitatively electrolyzed to hydrogen and oxygen at the platinum electrodes by the application of the dc voltage. Virtually all the current flowing through the cell is utilized to electrolyze the absorbed water, so that the current flowing through the micrometer gives a direct indication of the moisture content of the gas.

Keidel's instrument has been modified and improved by Cole et al. [60] for reliable measurement of the moisture content of organic liquids. In this method, moisture is removed from the sample stream by stripping and is then passed through a coulometric cell consisting of an anhydrous phosphorus pentoxide matrix between platinum electrodes. Using this system, accurate results can be obtained for

336   V.   ELECTRICAL AND ELECTRONIC METHODS

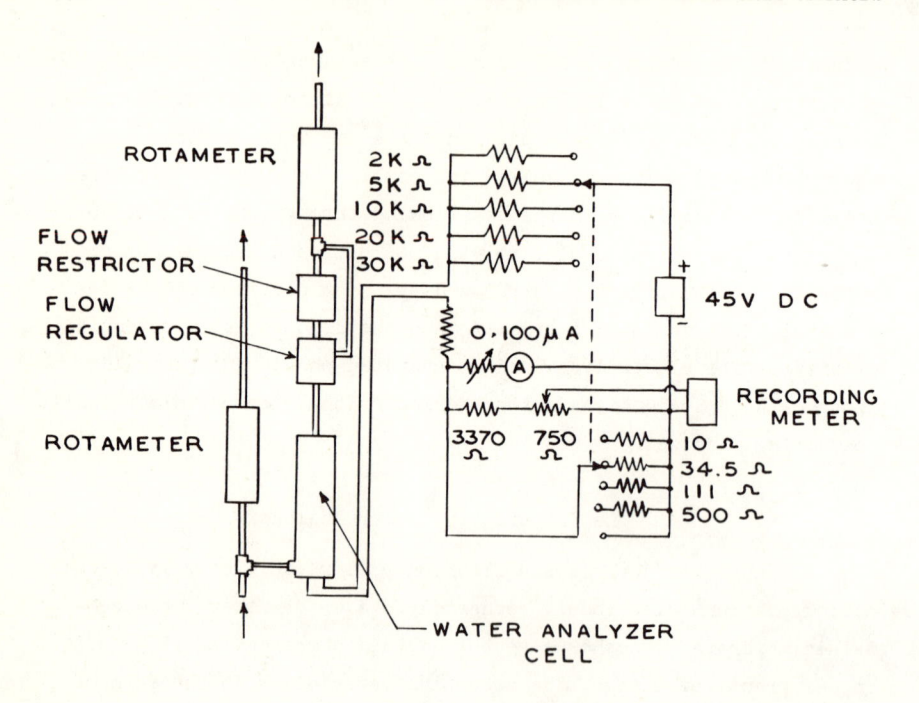

FIG. 5.36. Schematic diagram of an electronic water analyzer for liquids.

moisture levels down to 1 ppm and are comparable with those obtained by direct titration with the Karl Fischer reagent (Table 5.4), which shows good agreement between the two sets of values.

The method is applicable to any liquid whose vapors do not react with phosphorus pentoxide and is useful for analyzing most organic liquids over a wide range of moisture contents. Since the coulometric analyzer is electrolytic, extreme sensitivity is possible. The device is absolute in terms of the current and does not require calibration, as do most of the physical techniques of moisture analsis and measurement.

Based on Keidel's electrolytic cell principle, a moisture meter for solids has recently been developed and is commercially available from Consolidated Electrodynamics Corporation, USA. In this instrument, a weighed sample of the solid is placed in a small

TABLE 5.4

Comparative Data of Moisture Contents of
Some Chemicals as Determined by Electrolytic
Moisture Analyzer and the Karl Fischer Method

Sample no.	Chemicals (jet fuels)	Electrolytic moisture analyzer, ppm	Karl Fischer, ppm
1	JP-4	33	33 ± 3
2	JP-5	97	102 ± 5
3	Heavy lubricating oil	40	40 ± 3
4	Insulating oil	20	23 ± 3
5	Xylene	90	91 ± 4
6	Standard solvent	210	210 ± 7
7	Benzene	278	272 ± 8
8	Polypropylene glycol	300	316 ± 10

Teflon oven which is heated by a radiofrequency field (Fig. 5.37). Volatile matter from the sample is entrained by a carrier gas, usually dry nitrogen, which is kept flowing through the upper portion of the oven at a constant rate of about 100 cm^3/min. This carrier gas then conveys the volatile matter from the sample to the sensing elements, i.e., the platinum electrodes of the electrolytic cell. The cell, a solid epoxy resin cartridge, contains a glass tube through which the carrier gas passes. Two parallel platinum wires are wound in a helix on the tube's inner surface. The space between these wires is coated evenly with phosphorus pentoxide. The potential applied to the wires thus produces a measurable electrolysis current when moisture wets the pentoxide. Electrolysis of the water continuously regenerates the cell, thus enabling it to accept new water. A sensing circuit regulates oven temperature to prevent overloading of the cell with more water than it can absorb in a given time.

338   V.   ELECTRICAL AND ELECTRONIC METHODS

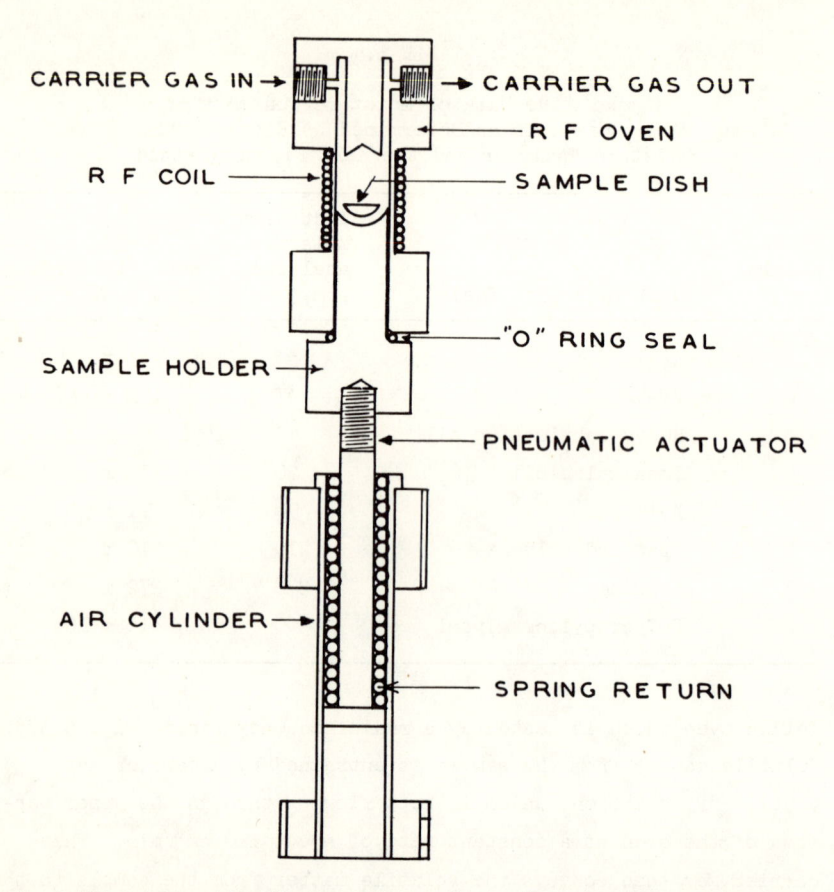

FIG. 5.37. Schematic diagram of an electrolytic water analyzer for solids.

The mass flow rate of moisture passing through the cell is represented linearly by the electrolysis current. To obtain a reading that is representative of total water in the sample, the cell current is integrated by a highly accurate motor that drives the indicator hands of the integrator dial scale. It takes about 10 min to complete one cycle of measurement. The instrument is claimed to be accurate to ±5 µg or down to 10 µg. Its sensitivity is 0.1 µg of water per division of the integrator dial and its dynamic range is 0.1 µg to 1.0 mg per complete cycle of the integrator. A variable timer, used to control the test cycles, permits completely automatic operation of the instrument. This instrument has a wide range of applications in such diverse fields as pharmaceuticals, chemicals, food, coal, and petroleum. Vitamins are tested to control moisture, which otherwise dilutes the vitamin concentration or adversely affects stability and blending qualities. Gelatin and other encapsulating materials are tested to ensure sufficient moisture content for rapid solubility, strength, and elasticity. Perfume stability and persistence also depends on controlled moisture content. Frequent measurements can be made to measure the moisture content of organic solids in either tablet or powder form. Detailed applications of this method are described in Chaps. XI to XIV.

4.4 Accuracy of the Measurement and the Temperature Effect

Accuracy of the instrument is normally limited only by the precision of the electrical and flowmeter components. A minimum error of ±5% in the reading can occur easily by using commercially available components. However, the accuracy is not affected by the exact value of the cell voltage so long as the voltage remains high enough to ensure complete and quantitative electrolysis of absorbed water. Usually at least 1 liter of gas sample is required for an analysis. In a few cases, an appreciable correction to the calibration based on Faraday's law has been found necessary at low concentrations of water, i.e., at few parts per million levels, because the efficiency is then somewhat less than 100%. Such cases include Freon hydrocarbons at low water concentrations. The application of the instrument to these materials has been fully discussed by Taylor [61]. This instrument is commercially available from a number of manufacturers in the United States and England and has been used successfully for the continuous determination of moisture in a number of gases, including air, nitrogen, hydrogen, carbon dioxide, argon, helium, hydrocarbons, refrigerants, and propellants.

Compounds which interfere with the proper working of such instruments are hydrogen fluoride, ammonia, and high concentrations of alcohols and acetones, as these chemicals react with the electrolyte, i.e., phosphoric acid. This technique has been successfully used for determining the water content of many volatile liquids which can be handled as vapors. Analysis of refrigerants and low-boiling point process liquids is also possible if water can be removed by inert-gas stripping. Common applications include the analysis of most aliphatic and aromatic hydrocarbons and their halogenated derivatives. Solid samples can also be analyzed by this method, using a modified stripping technique. Such applications include measurements of the extent of water absorption, adsorption, or hydration in both organic and inorganic materials.

Temperature Effect. For a fixed volumetric sample flow of 100 ml/min at normal temperature and pressure, 1 ppm of water produces a response of exactly 13.2 µA. At other temperatures the response is 13.2 times the ratio of 298 to the new temperature on the Kelvin scale. Thus instruments constructed for use at room temperatures read 0.3% lower for temperature rise of 1°C and higher by the same amount of temperature drop of 1°C in the region of room temperature. If wide deviations in temperature are encountered, the instrument flow can easily be altered to match the new conditions. Sudden changes of temperature, of the order of 5°C, cause transient fluctuations which amount to an appreciable percentage of the mean value of the moisture content. However, equilibrium is reattained as soon as the instrument and sample lines have reached the new temperature.

5 CONCLUSION

A great deal of interest in the development of electrical and electronic methods and techniques of moisture measurement has been generated recently as shown by a large number of technical articles and research publications [62-67] appearing on the subject. The reader interested in further detailed studies of such moisture meters is referred to these publications.

Electrical or electronic meters have a special role to play in industrial processes such as sizing, dyeing, and finishing in which chemical methods of moisture analysis cannot be applied, and it is not surprising to find them in industrial applications throughout the world. Further, it is such types of moisture meters that have been found to be most satisfactory for the continuous measurement and automatic control of moisture in industrial processes. The electronic moisture measuring devices are also economically the most competitive and are therefore being employed in a widening range of applications in testing and research laboratories.

REFERENCES

1. Kujirai and Akhari, Science Papers, Inst. Phys. Chem. Res. (Tokyo), 1, 94 (1923).
2. E. J. Murphy and A. C. Walker, J. Phys. Chem., 32, 1761 (1928).
3. M. Hasselbatt, Anorg. Allg. Chem., 154, 1761 (1928).
4. A. J. Stamm, Ind. Eng. Chem. (Anal. Ed.), 1, 94 (1928).
5. B. L. Banerjee and M. K. Sen, J. Sci. Ind. Res. (India), 15A, 24 (1956).
6. J. Kawasaki, J. Colloid Sci., 16, 405 (1961).
7. O. J. Sullivan, Brit. J. Text. Inst. (Trans.), 38, 277 (1947).
8. A. C. Walker, J. Text. Inst. (Trans.), 24, 123 (1933).
9. R. R. Williams and E. J. Murphy, Trans. Amer. Inst. Elec. Eng., 48, 289 (1929).
10. Sinijelnikoff and Walther, Z. Phys., 4, 246 (1927).
11. E. J. Murphy and A. C. Walker, J. Phys. Chem., 33, 200 (1929).
12. P. J. Geary, Control, 7, 303 (1963).
13. M. A. Rehman, J. Kishan, and B. I. Bali, Indian Forest Bull., 213, 1 (1956).
14. E. H. Jones, J. Sci. Instrum., 17, 55 (1940).

15. J. A. Reddick, S. C. Mayne, Jr., and E. E. Berkley, Text. Res. J., 29, 219 (1959).

16. B. L. Banerjee and M. K. Sen, J. Sci. Ind. Res. (India), 15A, 24 (1956).

17. B. L. Banerjee, Indian Patent 61607 (1957).

18. R. K. Toner and J. C. Whitewell, Text. Res. J., 16, 415 (1962).

19. R. K. Toner, E. F. Bowen, and J. C. Whitewell, Text. Res. J., 18, 526 (1948); 19, 211 (1949); 20 (1950).

20. Anonymous, A.D.R., 45, 935 (1956).

21. I. Hlynka, V. Martens, and J. A. Anderson, Can. J. Res. Sect. F, 27, 382 (1949).

22. E. M. Whitten and G. E. Holaday, Marketing Research Report 162, U.S. Dept. Agr., Marketing Service, 1957.

23. W. C. Wolfe, Anal. Chem., 35, 1885 (1963).

24. J. W. Rowen and H. R. Hope, J. Polym. Sci., 28, 225 (1958).

25. J. E. Fielden, British Patent 619,534 (1947); Indian Patent 37855 (1948); Electron. Eng., 21, 10 (1949).

26. N. F. Astbury, J. Sci. Instrum., 17, 26 (1940).

27. J. A. Van den Akker and K. W. Hardacker, Tappi, 35, 138A (1962).

28. A. Pande, Colourage (India), 8, 162 (1961); Instrum. Pract. (London), 15, 423 (1961); Indian Patent 67638 (1959).

29. A. Pande and S. R. Ranganathan, Instrum. Pract., 16, 415 (1962).

30. A. Pande, unpublished results, 1965.

31. H. E. Rasmussen and J. A. Anderson, Can. J. Res., 27, 249 (1949).

32. A. Pande, Instrum. Pract., 19, 650 (1965).

33. E. L. Ginzton and L. Holbingsworth, P.I.R.E., (USA), 29, 43 (1941).

34. F. Butler, Wireless World, 66, 386 (1960).

35. A. F. Brough and P. E. Puleston, British Patent 468,564 (1937).

36. A. E. Martin and D. Mounfield, U.S. Patent 2,874,564 (1950).

REFERENCES

37. A. Pande and S. Parthasarthy, J. Sci. Ind. Res. (India), 3, 1 (1945).

38. A. E. Crawford, Ultrasonic Engineering, Butterworths, London, pp. 306-338.

39. L. Von Bergmann, Der Ultrashall, S. Harzel, Zurich, 1942, pp. 151-205

40. K. F. Herzfeld and T. A. Litovitz, Absorption and Desorption of Ultrasonic Waves, Academic, New York, 1959, pp. 353-364.

41. P. Debye and F. W. Sears, Proc. Nat. Acad. Sci., 18, 409 (1932).

42. A. Pasynskii, J. Phys. Chem. USSR, 20, 981 (1946).

43. H. Shiio, T. Ogawa, and H. Yoshinashi, J. Chem. Phys., 27, 4980 (1959).

44. A. Watson, British Patent 697,956 (1959); Building Research Station Report A78 (1961); Building Research Station Report 493 (1963).

45. A. Kasteler, Proc. Colloquium on Water Molecules in Crystals and Solids Studied by Electromagnetic Waves, Editions du Centre Nationale de la Recherche Scientifique, Paris, 1940.

46. J. C. Slater, Microwave Electronics, Rev. Mod. Phys., 18, 44 (1946).

47. A. B. Bronwell and R. E. Beam, Theory and Application of Microwaves, McGraw-Hill, New York, 1947.

48. W. Gordy, Rev. Mod. Phys., 20, 668 (1948).

49. J. B. Hasted, Progress in Dielectrics, Heywood, London, 1961, p. 102.

50. S. K. Garg and C. P. Smyth, J. Chem. Phys., 43, 2959 (1965).

51. Anonymous, Instrum. Pract., 16, 314 (1962).

52. H. B. Taylor, A.E.I. Review (England), 4, 39 (1965).

53. H. B. Taylor, Ind. Electron., 3, 66 (1965).

54. A. E. Harrison, Klystron Tubes, McGraw-Hill, New York, 1947.

55. R. V. Pound, Rev. Sci. Instrum., 17, 490 (1946).

56. P. O. Vogelhut, Nature, 203, 1169 (1964).

57. A. D. Ince and A. Turner, Analyst, 90, 692 (1965).

58. M. F. Lagutin, A. Ja. Levcsinszkij, O. P. Mcsedlov-Petroszjan and G. A. Szalop, Moisture Measurement of Materials by Means of UHF and Ultrasonic Methods, Proceedings of Imeko Symp., 1971, p. 178.

59. F. A. Keidel, Anal. Chem., 31, 2043 (1959).

60. L. G. Cole, Anal. Chem., 31, 2048 (1959).

61. E. S. Taylor, Refrig. Eng., 64, 41 (1956).

62. Anonymous, J. Sci. Instrum., 39, 98 (1962).

63. A. Pande and C. S. Pande, Instrum. Pract., 16, 896, 1104 (1962).

64. H. Birr, Feingeratetechnik, 8, 306 (1963).

65. Anonymous, Instrum. Pract., 17, 896 (1963).

66. A. J. Borghorst, W. Arch. Met. Wein (B), 10, 533 (1961).

67. A. Pande, Lab. Pract. London, 12, 432 (1963); 12, 661 (1963); 12, 741 (1963).

Chapter VI

SPECTROSCOPIC METHODS AND TECHNIQUES

1 INFRARED SPECTROSCOPY

1.1 Introduction

During the past several years infrared spectroscopy has acquired a permanent place as a tool of analysis. It has been applied to a variety of problems that are both fundamental and applied in nature. The pattern of chemical analysis in thousands of research and control laboratories in industry, and research organizations has been profoundly influenced since the introduction of this analytical technique. The infrared spectrum of a chemical compound is probably the most characteristic physical property of that compound: it is known as its fingerprint.

There is a comparatively much smaller number of applications of this technique for routine moisture measurement as compared to other applications reported in the literature. However, this technique plays a very important role in specialized applications. The technique of infrared absorption spectroscopy is one of the most versatile and reliable methods of the detection and quantitative measurement of water content of various substances, especially at lower moisture content values and even up to the parts per million level. The composition of multicomponent liquids or gaseous materials can also be analyzed and the combination of extraction, dissolution, and spectroabsorption enables the analysis of even multicomponent solids. However, like other physical techniques, it is dependent on other techniques for calibration and accuracy.

1.2 Infrared Spectra of Water

<u>1.2.1 General</u>. It is well known that the infrared spectrum of water provides the basis of a quantitative and sensitive method for determining the water contents of many solids, liquids, and gases. Quantitative measurements are made possible because the intensities of the absorption bands are proportional to the concentrations of water. The infrared region chosen for the studies depends on the system in which water is to be determined, and both the fundamental and near-infrared regions can be used. The infrared spectrum of the water molecule has been investigated in great detail and with sufficient accuracy by a number of researchers [1-6]. Mecke and co-workers [2] have made a complete analysis of the rotational spectrum of the water molecule (Fig. 6.1). Nielson [3] has made a very thorough study of the near-infrared (bolometric region) spectrum of water vapor. Figure 6.2 shows the rotational-vibrational lines in the 3-µm water vapor band. Figure 6.3 shows the photographic infrared bands of H_2O at 9400 and 8200 Å in the solar spectrum. The actual forms of the normal vibration can best be understood by means of Fig. 6.4, which shows the modes of vibration of the fundamentals and overtones, respectively. The strong far-infrared spectrum as well as the rotation-vibration spectrum of H_2O and some other observations lead one to believe that H_2O is not a linear molecule, but has a plane of symmetry perpendicular to the plane of the molecule.

1 INFRARED SPECTROSCOPY   347

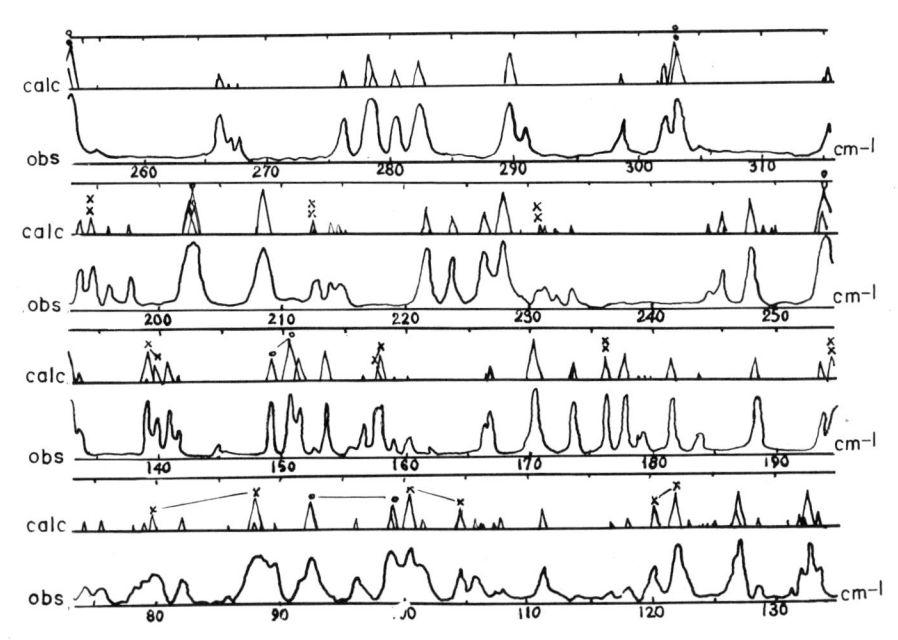

FIG. 6.1. Infrared rotation spectrum of water vapor.

1.2.2 The Near-Infrared Region. The near-infrared absorption region between 0.7 and 2.0 μm is particularly important for quantitative measurement. It has been the subject of several previous investigations, notably Hulburt and Hutchinson [4] and Collins [5]. Hulburt and Hutchinson [4] did their work in connection with an investigation

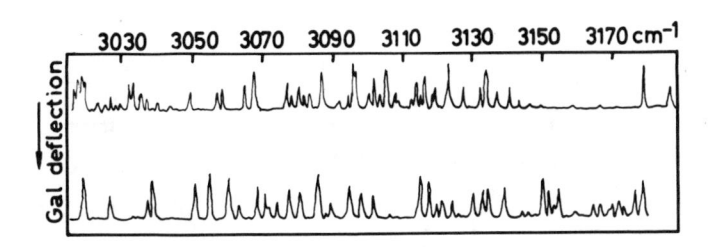

FIG. 6.2. Rotation vibration spectra of water vapor in the 3-μm region.

348   VI. SPECTROSCOPIC METHODS AND TECHNIQUES

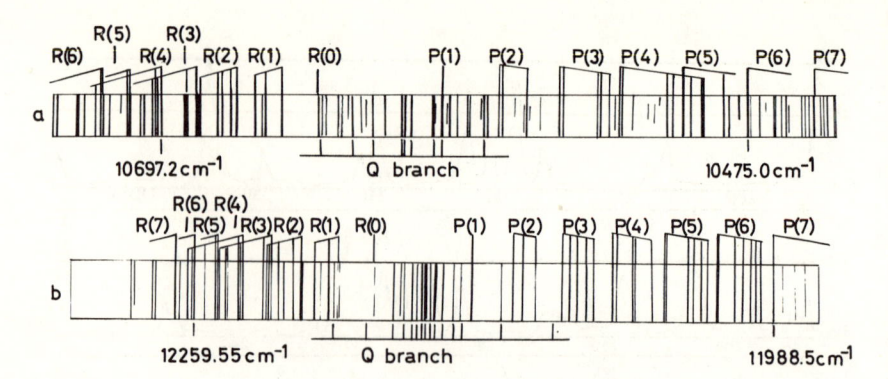

FIG. 6.3. Infrared bands of water at 9400 and 8200 Å in the solar spectrum.

of the infrared absorption by various salts in solution. Their water absorption data cover the wavelength range from 0.704 to 1.34 µm. In 1925 Collins [5] published water absorption data in the region of 0.70 to 2.1 µm. Curcio and Petty [6] investigated the spectral region from 0.70 to 2.50 µm and found that there are five prominent water absorption bands in the near-infrared region which occur at 0.845 µm. Collins [5] found that the intensity of the bands increases when the water temperature is raised above 90°C. Maximum absorption bands of water are given in Table 6.1.

Similarly, desorption bands of water in dioxane and in carbon tetrachloride are shown in Table 6.2. The intensities of these bands are considerably less than those in the fundamental region above 2 µm. Cell lengths of several centimeters can be used for the

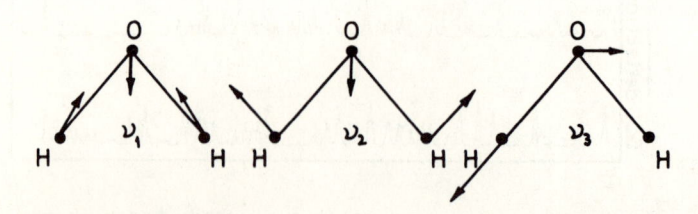

FIG. 6.4. Modes of vibration of water molecules in the fundamental as well as in overtones.

TABLE 6.1

Near-Infrared Absorption Bands of Water

Maximum absorption Wavelength (μm)	Frequency in wavenumber	Pathlength (cm)	Absorption coefficients at maximum absorption (cm^{-1})	Type of vibration
0.76	13,200	12.97	0.026	Overtone
0.97	10,300	1.99	0.46	Overtone
1.19	8,400	0.99	1.05	Combination
1.45	6,900	0.09	26.0	Overtone
1.94	5,160	0.02	114.0	Combination

TABLE 6.2

Maximum Absorption Bands of Water in Dioxane and Carbon Tetrachloride

0.1 M H_2O in dioxane		0.0075 M H_2O in CCl_4	
Wavelength (μm)	Frequency in wavenumber	Wavelength (μm)	Frequency in wavenumber
0.73	13,625	—	—
0.76	13,220	—	—
0.94	10,666	—	—
0.97	10,340	0.95	10,493
0.98	10,230	—	—
1.16	8,630	—	—
1.41	7,073	1.37	7,290
1.46	6,865	1.39	7,181
—	—	1.46	6,840
1.91	5,237	1.89	5,292

weaker bands below 1 μm compared to all lengths of fractions of a millimeter for bands above 1.5 μm. The spectra shown are for various thicknesses of water alone, 0.0075 M (free) in carbon tetrachloride, and 0.1 M (bound) in dioxane, for the region from 0.6 to 6 μm (ca 15,000 to 1500 cm^{-1}). Similar maximum absorption bands for water in dioxane and carbon tetrachloride have been observed by Greenacher and Mecke [7].

Vendt [8] has found that the absorption band in the near-infrared at about 1 μm is suitable for determining water in liquids such as acetone, acetic acid, acetic anhydride, methanol, ethanol, glycerol, and pyridine. A special filter was used to isolate the desired wavelength and a silver sulfide photoelectric element was employed. Water content was read from a series of standard curves prepared from data obtained in analyses of known mixtures. The same technique was used for estimating water up to saturation in compounds such as butanol, ethyl acetate, ether benzene, toluene, and chloroform. The band at 1.32 μm was found to be nearly specific for water in fuming nitric acid. The nearly specific absorption band at about 1.9 μm has been used for determining water in a variety of substances. In analysis of glycerol, Chapman and Nacey [9] found that the absorption band at 1.9 μm was clearly separated from that at 2.1 μm arising from hydroxyl groups in the glycerol. The standard deviation was about 0.06%. Usually the 1.9-μm absorption band is most likely to be free of interference from overlapping absorption by other groups. However, several percentages of methanol and ethanol were found to interfere, for example, 5% methanol or 5% ethanol in dimethyl hydrazine gave the same absorbance as 0.11 or 0.03% water, respectively.

Most of the relatively strong bands for water in the near-infrared are subject to interference by hydroxyl and amine groups. In the 2.5 to 3-μm region all hydroxyl and some amine groups absorb. In the 2.6 to 2.7-μm region, many hydrogen-containing compounds may interfere unless suitable compensation is provided. These interferences include those from alcohols, alkyl esters, hydrocarbons, and chloroform.

1.2.3 Intermediate-Infrared Region. The infrared spectrum of water in the region 2.5 to 6 μm has been studied extensively. In this region the wavelength for maximum absorption is affected by hydrogen bonding between water molecules or between water and other polar molecules. The nature and the extent of bonding are influenced by the concentration of water and the type of system in which the measurement is made. The water in liquid phase when present as moisture in solids and liquids is always in a polymer form such as $(H_2O)_2$, $(H_2O)_3$, and other higher complex forms. Water vapor, however, exists as a monomer, that is, H_2O. The wavelength of maximum absorption of the infrared depends on the polymeric form of water. Van Thiel and co-workers [10] established the assignments for monomeric and polymeric forms of water by using high-resolution spectrophotometers. Frequencies were determined by a matrix isolation technique in solid nitrogen at 20°K. They showed that the absorption bands of the monomer (water vapor) found at 3726 and 3627 cm^{-1} were due to symmetric and antisymmetric OH stretching vibrations. From studies of absorption bands by the dimer (liquid water) at 3691 and 3546 cm^{-1}, it is concluded that this polymer has a cyclic structure rather than the open or bifurcated structure usually proposed.

Absorption in the 6-μm region has also been used for analyses of certain materials such as gaseous mixtures containing oxygen, hydrogen, carbon monoxide, carbon dioxide, methane, propane, and ammonia. Process [11] found that the absorbance measured at 6.1 μm (1640 cm^{-1}) was better suited for analysis than at 2.7 μm (3700 cm^{-1}) since measurements at the latter wavelength required correction for carbon dioxide. However, carbonyl and carbon-to-carbon double bonds would interfere at 6.1 μm. Other groups that could interfere in the 6-μm region include amine and amide. The question of selecting a particular region, for the measurement of moisture content, thus depends on the substance in which the measurement is to be made. Knowledge of the infrared spectrum of the substance and previous experience are guiding factors in the choice of a particular band.

The intensities of absorption bands are proportional to the concentrations of water. In a system free of interferences, any of several wavelengths may be calibrated for quantitative analysis. The choice depends on the concentration, range of the water to be determined, and the nature of the sample. Most of the absorption bands are not specific for the water molecule alone. Absorption by hydroxyl groups in other compounds and other strongly absorbing groups may be coincidental with that by water or may cause such serious overlapping that certain bands will be inapplicable. Each system to be analyzed should be examined carefully before choice is made of the most suitable analytical wavelength. Known mixtures should be analyzed over the expected concentration range of the water. From this information, reliable absorptivities or calibration curves usually can be made. In some cases of intermolecular hydrogen bonding, a band associated with the nonaqueous component often is enhanced in proportion to the concentration of water.

1.3 Instrumentation

1.3.1 Introduction. Infrared instruments are designed to measure the characteristic vibration of a sample by passing infrared radiation through it and recording the wavelengths which have been absorbed, and the intensities of absorption. Since the amount of energy absorbed is a function of the number of molecules present, the infrared instrument provides both qualitative and quantitative measurements. The recorded infrared spectrum is a plot of the transmittance of the sample versus the wavelength of the radiation. It is a measurement of a fundamental property of the sample and can be used both to characterize the sample and to determine its concentration. The instruments for recording and measuring infrared absorption can broadly be classified as single-beam or double-beam instruments. The important constituents of a single-beam infrared spectrometer are as follows: (1) Source of radiation, (2) monochromator, (3) detector, and (4) amplifier and recorder.

1 INFRARED SPECTROSCOPY   353

In single-beam infrared spectrometers the emission spectrum of the radiation source is not constant for long periods, and therefore there are fluctuations in the sensitivity of the detector, the degree of amplification, the absorption of the atmosphere, or any of the many other possible variables. The larger the time interval between two such measurements, the more serious such alterations could be.

This is a fundamental defect of the single-beam operation and leads to the frequent repetition of measurements and their averaging to eliminate chance errors. In addition, single-beam instruments have other disadvantages, especially the greater time needed and the necessity of calculating the required spectrum from the measured curves delivered by the spectrometer. By a suitable slit-width mechanism, the Planck curve of the radiation emitted can be obtained for single-beam instruments and the atmospheric absorption bands can be avoided by evacuating the whole of the path of the beam or by replacing it with an atmosphere of pure dry nitrogen, but both of these methods need constant and careful manipulations.

Efforts to avoid and overcome the disadvantages of the single-beam instruments just mentioned have led to various alternative forms of construction; of these the most important are the double-beam instruments. The fundamental principle of this intrument is that the radiation emitted by the source is divided into two beams which are energetically, geometrically, and optically similar. At some point before entry into the monochromator, they are brought together again. In the path of one beam (the so-called measuring beam) is placed the substance to be investigated. The other beam (the so-called reference beam) contains no substance, but usually an empty cell, or for solutions the pure solvent is placed in it. By means of an optical switch (which in most cases takes the form of a rotating sector mirror) first the one and then the other beam is caused periodically at very short time intervals to be admitted alternately to the monochromator, and thus to the radiation detector. By means of electronic techniques, the radiation detector is caused to measure the difference in energy between the two beams. By a suitable setting both beams can be made of identical energy for a certain wavelength. Because of this, the detector reacts only when the substance under investigation shows absorption at a particular wavelength. The detector signal is a measure of the energy difference of the two beams and thus of the absorption of the substance. Usually this signal is made by lowering the energy in the reference beam using the optical wedge attenuator or the aperture stop.

The production of replica echellette gratings of high quality and low cost [12-13] has resulted in increased usage of such gratings for routine spectroscopic measurements. Wide-range grating spectrometers are now available commercially usually as modified versions of prism spectrometers. The advantages of a grating spectrometer compared with a prism spectrometer may be summarized as follows:

1. The high dispersion of a grating throughout its wavelength range results in a consistently high resolution. The resultant spectral bandwidth is generally a good deal less than the width of absorption bands in solid and liquid materials. Optical density data for these bands will therefore be relatively unaffected by moderate changes in slit width.

2. Due to the high dispersion of the grating, spectrometer slit widths are considerably larger at short-wavelengths by comparison with a rock salt prism spectrometer using a similar radiation detector. This makes the slit design critical with regard to quality and alignment of the slit jaws.

3. The effect of small amounts of optical aberration in the grating collimating system is small with wide slits, so that large aperture spherical mirrors can be used even with gratings of large areas.

4. The wavelength scale associated with a prism spectrometer is dependent on refractive index of the prism material and hence the calibration is dependent on temperature, but this is not the case with a grating spectrometer.

5. The angular rotation of the grating to cover a given wavelength range is considerably larger than that of a prism, so that the wavelength measurements on a grating spectrometer can be made with consistently high precision.

6. A preliminary stage of dispersion is desirable in a wide-range grating spectrometer and this results in a very low level of spurious radiation of wavelengths other than that being measured by the radiation detector.

Because of these advantages the grating spectrometer has assumed greater importance.

The constructional features of various types of infrared spectrometers together with sources of radiations and detection have been elaborately described in a number of books, research publications, and instruction manuals of instrument manufacturers, the reader is referred to these publications [14-23] for instrumental details. However, basic features of the various classes of spectrometers are discussed here so that an overall view of the techniques involved may be obtained.

1.3.2 Near-Infrared Region Instrumentation. The instruments used in this region (1 to 3 µm) have quartz prisms or grating monochromators and photoconductor detectors, such as a lead sulfide cell. Such instrumentation, which permits high resolution, has been available commercially only recently. There have appeared reviews of the research work in this region by Kaye [24], Wheeler [25], Goddu [26], and Rudko et al. [27]. The techniques of near-infrared spectroscopy are closer to those of ultraviolet and visible spectrophotometry. Quartz or glass cells may be used up to 2.4 µm. Special grades of silica and lithium fluoride are readily available for use up to 3 µm. Because of the sharpness of the absorption bands in the near-infrared, it is desirable to use special slit widths of the order of a few wavenumbers to attain high resolution. To date most analytical applications of near-infrared have been concerned with organic compounds and generally with quantitative functional groups analysis. This is because near-infrared spectra are mainly indicative of the hydrogen vibrations of the molecule, that is, C-H, S-H, O-H, N-H, etc., and few vibrations are dependent on the carbon or inorganic skeleton of the molecule. It is in the determination of these hydrogenic functional groups that near-infrared finds its greatest utility and promise.

Water in liquid form gives intense infrared absorption in the near-infrared region and for routine measurement, an infrared spectrometer suitable for one or a few of these absorption frequencies

of water is sufficient. All the spectrometers can be used in the
near-infrared region if the dispersion system is suitably selected.
Therefore, spectrometers have been developed and constructed specially for this purpose, in part as complete instruments and in part
as extensions to available instruments for the ultraviolet and
visible spectral regions. All these instruments use electrically
heated metal filament lamps as radiation sources, and photoresistance cells as radiation detectors. Registration mechanisms can be
obtained either with the instrument or separately. Since many of
the near-infrared bands are greatly affected by the solvent because
of intermolecular bonding, it is desirable that the same solvent be
used for calibration or reference spectrum as is used for the analysis of the unknown compounds.

1.3.3 Intermediate-Infrared Region Instrumentation. Vibrational
analysis shows that the majority of fundamental stretching and
bending frequencies occurring in organic compounds and inorganic
ions are observable within the wavelength region from about 2.5 to
15.5 μm. It is this portion of the spectrum which is popularly
called the "sodium chloride" region because rock salt prisms have
excellent dispersion characteristics throughout this region and
sample cells are transparent when constructed with windows of the
same material. The fundamental vibrational modes, i.e., the normal
modes, are virtually universally those which are most useful for
both qualitative and quantitative analysis. This situation obtains
because the absorption bands associated with the normal frequencies
are the most intense ones among the spectroscopically active vibrations. Overtone bands are always of far lower intensity than the
majority of active fundamental bands. A great simplification in the
correlation of infrared band positions for purposes of structural
identification arises because of the existence of certain group frequencies which are relatively constant, irrespective of the other
molecular moieties present in the species under consideration. This
absence of appreciable coupling between molecular motions of many
groups in complex compounds allows a systematic treatment of infrared

1 INFRARED SPECTROSCOPY

spectroscopy which would not otherwise be possible. For a given vibration to be infrared active there must be a change in the dipole moment of the molecule as a result of the molecular motion. Details of the application of the selection rules governing the active and silent frequencies for the different symmetry classes are discussed fully by Herzberg [28].

1.3.4 Far-Infrared Region Instrumentation. According to current practice, the far-infrared region is considered to be that part of the electromagnetic spectrum between the sodium chloride prism cutoff (about 15 μm) and the wavelengths at which microwave techniques may be successfully employed. The far-infrared tends to be pushed continually to longer wavelengths by the development of better optical materials and instrumentation and now overlaps the microwave region to some extent. The microwave region is merely an extension of the far-infrared from the theoretical aspect but involves different experimental techniques [29]. In the long-wavelength region, infrared absorption is due to pure rotational and to vibrational-rotational transitions in gaseous molecules, to molecular vibrations in liquids and solids, and to lattice vibrations and molecular vibrations in crystals [30]. To a considerable extent, the present discussion will be limited to these regions of the far-infrared which can be studied with commercially available double-beam infrared instruments and in which absorption arises primarily from the vibrational modes of the molecules. These include only a small portion of the far-infrared, namely, the potassium bromide and cesium bromide regions, but it is this portion that is of most interest in analytical applications. This is true because most of the low-lying vibrational frequencies occur in these regions. Furthermore, the interesting possibility exists of using a cesium bromide prism which is not markedly inferior to the potassium bromide prism from 15 to 20 μm, and the convenience of being able to use a single prism for the whole 15 to 35-μm region is obvious [31]. Physical methods of analysis involving spectra in the cesium bromide region have not found widespread applications until recently. This has been due primarily to the instrumental difficulties of obtaining useful spectra in this region in short periods of time. Low-energy atmospheric absorption and stray radiation are the principal sources of difficulty in the design of fast-recording double-beam instruments for the far-infrared. These difficulties are being greatly reduced by improved gratings, detectors, and radiation sources, by new kinds of filters, by the use of vacuum housings or of vigorous sweeping of the optical path by dry gas, and by modern techniques of amplification.

1.4 Sampling Techniques

Different types of materials in different states require varied types of cells and sampling techniques. However, the cell windows are usually made of rock salt, even though it is difficult to handle (while polishing). Also, it is fragile and is attacked both by water and by methyl alcohol. Calcium fluoride is a good window material up to about 8.5 μm and can be used for aqueous solutions. Calcium fluoride is not easily polished, but once it is polished it will remain clear. Other window materials include potassium bromide, thallium bromide, barium fluoride, and sapphire. Besides lead amalgam, aluminum, indium, polyethylene, stainless steel, and brass may be used for spacing the cell windows. The chemically resistant plastics, such as polyethylene, and the fluorinated plastics are useful and they make a spacing material which generally can be reused. The techniques of sampling to be followed in each case are described below.

1.4.1 *Solid Materials*. Three general methods are usually used for the examination of solids in their crystalline form. All involve the reduction of a solid to very small particles, which are then diluted in a mull and introduced in an alkali halide (KBr) disk, or spread as pure solid on a cell plate surface. The mulling technique is probably the quickest for most samples, and the cheapest. For mulls, Nujol (high-boiling fractions from petroleum) is the most commonly used reagent. Perfluorokerosene, a mixture of fluorinated hydrocarbons and hexachlorobutadiene, has also been employed as a mulling agent. The fluorinated hydrocarbon mixture, however, is difficult to remove from cell plate surfaces and sample recovery is troublesome. Care should be taken to avoid the loss of moisture by the sample, because of the heat of the source. Methods of incorporating samples in potassium bromide, which is pressed to form a "window," are sometimes found very suitable. The dispersion is readily accomplished by grinding the sample with potassium bromide in a ratio of one part of sample to 200 parts of potassium bromide. Demountable cells with single or double plates are obtainable in a range of plate thicknesses for use in conjunction with mulls. In the preparation of suspensions of finely divided solids in viscous liquid, a widely practical technique consists of intimately grinding the solid with Nujol, fluorolubor hexachlorobutadiene [32-33]. For qualitative analysis the mull technique is highly satisfactory, but there are difficulties in its application to quantitative determinations. Since the sample thickness is generally unknown, it is required that an internal standard be added during the preparation of the system for spectroscopic analysis, provided one is interested in directly measuring the absolute concentration level of the components.

Potassium bromide and other alkali halides have recently proved of great utility in both quantitative and qualitative infrared spectroscopy [34-35]. These halides are readily fused at room temperature to yield transparent disks at pressures of approximately 10,000 psi. The dies are evacuated to preclude the entrapment of air bubbles in the disks. Specially prepared forms of the alkali halides are commercially available for infrared work. The low solubility of numerous polar compounds, e.g., benzene polycarboxylic acids in infrared solvents, necessitates the study of these substances in solid form if spectra are to be measured with the sample near room temperature. The alkali halide method is not without complications which arise from the fact that true solutions may not be formed in the preparation of the pellets. The dispersions of solid samples may show spectral features originating from orientation effects, polymorphism, adsorption, isomerization, formation of mixed crystals, and other less well-defined phenomena. In applying both the mull and alkali halide procedures, the grinding time should be varied in order to locate the optimum period for mixing of both the sample constituents and the internal standard, if any. It is unnecessary to employ an internal standard with the alkali halide method provided the same die is always employed and a semimicrobalance is available for weighing the sample.

1.4.2 *Pure Liquids, Solvents, and Solutions.* Pure liquids and solutions of solids, liquids, or gases can be examined in the infrared. Liquids are generally not examined in solution, thus avoiding solvent absorption interference, though a solution spectrum may remove some of the intermolecular interactions existing in the pure liquid. Solutions may also be necessary when sample absorption is strong and insufficiently thin films are readily and accurately available. The most universally useful infrared absorption cell for liquids is the sealed type by which samples may be introduced and removed through two openings pluggable with Teflon stoppers. These cells are available in a range of thicknesses varying from 0.025 to 1.0 mm or more. They are obtainable in matched sets for double-beam spectroscopy. In addition to the regular macrosealed liquid absorption cells, micro and ultramicro liquid cells have been developed. These cells are fillable at 0.1-mm thicknesses with quite small volumes of liquid, that is, 0.002 to 0.02 ml. These are of considerable assistance in the study of samples trapped from gas chromatographic columns. Wedge- and micrometer-type liquid absorption cells provide the experimenter with a means of varying sample thickness without resorting to the inconvenience of changing cells.

According to Nicholson [36], variable-thickness cells should not be used as sample containers in quantitative analysis. They are, however, exceedingly useful for qualitative work. To permit some freedom in the interchange of intensity data for quantitative purposes in cells of different thickness, the interference fringe method of measuring cell pathlengths is used. A single empty cell is placed in the light beam of the spectrometer and scanned from about 2 to 15 μm on a double-beam instrument, as though a qualitative analysis were being made. A series of maxima and minima will be readily observed for cases in which the spaces are approximately 0.02 to 1.0 mm. From the relationship $t = N(\lambda_2 - \lambda_1)/4000$ (where t is the cell thickness in millimeters and N is the number of complete waveforms in the wavelength interval encompassed from λ_2 to λ_1 in micrometers) it is obviously a simple matter to obtain the value of t. Other methods of determining the thickness of infrared cells are (1) using a vernier microscope on the assembled cell and (2) measuring the absorption of a compound having a known extinction coefficient.

Infrared spectra for analytical purposes are usually obtained with the sample in solution in a liquid solvent. When employing the thinnest (0.020 mm) cells available, the more intense absorption bands of the majority of compounds approach 100% absorption, and some dilution of the sample is therefore frequently essential. The spectra of greases, high polymers, and samples which are corrosive to cesium bromide plates can be obtained by using cells of polyethylene and KRS-5 to support the materials.

The cesium bromide and iodide plates are soft and easily polished with paper towels. In an air-conditioned room, corrosion by atmospheric water vapor is not very serious, and with careful handling the cesium bromide cells are as easy to work with as potassium bromide or sodium chloride cells. For the most part a cell with a longer pathlength is required for the far-infrared. For the cesium bromide region one of the most useful cells is 0.50 mm in pathlengths, but the highly polar materials require cells with pathlengths of 0.05 mm or less and the less polar materials require cells with pathlengths of 2 mm or more. Chloroform, carbon tetrachloride, and carbon disulfide are the three solvents most commonly employed in cells of 0.1 mm to 1 cm thickness. The conventional types of infrared absorption cells of 1-mm thickness have volumes of the order of 200 to 500 µl.

If only the minimum volumes of solution are prepared, it is difficult to avoid errors in moisture measurement because of evaporation losses in manipulating the volatile solvents. These losses are proportionately less if the total volume of solution is increased, and for accurate quantitative work it is desirable to have as large a volume as possible.

1.4.3 Gases. Determination of moisture in gases requires a change in the technique. In view of their reduced molecular concentrations, gas-cell pathlengths in centimeters rather than in fractions of millimeters are used. Special techniques have been developed for weighing small quantities of the gas and effecting total transference to the gas cell. In a common procedure, however, the quantity of gas admitted to a standard volume cell is known from measurement of its pressure. To fill the cell it is first evacuated and the gas is then passed in along the pressure gradient. For analysis of traces of moisture long-path gas cells can be used. A 10-cm pathlength is suitable for most compounds provided that the vapor pressure at room temperature of the substance is between approximately 25 to 500 mm. Cells having variable pathlengths up to 10 m are currently available as stock items and have proved of great value in trace analysis of moisture in air and in other gases.

The majority of infrared bands observed in fairly simple molecules (e.g., benzene) are subject to pressure-broadening effects; with increasing pressure the band intensities increase. The problem of pressure broadening in quantitative infrared spectroscopy, however, is simplified to some extent by the fact that the effects are similar for many different gases and one may compensate by adjusting to equal total pressures in calibrating by means of diluents such as hydrogen or nitrogen and in studying mixtures of components included in the calibration procedure. Microgas cells having a pathlength of 60 cm and designed for 22-ml volume have recently become available [37]. These cells have a comparatively high fraction of the sample molecules actually exposed to radiant energy. A beam-condenser apparatus is required for proper use of the gas microcell.

1.5 Attenuated Total Reflectance Techniques

1.5.1 Introduction. This new technique greatly simplifies one of the fundamental problems of infrared spectroscopy, viz., that of properly preparing a sample so that a characteristic infrared spectrum can be obtained from it. It permits the direct examination of solid and liquid materials without such special treatment as dissolving, pulverizing, mulling, or slicing, and without regard to sample thickness. Attenuated total reflection spectra are similar to absorption spectra. They provide a very practical means for the qualitative analysis of most organic and many inorganic materials. In addition, they contain a wealth of new information that will provide added fundamental knowledge of molecular structure.

1.5.2 Principles of Attenuated Total Reflectance. A complete treatment of attenuated total reflection has been given by Fahrenford [38]. In somewhat oversimplified terms, the phenomenon may be explained as follows. It can be shown mathematically that when a beam of radiation is totally reflected internally from a surface, as in a prism, there will be an exchange of energy between the prism and the medium in contact with it. This exchange is roughly inversely proportional to the ratio of the index of refraction of the prism and that of the medium in contact with it. Since air has a low refractive index (1.0), a radiation beam being totally reflected internally suffers no attenuation. If a material with an index equal to or greater than that of the prism is contacted to the prism, all of the energy will pass into the second medium. Further, the index of refraction of a material as a function of wavelength undergoes a rapid change at the wavelength where absorption takes place. Hence, when such a material is brought into contact with a prism, the internally reflected beam will lose energy at these absorbed wavelengths (where the index is high) so that a plot of the reflected energy will produce a curve that is very similar, but not identical, to a conventional transmission spectrum.

The overall effect is as if a little of the energy escaped from the reflecting surface of the prism and penetrated a few microns into the surface of the material in contact with it and then returned to the prism. The amount of apparent penetration of energy into the sample is a function of the prism index (high index, low penetration) and the angle of incidence of the beam of radiation (high angle, high penetration). The actual thickness of the sample has no effect on the spectrum and herein lies the real importance of the total attenuated reflectance technique to the spectroscopist. It is not necessary to prepare a thin film for the infrared energy to pass through. One can obtain an equivalent spectrum by merely contacting the sample to the reflecting face of the prism. In general, any sample that has a surface smooth enough to be contacted to the reflecting surface of the prism will produce the infrared spectrum. Continued study of the attenuated total reflection technique has provided ample evidence that this new method of infrared analysis will greatly add to the general usefulness of infrared spectroscopy. The prime reason for this is that this technique, for the first time, permits the spectroscopist to examine solid samples in situ without any special preparation such as grinding, dissolving, mulling, pressing, and the like.

1.5.3 Instrumentation of Attenuated Total Reflectance. The instrumental requirements of a system to produce ATR infrared spectra are (1) a means for providing an adjustable angle of incidence of the infrared beam on the internally reflecting face of a prism; (2) an infrared transmitting prism of higher index of reflection than that of the sample to be examined; and (3) a means of holding the sample in close contact with the prism. A reflectance attachment developed by the Connecticut Instrument Corporation (USA) provides the necessary variable angle of incidence optical system, where prisms of silver chloride, KRS-5, and germanium, or specially designed, pressed AgCl plates [39-40] serve as the high-index reflectors. Solid and liquid sample holders serve to hold the samples against the reflecting surface of the prism. To obtain the ATR spectrum the investigator simply cuts his sample to fit the holder, clamps it in place, inserts the holder in the ATR unit, and starts the spectrophotometer. Since ATR measurements are made on the upper few microns of the surface of the sample rather than by transmission, sample thickness has absolutely no effect on the resulting spectrum. The penetration into a sample may be varied by changing the prism material (to get a different refractive index ratio) or by varying the angle of incidence.

1.5.4 Special Applications of Attenuated Total Reflectance. There are many worthwhile fundamental studies that could be undertaken by attenuated total reflection techniques but it is highly probable that by far the most widespread application will be in the analysis of competing products. Attenuated total reflectance can provide infrared spectra on such items as floor tiles, rubber products, paper coatings, synthetic leathers, detergents, etc., without any chemical or mechanical preparation. Because the effective penetration of the beam into the sample is only a few micrometers, water, for example, is quite transparent throughout the range.

The intensely absorbing solvents show significant gains in the effective transmission of energy with ATR compared to normal transmittance technique. The highly polar and very intensely absorbing solvents best illustrate the advantages of ATR over conventional transmittance methods. The transmittance spectra of the alcohols and glycol ethers are opaque over almost the entire rock salt region. The spectra are simple, and only the vibrations associated with the O-H and C-O stretch and O-H deformation produce bands in the opaque region.

Special absorption interferences contributed by solvents are reduced by ATR. Solvents with increased solubilizing power can be used for qualitative and quantitative infrared solution studies of materials which hitherto were insufficiently soluble in solvents used for transmittance analyses. However, a major disadvantage of

ATR for solution analysis is the requirement of a relatively high concentration of sample in the solvent.

1.6 Laws of Absorption

When a parallel beam of monochromatic radiation passing through a homogeneous transparent medium is absorbed, the mathematical relationship of absorption, the sample thickness, and concentration is governed by two fundamental laws, i.e., Beer's and Lambert's laws. Beer's law relates to the absorption of the radiation with the thickness of the sample, and Lambert's law relates the absorption with its concentration. The two laws can be combined. The intensity of a monochromatic beam of radiation passing through a homogeneous medium falls by absorption exponentially to its concentration and thickness and is mathematically expressed as follows:

$$I = I_0 e^{-kcd} \tag{6.1}$$

where I and I_0 are the transmitted and incident radiations, respectively; k is the extinction coefficient; c is the concentration of the substance; and d is the thickness of the sample in centimeters. From the above equation

$$kcd = \log \frac{I_0}{I} \tag{6.2}$$

Putting kcd = A and I/I_0 = T from the above relation, we have A = log T, where A is called optical density and T is the ratio of transmittance. This relates transmittance T with optical density A and the magnitude of A is a measure of the amount of absorption. Arising from these equations an abundance of terms are used in the literature which have been summarized by Brode [41].

The substances which obey Beer's law can be quantitatively analyzed by calculation directly from the spectrophotometer data by means of a simple system of linear equations. Substances which

1 INFRARED SPECTROSCOPY

do not obey Beer's law can be analyzed only by the use of analytical curves; empirical calibration curves are obtained by measuring known concentrations of the substance at an appropriate wavelength and then plotting concentration vs transmittance or concentration vs absorbance.

1.6.1 Deviation from Beer's Law. The linear relationship of optical density with the concentration is logical and can be empirically justified for certain regions of concentrations, but certainly not for all cases. It is found that Beer's law is always obeyed for sufficiently small pressures or concentrations, but that for larger concentrations or pressures deviations appear, for some substances earlier than for others. There are many substances which do not obey this relationship.

There are two reasons for the appearance of such deviations from Beer's law. The first is due to the nature of the substance investigated. The absorption measured is not simply the sum of equal absorptions for all the individual molecules, but is due to the formation of molecular aggregates, regardless of whether these aggregates are formed by the association of the molecules of the substance with each other or by interactions of a definite type with molecules of the environment, e.g., the solvent. For sufficiently small concentrations or pressures these do not appear and therefore Beer's law is obeyed. The aggregates only appear with an increase in concentration or an increase in pressure and then the deviation from Beer's law mentioned is observed. Such deviations are thus due to intermolecular interactions. Physical effects, particularly intermolecular association (e.g., hydrogen bonding), causes deviation from Beer's law. Bands change shape and position and only the calibration-curve method may be used for quantitative studies. Chemical effects such as dissociation and polymerization also lead to deviation from Beer's law.

The other reason for such deviations is the fundamentally unsatisfactory nature of the instruments used. Rigid control of operating conditions is vital; speed of scan, for example, should be slow and constant. Beer's law holds rigorously only for true monochromatic radiations. Thus the major cause of deviations is due to the finite slit-width effect, for no monochromator provides absolutely pure monochromatic light at the exit slit. The light emerging from the exit slit covers a narrow frequency range. Well-constructed gratings, however, give light more nearly monochromatic than any prism can provide.

1.7 Measurement of Intensity

The measurement of the intensity is done by a number of instruments, the most suitable being the spectrophotometer. Current instruments permit direct readings of absorbance instead of percent transmittance in terms of the parameter A. Calculations based on band heights give extinction coefficients which may be "true" or "apparent," depending on the conditions of measurement. For comparison of intensities of differently shaped bands, or in cases where finite slit errors are introduced, band areas should be measured. Absorption band areas (integrated absorption intensities) may be evaluated by the standard graphical procedure using a planimeter, by weighing paper profiles of the bands, or by counting squares. Electrical band intensity integrators are available for some instruments where the pen moves on a slide wire which serves also as a potentiometer wire. The major advantage of determining integrated absorption intensities is their virtual independence of slit width, whereas measurements of absorbance or molecular extinction coefficient vary with slit width.

1.8 Procedures for Calibration of Spectrophotometers

Wavelength calibration on typical modern commercial double-beam spectrometers is unnecessary except, of course, as a precautionary measure. The instrument dial discloses the wavelength setting of

1 INFRARED SPECTROSCOPY

the monochromator to an accuracy of ±0.01 μm. Polystyrene films in suitable thicknesses are supplied by the manufacturers; these films are useful in making checks of both wavelength accuracy and reproducibility of absorbance. In the event that reference standards are needed in which the half-bandwidths are perceptibly narrower, a number of gases are recommended: (1) carbon dioxide at a pathlength of 25 cm and pressures of 27 and 50 mm for the doublet at 4.27 μm and the perpendicular band at 14.97 μm; (2) ammonia vapor having a pathlength of 25 cm and pressures of 100 mm for the Q branch near 2.988 μm, also the P branch exhibits a strong line near 11.008 μm; (3) water vapor shows a series of rotational bands between about 5.5 and 6.5 μm which provide excellent calibration points in a 25-cm cell at pressures of 5 to 10 mm. The carbon dioxide and water-vapor bands may be observed quite conveniently without recourse to special gas cells merely by exposing the monochromator to the atmosphere for a few minutes preceding a calibration experiment. It is a good policy to conduct a series of linearity checks when a new spectrometer is obtained for quantitative analysis even though extensive calibration curves may ordinarily be established later for ensuring maximum accuracy. For purposes of studying any instrumental contributions to nonlinearity, in a plot of absorbance versus concentration, it is preferable to choose thick cells (1.0 mm) and minimum slit widths insofar as consistent with acceptable signal-to-noise ratio. Such cells are necessary in order to work with dilute solutions whereby the absorption errors attributable to finite solute volumes are negligible. All absorbance measurements should be made, of course, using the same sample and reference cells over the absorbance range from about 0.3 to 0.9 μm. It is not absolutely essential that a spectrometer be highly linear; it is possible to obtain exceedingly accurate analyses on an instrument exhibiting marked apparent departures from the Beer-Lambert law through the expediency of obtaining a calibration curve.

1.9 Application of the Infrared Spectroscopic Techniques in Moisture Measurement

The moisture in any sample can be detected by its absorption of infrared radiation at certain characteristic frequencies. However, for determining the amount of moisture content one has to measure the intensity of such absorption bands since the depth of an absorption band is proportional to the concentration of the component responsible for that band. The amount of any material present in a sample can be determined by comparing the depth of the band of interest with the depth of the same band in known concentrations of the sample. A working curve of absorbance versus concentration for different amounts of moisture is usually obtained from which the concentration of the unknown sample may easily be determined. The spectrum of a mixture is a superimposition of the spectrum of the pure components. Absorption wavelengths unique to each component are chosen and the sample transmittance at the chosen wavelength is measured and related to the concentration. Thus comparison of absorption intensities or determination of their individual values is the basis of quantitative measurement. The most reliable results are obtained by comparative methods since, despite much refinement of instrumental design and of operating procedures, reproducibility of absolute intensities of absorption on different instruments is difficult to achieve.

The presence of water in a sample reduces the sharpness of individual bands resulting in a general blurring of the spectrum and the clearance of extra bands. High concentrations may be necessary to clearly observe the extra bands due to moisture. An approximate curve for the moisture is produced by a subtraction curve of the pure compound (reference beam) from the same beam. This differential analysis procedure allows identification of moisture. This approach can form the basis of moisture control on an industrial or small laboratory scale. A refinement of the impurity analysis procedure is necessary for accurate measurement of moisture forming a two-component system with the dry substance.

1 INFRARED SPECTROSCOPY

The analyst is required to estimate, as accurately as possible, the amount of water present in the sample. Using infrared spectroscopy this determination rests solely on comparative absorption intensities, and the absorption intensities of the dry sample must be known for at least one characteristic strong band in the spectrum of each component. Accurate measurement of the sample containing moisture and of the thickness of the absorbing specimen then allows calculation of component concentration on the basis of Beer's law. Alternatively, each component is examined in its pure form at a series of concentrations and a calibration curve is obtained of concentration against absorption intensity for a selected band. Using the same pathlength cell for the sample having moisture, the concentration of the components may be obtained by the measurement of the intensities of a characteristic band for each component and reading from the relevant calibration curve the corresponding component concentration. This method obviates the necessity of measuring cell width (pathlength) by interferometric methods, and cancels errors due to nonparallel cell window surfaces, besides permitting quantitative analysis of substances which do not obey Beer's law.

A further factor which must be considered is the possible absorption by water at the same absorption frequency as the dry sample. This complication may be resolved generally by the study of two band intensities for the component. In both of the procedures outlined, better accuracy can be obtained by working with absorption bands having transmittance of 25 to 65%. These two procedures discussed above are applied generally to water measurement in liquids or in gases. A similar approach has been developed for moisture measurement in solids examined spectroscopically by the alkali halide disk technique. Here an internal standard, potassium thiocyanate potassium bromide standard mixture, and the ratio of CSN ion absorption at 2.135 cm^{-1} (4.7 μm) to a chosen sample band absorption is plotted against percentage concentration of sample; a calibration curve is obtained. Using the same thiocyanate-bromide mixture as standard disk material the concentration of the substance in any mixture may then be read off from the curve. A critical factor is the need for a constant grinding time in disk preparation. This procedure eliminates the need to measure the disk thickness and allows examination of substances which do not conform to Beer's law. Quantitative analysis using an internal standard in Nujol mulls has also been used.

It may be mentioned that the best advantage of this technique is obtained in those cases where very small amounts of moisture contents (even in trace quantities) are required to be measured very accurately and where the results are to be compared with those obtained by other methods such as mass spectroscopy and nuclear magnetic resonance (NMR) techniques. Measured water contents are probably accurate to about 0.05% or even better for samples of good optical quality. For scratched samples the accuracy of measurement is reduced as a result of loss of radiation due to scattering. This difficulty can be overcome by using an internal-standard method of measuring absorption.

Only a few typical applications are mentioned here to show the uniqueness of the infrared spectroscopic methods and techniques. Details of the applications in these and similar materials are discussed in Chaps. XIII and XIV. Infrared spectrometry has been applied for the measurement of moisture contents even up to the parts per million range in hydrazines [42-43]. The absorption band in the 1.9-μm region has been found to be quite suitable for the determination of water in monoethylhydrazine and 1,1-dimethylhydrazine. It has also been applied successfully for accurate measurement of moisture contents in Freon fluorine refrigerants in the range of 0 to 10 ppm with an accuracy of 1 ppm by studying the absorption of infrared radiation at the 2.7-μm water band [44-45]. The water contents of methanethiol and ethanethiol have been measured by Matsuyama [46] who selected the large infrared absorption of the OH stretching frequency at 2.8 μm. Earlier the water content in these chemicals and mercaptans of higher molecular weights were determined by Mitchell and Smith [47] using Karl Fischer reagent.

1 INFRARED SPECTROSCOPY

Coulson et al. [48] have utilized infrared spectroscopy for the measurement of the water contents of highly purified samples of pyridine α-, β-, and γ-picoline, and 2:6 lutidine, in which water is usually present in the liquid phase, an absorption band at 3420 cm^{-1} being present. It was found by them that 3% water by volume with pyridine in the vapor phase produces no detectable difference in the absorption spectrum at 3420 cm^{-1}.

Dalmon and Freymann [49] found that the addition of water to pure fuming nitric acid causes a weak absorption band to develop at 0.07 μm. The strength of the band increases with increase in concentrations of water. Kinsey and Ellis [50-51] observed that the absorption bands of pure liquid water at 1.92 and 3.0 μm in 95% nitric acid were almost unaffected except for a slight shift in wavelength and some sharpening of the bands. The interpretation of the infrared absorption in nitric acid is based on the assumption that the absorbance of the sample is a linear function of its "species water content." (Species water content is the sum of the water content from self-dissociation and the water content determined by chemical analysis.)

The Beckman Model DU quartz spectrophotometer has been modified [52] to record absorption spectra from 2.1 to 2.7 μm automatically. This improvement has been achieved through replacement of the red-sensitive phototube with a photomultiplier tube, provision of a rotating slotted drum to interrupt the light beam, and use of an electronic recorder. The modification of the Beckman Model DU spectrophotometer considerably increases the utility of the instrument for three reasons: first, the automatic recording greatly increases the speed at which spectrum data may be accumulated; second, the use of a lead sulfide detector permits the instrument to be used in the near-infrared region of the spectrum; and third, the photomultiplier tube permits much greater resolution in the ultraviolet region.

Perhaps the greatest usefulness of this technique is found in the analysis of water in organic liquids. The precision of the analysis depends on the ratio of extinction coefficients of the water and the organic liquid in question. For most hydrogen-containing materials, this ratio is such that the precision will be of the order of a few hundredths of a percent of water. If the liquid in question does not contain hydrogen, the analysis for water may be performed when it is present in a concentration of a few parts per million. The OH groups in alcohols and acids do not absorb at the same wavelength as the OH group in water; hence, all of these materials are subject to near-infrared analysis. In all of these analyses for OH groups, consideration must be given to hydrogen bonding. The extinction coefficient of a bound OH group is smaller and at a different wavelength from that of a free OH group. Fortunately, the hydrogen bonding between molecules may be broken easily by diluting with a nonpolar solvent, such as carbon tetrachloride. Hydrogen bonding within a given molecule such as an amide is not broken so easily.

Using a modified Beckman DU quartz spectrophotometer Cahn [53] and White and Barrett [54] have determined the absorbance at 1.423 μm of samples having up to 5% water. The accuracy obtained by the infrared spectroscopic method is comparable to the Karl Fischer method employed by Moberg et al. [55]. The traces of water in acetic acid have been accurately measured by Bruckenstein [56] with a Cary recording spectrophotometer using 2-cm quartz cells with ground-glass stoppers. The water content was found to be 0.0015% which is in satisfactory agreement with the value estimated by the visual Karl Fischer method, which is 0.001 to 0.002%. This method has also been used to establish the absence of acetic anhydride in acetic acid as purified according to the method of Eichelberger and Lamer [57].

The infrared spectroscopic method has been combined with azeotropic distillation technique by Brandenberger and Bader [58] for the measurement of the moisture content of instant-coffee powders. This method excludes most of the error possibilities encountered in the drying procedures and determines the water content in the dioxane distillate at a specific absorption band for water in the near-infrared region.

1. INFRARED SPECTROSCOPY

Direct spectrophotometric determination of moisture contents of grains and seeds have been made by Norris and Hart [59]. The water absorption bands at 0.76, 0.97, 1.18, 1.45, and 1.94 μm were investigated for spectrophotometric measurement of the moisture contents of grains and seeds. The near-infrared spectrum of polymethyl methacrylate (perspex) has been investigated by Jones [60] for moisture measurement. He obtained an absorption band at about 2 μm due to absorbed water; this band has been found to be suitable for quantitative measurement. Elliot et al. [61] have extended the method and technique developed by Jones [60] for the measurement of moisture content of textile materials, and have suggested that the moisture content of textile fibers can be estimated from the overtone band at 5150 cm^{-1} which was used successfully for this purpose. Hecht and Wood [62] give the analytical curve for protein materials covering a range of 0 to 20% water.

The scope of application of infrared techniques in measurement of moisture in different chemicals can be observed from Table 6.3 wherein the absorption bands studied have been indicated.

1.10 Continuous Monitoring of Moisture by Infrared Spectroscopy

It is well known that the corrosion becomes excessive in a sulfur dioxide gas-oil extraction unit in refinery operations if the water content of the liquid sulfur dioxide exceeds 0.2% by weight. In order to maintain maximum capacity in the extraction operation and to protect the plant against excessive corrosion, an accurate, reliable, and rapid continuous water analyzer sensitized to 2.7 to 2.8 μm absorption doublet of water has been developed [63]. Figure 6.5 shows the infrared spectra obtained with a sodium chloride prism for samples of liquid sulfur dioxide from the extraction unit which contains varying amounts of water. This figure also shows the spectrum of a sample of chemically pure sulfur dioxide which contains about 0.15 wt % water. Examination of these spectra reveals that the weak bands at 2.3 to 2.5 μm and the strong bands at 3.4 to 3.5 μm are due to hydrocarbons present in the liquid sulfur dioxide from

TABLE 6.3

Typical Applications of Infrared Spectroscopy for Measurement of Water

Sample No.	Material	Analytical wavelength, approx. μm	Analytical wavelength, approx. cm^{-1}	Range studied, wt % H$_2$O (ppm)
1	Misc. organic compounds	1	10,000	0.1- 1
2	Nitric acid, fuming	1.423	7,025	0.1- 6
3	Acrylic resins	1.9	5,260	0.0- 1.2
4	Cellophane	1.9	—	—
5	Glycerol	1.9	—	1.0- 20
6	Hydrazines	1.9	—	0.1- 15
7	Sulfur dioxide	1.9	—	—
8	Vinyl acetate	1.9	—	—
9	Freon fluorine refrigerants	2.67	3,750	0.0-100
10	Sulfur dioxide	2.7	3,700	—
11	Mercaptans	2.8	3,570	0.0- 0.2
12	Pyridine and homologs	2.02	3,420	0.0- 3
13	Gases	5.5-7.5	1,800-1,350	—
14	Propane gas	5.8-6.3	1,700-1,600	0.0- 13
15	Chlorine liquid	6.1	1,640	—

the extraction unit. Being well separated from the water absorption at 2.7 to 2.8 μm these hydrocarbon absorption bands do not interfere significantly with water analysis.

In the production of many polymers it is important to control the water content of reactor feed streams in the range 1 to 10 ppm because catalyst may be modified or consumed, altering the properties of the finished polymer significantly. Commercially available electrolytic moisture monitors utilizing absorption on P_2O_5 are not directly useful on liquid streams, nor on unsaturated hydrocarbon streams because of their reactivity with phosphorus pentoxide. Infrared instruments for direct determination of water have lacked

1 INFRARED SPECTROSCOPY

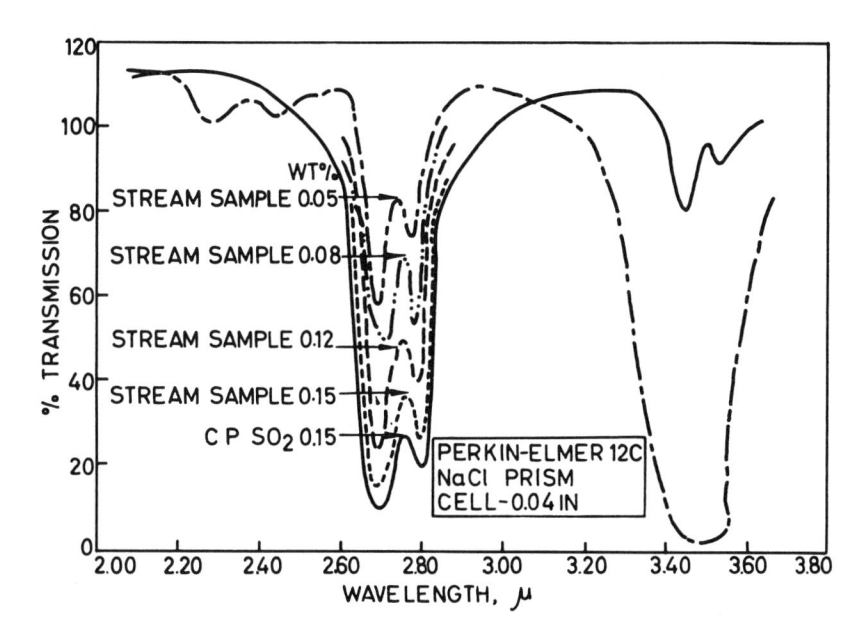

FIG. 6.5. Infrared spectra of liquid sulfur dioxide obtained with a sodium chloride prism.

sensitivity in such cases. Therefore, a trace water analyzer has been developed by Abrams and Smith [64] for automatic analysis of process streams by estimating acetylene obtained from the sample by reaction with calcium carbide. Acetylene has a sharp absorption band at 3.05 μm, which is well separated from the C-H stretching band of the hydrocarbons, which occurs at 3.45 μm. It is therefore possible to use this acetylene absorption band for the water measurement. Water is converted to dissolved acetylene in the liquid stream the acetylene is then measured at 3.05 μm by a nondispersive infrared analyzer so arranged as to compensate for moderate changes in the sample background absorption. When water contacts calcium carbide, acetylene is produced according to the reaction:

$$2 H_2O + CaC_2 \rightarrow C_2H_2 + Ca(OH)_2 \tag{6.3}$$

In the automatic process stream analyzer the acetylene in the original sample after reaction with calcium carbide is monitored by the infrared spectroscopic technique. A schematic diagram of the analyzer arrangement and flow system is shown in Fig. 6.6. When the valve is set so that the untreated sample flows through both the reference cell and sample cell, the detector signals are equal and the instrument is in null position. If the valve is now switched to permit flow of sample through the calcium carbide bed, any water present is converted to acetylene; the resultant absorption causes a deflection of the recorder. The sample normally flows through the bypass (while the sample filling the reactor tube is static), and is directed through the reactor tube for a short time; this sequence is repeated at regular intervals. During the short flushing periods acetylene formed in the preceding time interval flows through the measuring sample cell and produces a recorder deflection. The instrument has added gear for temperature control, sample switching, heat exchange, etc. Sample cells for the application were designed [64] with special attention to rapid mixing and clearing of sample and to withstand the pressure of approximately 150 psi. Four small

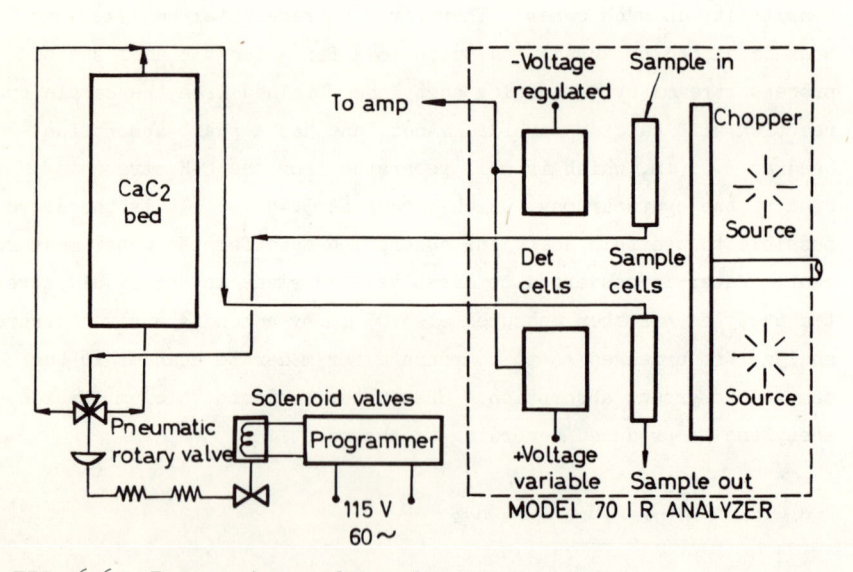

FIG. 6.6. Trace water analyzer for process streams.

1 INFRARED SPECTROSCOPY

inlets at the bottom distribute sample through the body of the cell; the outlet is to a single opening at the top. The resulting recorder displays peaks much like those commonly obtained in gas chromatography analysis comprising a zero baseline with sharp peaks at 20-min intervals. In principle any double-beam instrument adaptable to liquid measurement and of the requisite sensitivity will be satisfactory for the measurement in this case as well.

Although conversion of water to acetylene is quantitative with the reactor and residence time used, it is necessary to obtain an empirical calibration of the overall system including the infrared analyzer and reactor because separate calibration of the analyzer for acetylene is not convenient, particularly in plant operation. The calculated ultimate sensitivity (range) of the instrument is 0 to 12 ppm full scale. For applications in which higher sensitivity is required, another method utilizing solvent exchange of inert-gas stripping, followed by measurement at 13.7 µm, may be used [65]. Figure 6.7 shows a typical recorder chart for a few parts per million of water in benzene. The analyzer should be applicable on many organic liquids and gas streams. The principal requirements are that the sample should have adequate transmission at 3.05 µm, and not contain components, other than water, which will react with calcium carbide.

1.11 Continuous Monitoring of Moisture Content

Tripeer [66] has developed a process stream analyzer for continuous and unattended analysis of water in solids, liquids, and gases. He has used a filter-photometer type of analyzer which offers significant advantages for process stream analysis by combining the wavelength selectivity of the dispersive analyzer with the high photometric sensitivity and simplicity of the self-filtering analyzer. The mechanical and optical simplicity of filter photometers permits a rugged, low-maintenance design capable of extremely high analytical sensitivity. The increasing availability

380   VI. SPECTROSCOPIC METHODS AND TECHNIQUES

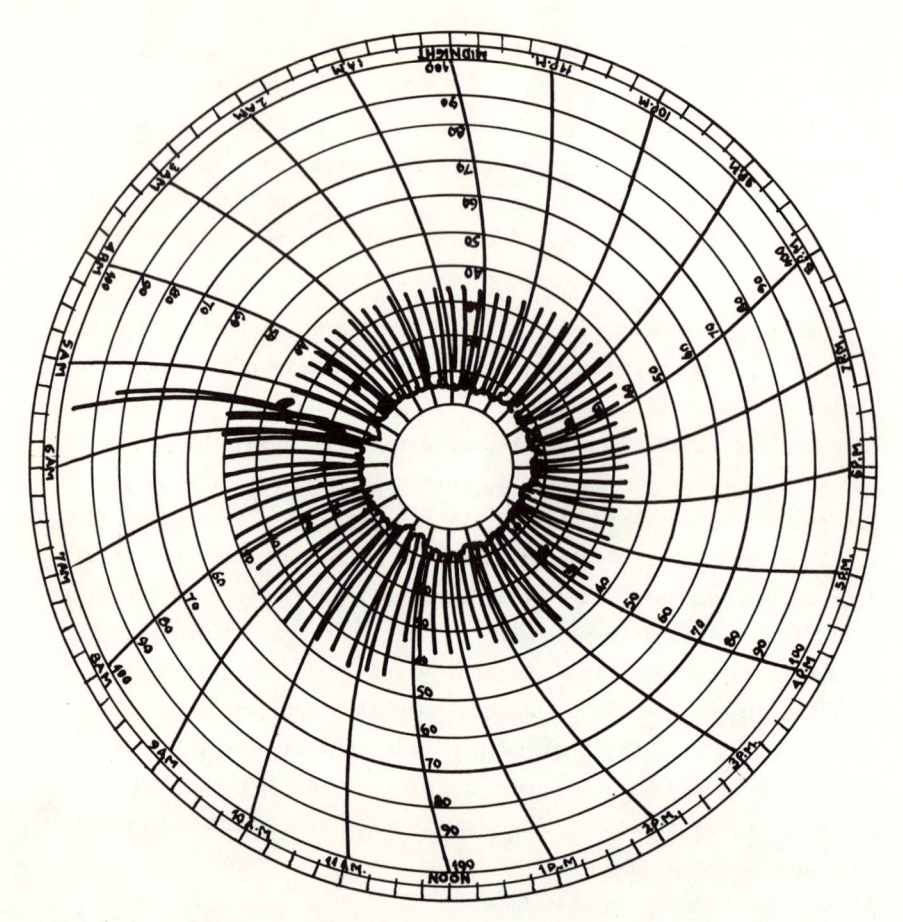

FIG. 6.7. Infrared spectra of benzene showing presence of a few parts per million of water.

of a wide selection of suitable narrow-band filters will make the filter photometer more generally accepted for continuous, high-sensitivity analysis. The above features and the many advantages of analyzing at near-infrared wavelengths make the filter photometer ideally suited for water analysis. This analyzer has several advantages over similar instruments developed earlier by other workers. These advantages are as follows:

   1. It eliminates adverse effects of sample radiation by modulating between the source and sample.

2. It provides selectivity by the use of narrow-bandpass filters or a monochromator.

3. It minimizes the effects of particulate matter, bubbles, etc., in the sample by the use of collimated radiation in the sample areas.

4. It provides first-order compensation for other absorbing materials by simultaneously measuring the same area of sample with both wavelengths.

This analyzer has been applied for the measurement of water in dimethylformamide (DMF). Precise control of water content in DMF to less than 50 ppm is required in process analysis with a sensitivity of 10 ppm or less. Using a 0.284-in. thick sample cell and analytical and reference wavelengths of 1.930 and 1.980 µm, respectively, Tripeer [66] has obtained a full-scale sensitivity of 300 ppm (or 3 ppm per chart division) when the analyzer "span" is set at 0.03 absorbance. This performance is obtained with a noise level of less than one recorder division. The analyzer is normally standardized once every 24 hr using solutions of known water content or, if desired, by independent analysis of a grab sample.

Another application of this analyzer has been made in the measurement of moisture in paper. Adequate control of the drying step of paper processes requires a sensitive method of process analysis. A simple modification of this analyzer in which use is made of a focused beam at the plane of the sample instead of the normal collimated beam, provides sufficient optical efficiency to permit high-sensitivity infrared measurements on many types of papers at thicknesses up to 10 mils. Typically, a full-scale sensitivity of 0.5% water is possible on a 5-mil thick paper using an analytical wavelength of 1.9 µm and a reference wavelength of 1.80 µm. To obtain the analysis on a weight percent basis, an independent measure of thickness and appropriate correction will be needed. Though only two applications are given here, it is claimed by du Pont Company, where this instrument was developed, that this analyzer can be used effectively for determining moisture content of substances in any one of the three phases with a very high degree of accuracy even at high temperatures and pressures up to 300°C and 2000 psi, respectively. Typical sensitivity obtained is 200 ppm full scale of water in a hydrocarbon, and sometimes photometric sensitivities as high as one part in 1500 have been obtained.

1.12 Application of Infrared Spectroscopy for Measuring the Quality of Steam

1.12.1 <u>Introduction</u>. The efficiency and life of steam-powered equipment are affected by the quality or wetness of the steam used. Steam quality is defined as the ratio of the weight of water vapor to the total weight of steam, which may consist of both water vapor and liquid water. Dry steam or steam of 10% quality consists solely of water vapor. In an operating steam system liquid water may be introduced into dry steam by physical carryover of liquid water droplets from the boiler or as a result of condensation due to a pressure or temperature drop in some part of the system. In steam turbine systems, these water droplets impinge upon the turbine blades and cause erosion on the back and inlet edges. In addition, such droplets often contain entrained solids originating in the boiler water. These solids deposit on the turbine blades causing unbalance and necessitating difficult cleaning operations.

Wet steam contains less usable energy than dry steam. This is particularly significant in critical applications of steam thrusts such as the steam catapult. Here, the delivered thrust of the system is empirically determined for each combination of the variables of pressure, temperature, and time of cycle. As a result of the lack of a suitable measuring device the quality of the steam used is not measured and is assumed to remain constant. In operation, however, occasions do arise where the quality of the steam used has changed. In cases such as these the delivered thrust deviates from the empirically predetermined value and launching failures may occur. It is therefore desirable to continuously monitor the quality of steam.

1 INFRARED SPECTROSCOPY

1.12.2 The Principle and Working of the Instrument. The method of the measurement of the quality of the steam depends on the differential infrared absorption of liquid water and steam in the vapor phase. It has been observed [67] that the maximum absorption of liquid water at 92°C occurs at 2.81 μm, whereas dry steam at 100°C has its maximum absorption at 2.62 μm. This differential absorption property has been utilized by Greenberg [67] to develop an instrument which can detect only liquid water from a mixture of liquid water and steam, thereby making the instrument insensitive to steam pressure changes. It measures the attenuation of infrared radiation by steam, which may consist of both water vapor and liquid water droplets. Attenuation by water vapor is through the process of simple absorption and is affected only by the concentration of water molecules and the pathlength traversed by the radiation. This is mathematically expressed by the Beer-Lambert equation. The pathlength is fixed by the diameter of the sample section of the instrument and the concentration of water-vapor molecules is directly related to the steam pressure. The attenuation due to the water vapor has been empirically determined by measurements on dry steam at various pressures. It is constant at any specified pressure and is included in the calibration of the instrument.

The instrument developed by Greenberg [67] operates in the 1 to 3-μm region. This region has been selected because of its high sensitivity to attenuation by wet steam and because of the availability of sensitive, rugged photoconductive detectors, steam-resistant window materials, and energy-rich sources which operate efficiently. Water absorption bands occur at 2.97, 1.98, 1.46, 1.18, and 0.98 μm. The intensities of these bands decrease with decreasing wavelength. The 2.9-μm absorption band is a result of the fundamental vibrational mode of the water molecule and is the strongest absorption band. The other absorption bands are a result of combinations and harmonics of frequencies of the fundamental vibrations. The tungsten lamp source used emits a continuous band of radiation covering the visible and near-infrared regions up to 3.5 μm, which is the cutoff wavelength for the lamp's quartz envelope. A broadband transmission filter mounted in front of the detector rejects 99% of the radiation from the source below 0.8 µm and transmits 76% of the radiation over the 1.5 to 2.7-µm range. The lead sulfide detector used has a peak sensitivity at approximately 2 µm with a cutoff at approximately 3.3 µm.

In a heterogeneous material such as wet steam, attenuation is due to both absorption and scattering. Complex absorption and scattering occur in spherical water droplets as a result of multiple internal reflection and reflection of incident radiation from the surfaces of the small water droplets. These are the major infrared attenuating mechanisms, and they both are related to the particle size distribution and concentration of the liquid water particles in the steam. An investigation leading to the development of this instrument showed that infrared transmission is not significantly affected by changes in mass steam-flow rate above a limiting value and by other operating conditions such as temperature and pressure after a correction for water-vapor absorption has been applied. Therefore, it is reasoned that the water droplet size distribution for a steam system is a constant characteristic over a wide range of operating conditions and that the concentration of water droplets is the only variable related to the infrared attenuating properties of the steam. Steam quality, being directly related to the concentration of the water particles, should be related to the instrument's reading. Actual measurements made on wet steams over a wide range of qualities show this to be true.

1.12.3 Constructional Features of the Infrared Steam Quality Analyzer. The instrument (Fig. 6.8) consists of the following major units: (1) source section, (2) sampling arrangement, (3) detector system, and (4) associated electronics circuit. For description of these units, the reader is referred to the original publication [67].

1.12.4 The Procedure of Measurement and Interpretation of Data. The instrument is activated by switching on the source lamp, beam

1 INFRARED SPECTROSCOPY

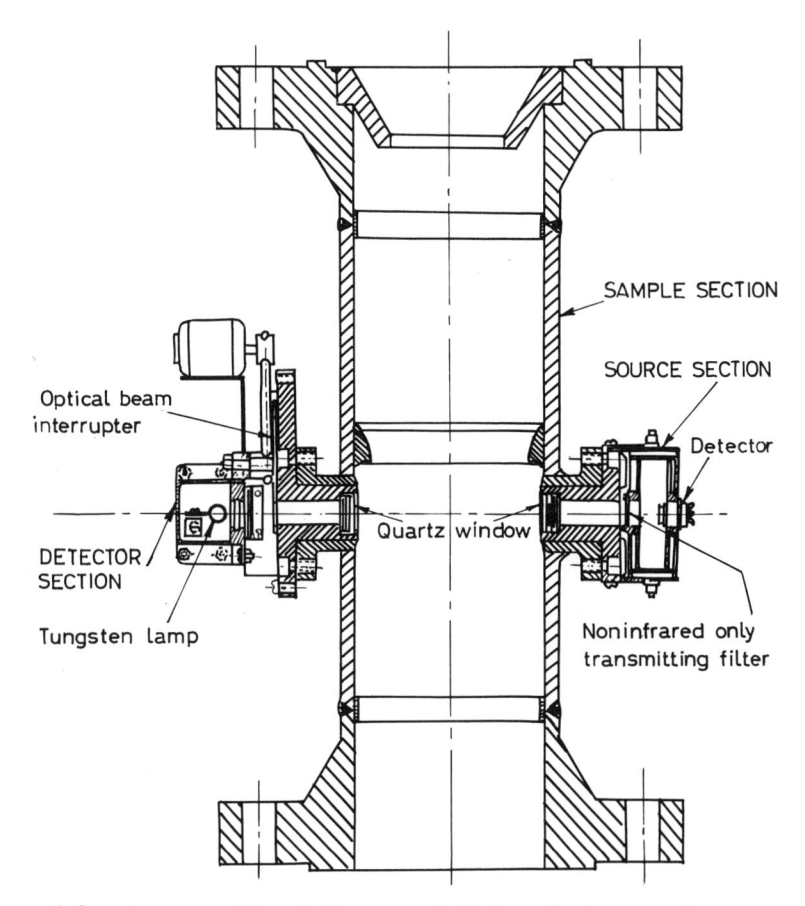

FIG. 6.8. Cross-sectional diagram of infrared steam analyzer.

interrupter, amplifier, detector bias voltage, and recorder, and by turning on the detector housing cooling water. A half-hour warmup period is recommended. It is necessary that the detector housing cooling water be left on continuously during steam operation. The instrument is standardized by inserting in the beam a calibration plate. With the instrument on, an air path in the sample section and the standardizing plate in position, the shutter is adjusted until the recorder or instrument meter reads a previously determined calibration value. The setting of this value assures the proper operation of all components and the original calibration of the instrument. This standardizing procedure can be accomplished on an operating steam system by directing the steam flow through a bypass line until this operation is complete.

The theoretical basis for the pressure effect on the instrument reading is understood when one considers that the steam quality analyzer responds directly to the density of the water molecules in the optical path. Hence, an increase in steam pressure increases the density of the water-vapor molecules and changes the background absorption of the system. This has the effect of translating the calibration curve in the direction of lower instrument reading in the case of a pressure increase, and in the direction of higher instrument reading in the case of a pressure decrease. The magnitude of the pressure effect is shown in Fig. 6.9. The shaded area is the range of variation in instrument reading for changes in pressure over the 100 to 400-psi range. When highest accuracy is required, one must refer to a calibration curve of a specific pressure of interest; however, when an accuracy of ±2% quality is permissible, the pressure effect over this range can be ignored and the median calibration line (broken line, Fig. 6.9) can be used.

It is difficult to evaluate the reproducibility of the steam quality analyzer under actual steam operating conditions because wet steam consists of a dynamic equilibrium of water and water vapor which is difficult to maintain. Therefore, in considering data taken under actual steam flow conditions, one must keep in mind the effects of variations in steam quality and pressure which are uncontrollable. Figure 6.10 shows the median calibration lines for two runs. It is seen that the greatest variations between these runs occur in the region of poorest steam qualities. It is interesting to note that the ability to generate and maintain constant-quality steam in this poorer-quality region is more difficult. With this in mind as a major source of reproducibility error, it can be seen that the maximum variation in three runs is ±1% quality.

1 INFRARED SPECTROSCOPY   387

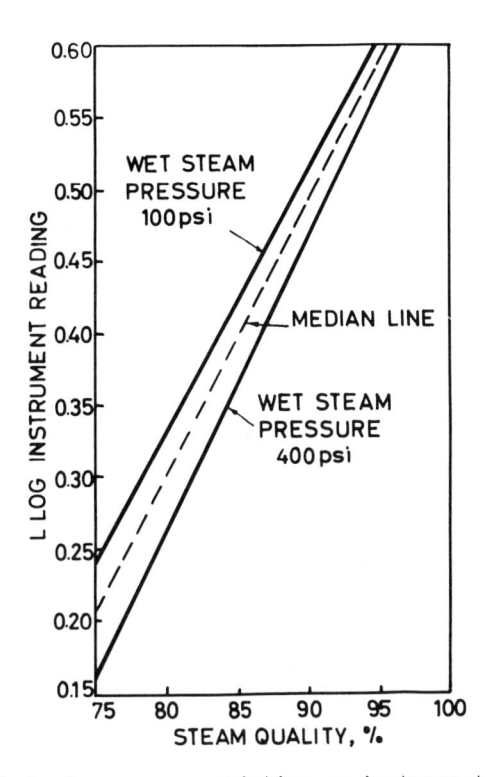

FIG. 6.9. Effect of pressure variation on instrument readings.

1.13 Determination of Stratosphere Moisture

Meteorologists are very much interested in determining the concentration of water vapor at heights greater than those at which the weather is made. Water vapor at these higher altitudes determines the absorption and reemission of radiant energy in the stratosphere and thereby stratospheric temperatures. A rather unusual but interesting example of the use of infrared spectroscopy is furnished by the National Bureau of Standards' methods for determining the moisture in the stratosphere at heights above 15 km. Atmospheric humidity measurements at such heights today have been made by hygrometers and recorders which have been sent aloft and recovered on

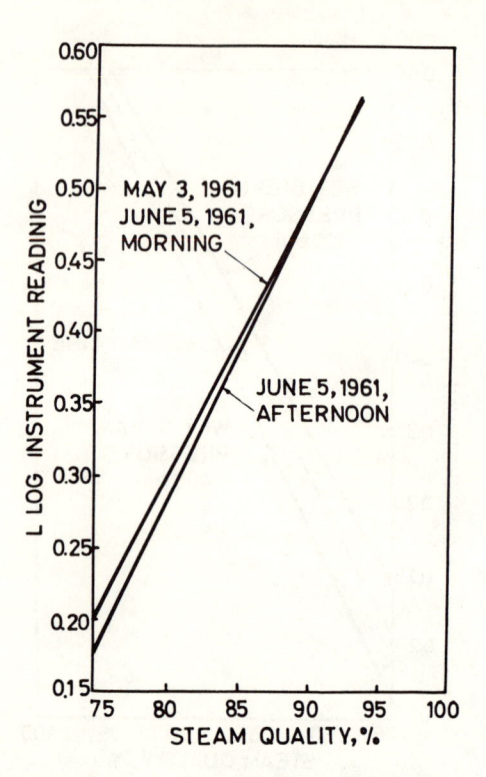

FIG. 6.10. Reproducibility of calibration curves.

on their return to earth. This method has provided reliable measurements up to about 15 km (nearly 50,000 ft) and less reliable results above this altitude, but does not give much information above 30 km. The infrared method worked out by Gates [68] is based on the evaluation of data obtained from infrared spectrometers carried aloft by balloons. These data are used to compute the amount of precipitable moisture in the line-of-sight path from the spectrometer to the sun. Water vapor selectively absorbs certain frequencies passing through it; the greater the concentration of water vapor, the greater the absorption at these discrete bands and lines. This absorption is a consequence of the vibration-rotation bands in the near-infrared and the pure rotation spectrum in the far-infrared. If the radiation from the sun is known to be evenly distributed over

1 INFRARED SPECTROSCOPY

part of its spectrum, a spectroscope can be used to determine at what frequencies the radiation has been absorbed en route and the absorbants can thus be identified.

Several strong lines in the vicinity of the 3.3-μm wavelength can readily be used to indicate the presence of water vapor in the radiation path. Evaluation of absorption at these frequencies can be used to calculate how much water vapor must have passed through on its path toward the earth. This calculation is facilitated by computing total precipitable water vapor above various altitudes for specific assumed mixing ratios and the transmission for any frequency at varied water-vapor concentrations. The latter calculation is based on the quantum mechanics of water-vapor molecules and the absorption caused by the ν_1, ν_2, and ν_3 vibration-rotation bands of the water-vapor molecule near 2.7 μm. Using high-resolution spectrum data recently obtained, Gates [68] has calculated that water vapor is present in a concentration of 30 μm above the 15-km level. This value is for the slant path of 71° from the vertical; however, it is equivalent to only 9 μm of water vapor straight up from the 15-km level. Analysis of additional spectra obtained from British Aircraft flights shows a dry stratosphere with less than 10 μm of water vapor above 45,000 ft (nearly 15 km). Such small amounts indicate that the mixing ratio is less than 10^{-5} g H_2O/g air, if the water vapor is uniformly mixed above these heights.

For further study of the subject the reader is referred to a recent monograph <u>Modern Hygrometry</u> by Pande [69]. In this publication different types of infrared absorption hygrometers are described.

1.14 Analysis of Heavy Water by Infrared Spectrometry

In the production of heavy water, it is necessary to monitor the deuterium content of heavy water in the following concentration ranges:

1. 99.6 to 100% D_2O

2. 50% D_2O
3. 3% D_2O } with increased accuracy over
4. 0.2% D_2O } that previously obtained
5. Natural range

Gaunt [70-71] has developed infrared spectrophotometric methods for the analysis of the deuterium content of heavy water in the concentrations given above and obtained a high degree of accuracy which varies from one range to another.

In order to analyze the five ranges of heavy water on a routine basis a minimum of three infrared spectrometers would be required which would have the different degrees of accuracy in these ranges. These should be as follows:

1. For the 99% range an instrument set at 2.94 μm equipped with PbS cell and 800-Hz amplifier, with 0.25-mm silica cells.

2. For the 50% range an instrument set at 1.445 μm (second order), equipped with PbS cell and 800-Hz amplifier, with 5-mm glass cells.

3. For the 3%, 0.2%, and natural ranges an instrument set at 3.98 μm, equipped with thermocouple and 10-Hz amplifier, using 0.07-, 0.19-, and 0.25-mm cells with windows of calcium fluoride or synthetic sapphire.

The data (Table 6.4) obtained by Gaunt [70-71] compare favorably with those obtained from theoretical calculations, and spectroscopic and nuclear methods.

1.15 Continuous Spectrophotometric Analysis of Heavy Water

Plant-control infrared spectrometers for flow analysis of heavy water have been developed by Woodhull et al. [72] and Savitzky and Bresky [73] which employ dispersive and nondispersive systems, respectively. The infrared dispersion analyzer developed by Savitzky and Bresky [73] is known as the Bichromator. It is essentially a single-beam instrument using the dispersion principle but analyzing at two wavelengths simultaneously to give an automatic continuous

TABLE 6.4

Comparison of Calculated and
Experimental Values of Deuterium

Sample No.	Calculated mole % (D)	Experimental mole % (D)
1	49.4	48.4
2	24.9	26.1
3	78.9	77.3
4	57.5	55.6
5	37.7	36.0

measurement of a ratio according to the widely used baseline density technique. This method of taking the ratio of transmissions at a sample wavelength and at a reference wavelength produces an indication of sample concentration relatively independent of cell window fogging and source emission variations, as well as changes in the optical path which can adversely affect the operation of double-beam-type analyzers. Use of this single-beam method not only simplifies the instrument optically but also allows compensation for variable interference owing to a second component which also absorbs at the sample wavelength. This compensation is achieved by selecting the reference wavelength so that the absorptivity of the interferent is equal to that at the sample wavelength; absorption being exponentially dependent on concentration, the ratio of transmissions then remains a function of the sample concentration only. Designed for continuous in-plant operation the Bichrometer analyzer makes use of the optical null principle to eliminate the effects of gain changes in the electronic amplifiers, source deterioration, and fogging of optics.

1.16 Conclusion

As will be seen from the foregoing descriptions, great interest has been generated in the applications of infrared spectrophotometric methods and techniques for the measurement of moisture content of a large number of substances in solids, liquids, or gases by employing suitable wavelengths at which maximum absorption is expected to occur. A few typical applications are given in Table 6.3. Like every method or technique this also has its own limitations because the choice of a suitable wavelength for experimental purposes depends on the concentration and range of water and the nature of the sample. Actually, most of the absorption bands are not specific for the water molecule. Absorption by hydroxyl groups in other compounds and other strongly absorbing groups may be coincidental with that by water or cause serious overlapping so that certain bands will be inapplicable. Each system to be analyzed should be examined carefully before choice is made of the most suitable analytical wavelength. Known mixtures should be analyzed over the expected concentration range of the water. From this information, reliable absorptivities or calibration curves can be obtained. In some cases of intermolecular hydrogen bonding, a band associated with the nonaqueous component often is enhanced in proportion to the concentration of water. Most of the relatively strong bands for water in the near-infrared are subject to interference by hydroxyl and amine groups. In the 2.5 to 3-μm region all hydroxyl and some amine groups absorb. In the 2.6 to 2.7-μm region many hydrogen-containing compounds may interfere unless suitable compensation is provided. These interferences include those from alcohols, alkyl esters, hydrocarbons, and chloroform.

Infrared techniques are being very widely used in many laboratories and continuous analyses are being performed either semiautomatically or completely automatically. However, they have not reached their full potential in the application of measurement and control of moisture. This is perhaps due to inadequate understanding of the conditions needed for reproducible analysis and the unavailability of commercial instrumentation designed for use at the wide range of frequencies required under different operating conditions. The versatility and selectivity of infrared techniques can provide significant advantages over other instrumental methods, if these drawbacks can be overcome. However, attempts have been recently made to overcome these difficulties (with a substantial amount of success) by the development of the process stream analyzer and the heavy water analyzer which have been described earlier.

2 MASS-SPECTROMETRIC METHOD OF MOISTURE MEASUREMENT

2.1 General

Mass spectrometers were originally developed for the measurement of isotope abundance ratios and other relevant quantities. However, recently it has been utilized successfully as a tool of chemical analysis with remarkable success. For example, a rapid analysis of complex hydrocarbon mixtures in the petroleum industry which is very difficult and time-consuming otherwise can be done conveniently by this technique. After the notable success of this instrument in such fields, because of similarity of structure and chemical inertness of the compounds, analytical scientists have extended its applications to other fields, including estimation of moisture content in liquids and gases. It is capable of giving fairly reliable results of moisture content over a wide concentration range.

2.2 Instrumentation

The mass spectrometer and mass spectrograph, though based on the same principle, are quite different. The spectrograph is employed for precise measurement of mass, whereas the spectrometer is designed to measure precisely the relative abundance of ions, which is discussed here. In a mass spectrometer, the sample to be studied is first introduced in a vacuum chamber and is reduced to low vapor pressure by suitable heating. The vapor thus formed is passed through a beam of electrons, where ionization occurs. The ions thus produced are accelerated by a suitable electric field and passed into the magnetic field. A charged particle traveling at high speed follows a curved path, the radius of which depends on the speed of the particle and its mass-to-charge ratio (m/e). By varying either the velocity of the particles (by changing accelerating voltage) or by changing the magnetic-field strength, ions of various m/e ratios can be focused on a collector plate and thus grounded. The resulting current is amplified and recorded by a suitable electrometer circuit. The plot of mass versus intensity is known as mass spectrum. It is reduced to a mass pattern by dividing each of the peak intensities by the intensity of the largest or base peak.

2.3 Construction of Mass Spectrographs and Spectrometers

Mass spectrometry is of very recent origin and in a short period of time a number of instruments have been experimentally developed and commercially manufactured. The mass spectrographs and spectrometers can be classified into the following categories:

1. Static instruments
2. Direction-focusing mass spectrometers
3. Double-focusing mass spectrographs
4. Cycloidal-focusing mass spectrometers
5. Dynamic instruments (ion-resonance type)
6. Time-of-flight mass spectrometers
7. Quadrupole mass spectrometer
8. Magnetodynamic instruments

Only two of these instruments, i.e., double-focusing and dynamic instruments, which are most used for chemical analysis, are briefly described here. For a detailed study of the rest of the mass spectrographs and mass spectrometers, the reader should consult the references [82-91].

2.4 Double-Focusing Mass Spectrographs and Mass Spectrometers

In the double-focusing mass analyzer advantage is taken of the ion optical properties of a radial electric field established between the plates of a cylindrical condenser. The instrument functionally

consists of an analyzer, a vacuum system, an electric system, an
optical lens system, and a vacuum chamber for photographic plate
(Fig. 6.11). The analyzer consists of an ion source, an accelerating
slit, a main slit, an electrostatic-field entrance slit, electrostatic-field electrodes, an electrostatic-field exit slit, a monitor,
a magnetic-field entrance slit, and a magnetic field. In the double-
focusing mass spectrograph (Fig. 6.11) the electrostatic and magnetic
fields are connected in tandem. Mass spectrographs embodying a
double-focusing analyzer of this type provide high resolution necessary for accurate atomic mass determinations. In recent years
double-focusing instruments have been applied increasingly to problems of chemical analysis.

2.5 Description of Radiofrequency (Ion Resonance) Mass Spectrometer

The ion-resonance mass spectrometer (Fig. 6.12) developed by
Morgan et al. [74] consists of three major constituents: (1) the
vacuum pumping system, (2) the mass spectrometer tube, (3) associated electronic components. The radiofrequency mass analyzer is
shown in Fig. 6.13. The principle of operation is basically quite
simple. Ions are formed by bombardment of the molecules of the
sample gas with electrons emitted from a hot filament. In the ion-
resonance tube the ions formed about the electrons' beam are immediately separated according to their mass-to-charge ratio as they are
accelerated by a radiofrequency (rf) voltage toward a small collector
inserted in the ion source. Only ions of a particular m/e ratio
having a normal resonant frequency in the magnetic field equal to
the frequency of the rf voltage can obtain enough energy to reach
the collector. Thus, it is possible to detect ions of a given m/e
ratio by application of an rf voltage of the appropriate frequency.
An ion beam homogeneous in energy passes through a succession of rf
modulator stages separated by field-free drift spaces. Ions having
a certain velocity are preferentially accelerated and can overcome
a static retarding field, while ions having other velocities are
rejected. Because of the homogeneity in energy of the incoming beam,

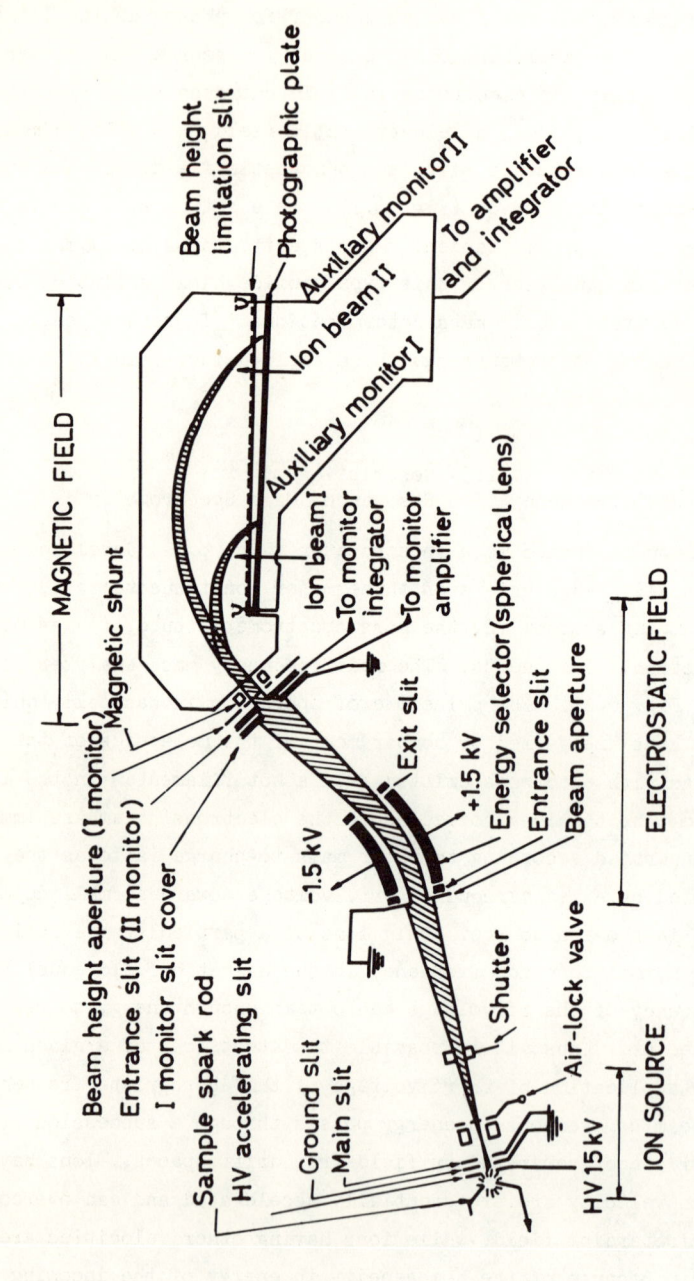

FIG. 6.11. Schematic diagram of the Mattauch-Herzog double-beam-focusing mass spectrograph.

2 MASS-SPECTROMETRIC METHOD

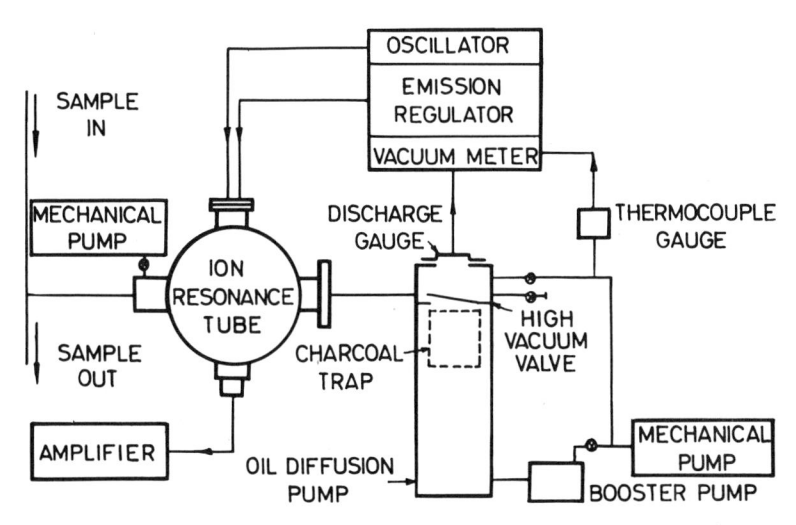

FIG. 6.12. Block diagram of ion-resonance mass spectrometer.

the velocity of an ion is characteristic of its mass. Hence the velocity analysis achieved in the spectrometer is equivalent to mass analysis. Each modulator stage of an rf analyzer consists of an odd number of plane, parallel grids divided by equal gaps. In the ion-resonance mass spectrometer the mass spectrum is scanned by varying the frequency of the applied rf voltage. Bennet [75] has developed three axial-field rf mass spectrometers which have served as models for subsequent designs. Several advantages result from the use of the ion-resonance principle; some of them are given below:

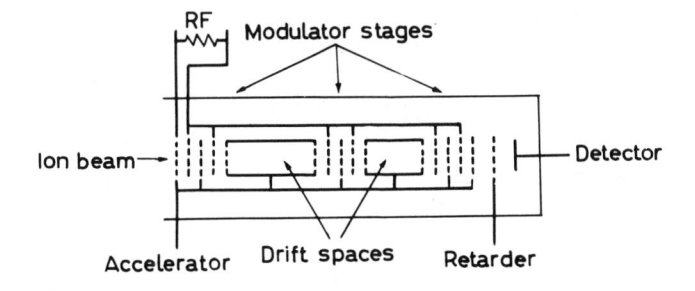

FIG. 6.13. Radiofrequency mass analyzer.

1. There are no high potentials applied to the tube, so the electrical leakage problem is virtually eliminated.

2. There are no slits for resolving the ion beam, so the effects of surface potentials and deposits as well as the problem of dimensional stability are minimized. The absence of slits also contributes to the high sensitivity of the instrument.

3. The resolution of the tube is variable by means of externally controlled potentials. This readily permits maximizing sensitivity for detection of trace constituents of maximizing resolution for special analysis.

4. Because of the spiral path of the ions in the strong magnetic field, high resolution can be obtained in a small compact tube that serves as both ion source and analyzer.

2.6 Technique of Mass Spectrographic Analysis

A brief description of the procedure of mass spectrographic analysis is given below.

1. Since a sample to be analyzed is used as an electrode and ionized by rf arcing in high vacuum, it must be prepared in proper shape. The powdered sample can be filled in a tube made of other pure materials.

2. Since impurities clinging to a sample bring serious problems when a mass analysis is carried out with very high order of detection, it is desirable to prepare the sample with utmost care so as not to allow the clinging of any impurities, and to use it as the electrode without washing or other similar treatments.

3. In the strict sense of the word, the relative sensitivity of respective elements with respect to the instrument should have been determined in advance by use of a standard sample, and corrections thereby be made upon the quantitative analysis.

4. Photographic plates to be used are darkened by attached ions on the emulsion surface and the line density depends on the number of attached ions; therefore the atomic concentration is given by a calculation based on the above fact. Accordingly, it can be converted into the weight concentration which is used for ordinary chemical analysis, weight concentration (ppm), and the ratio of atomic weight of impurity element to atomic weight of standard element.

However, in quantitative analysis the problem is somewhat different. Prior knowledge of the quantitative analysis of the sample is required for calibration. The mass spectrum of a mixture then is simply the sum of the spectra of the components in the ratio of their partial pressure in the sample. The method of establishing the ratio of components depends on the components in the sample. Each component gives rise to a characteristic ion not formed by any other component, and a direct breakdown of the mixture is possible. Mass spectrometric analysis is relatively rapid, an hour or two being sufficient for the analysis of a complicated mixture. This time can be further reduced by utilizing special computation facilities where a large number of samples of the same type are to be examined. The precision and accuracy of the instrument depend on the type of sample being examined. Figure 6.14 shows the mass spectrum of water and heavy water [74]. This technique has found wide applications in the estimation of deuterium oxide (D_2O) in water.

2.7 Applications

Mass spectroscopy is often considered unsuitable for the quantitative determination of water; the technique is, however, capable of giving fairly reliable results over a wide concentration range. Its particular value is in estimating water as part of the complete analysis of a complex mixture of gases or liquids. Only small samples are required, about 0.1 cm^3 of gas at STP or few microliters of liquid. These requirements can be reduced further by sealing off the ballast volume in the mass spectrometer's inlet system; gas samples as small as 1 µl can then be analyzed. Electron bombardment of water molecules produces a mass spectrum consisting primarily of the mass 18 peak due to $^{16}HOH^+$ ions commonly referred to as the parent mass (or water). Actually many ions are produced by direct bombardment and by secondary collisions of some of these ions with neutral molecules [76]. In the range of masses 16, 17, and 18, the relative intensities are 2.3, 24.5, and 100.0, respectively [77].

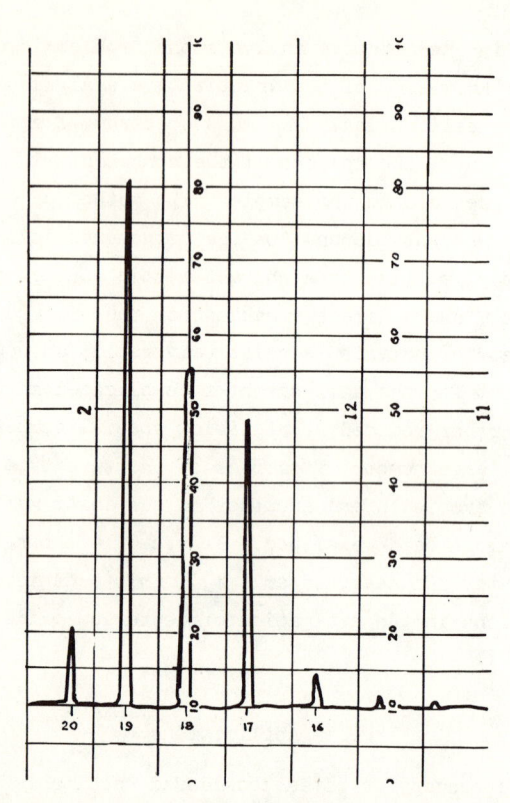

FIG. 6.14. Mass spectra of light and heavy water.

Calculations based on mass 18 are best suited for determining water. Usually contributions to this mass by other compounds are relatively small.

2.8 Estimation of Water Content in a Mixture of Organic Chemicals

Though in the early years of the development of mass spectrometers (the 1950s) experimental models of mass spectrometers were used, at the present time commercial instruments developed by a large number of instrument manufacturers are being used for routine experimental observations and laboratory analysis. By using one such commercial mass spectrometer Gifford et al. [78] have analyzed mixtures of methanol, ethanol, and methyl ethyl ketone first in dry condition and later on in wet condition by adding measured quantities of water. These results show that the water fractions showed the same accuracy as other components. Taylor et al. [77] have employed the mass spectrometric method for the analysis of ethanol-ether-water mixture. These results show good agreement with the known composition in spite of the fact that water and alcohol are two components strongly absorbed on the walls of the inlet system.

A mixture of ketones, aldehydes, alcohols, and water has been analyzed by Thomas [79] using a commercial mass spectrometer, and excellent results were obtained. The results of determinations of water by mass spectrometry obtained by a number of research workers are summarized in Table 6.5. From this table it will be observed that there is good agreement between the experimental results and theoretical calculations.

2.9 Conclusion

The subject of mass spectrometry has in the past decade or so developed very rapidly, and at the present time, mass spectrometers are being very commonly used for a number of routine analyses. Their main importance lies in being able to analyze simultaneously a large number of components separately out of a complex mixture of chemical compounds. The application of the mass spectrometer for the measurement and control of moisture forms a part of this broad analytical technique. It has a few drawbacks, which are briefly narrated here.

One of the major instrumental problems encountered when running water samples on a mass spectrometer is the so-called "memory effect." When a water sample having a deuterium concentration different from the samples previously run is introduced in a mass spectrometer, the ratio of peaks obtained does not immediately indicate a concentration corresponding to the new sample. The indicated concentration changes gradually from the concentration of the previous samples to the concentration of the new sample. The instrument, in effect, "remembers" the previous samples.

TABLE 6.5

Determination of Water by Mass Spectrometry

Sample	Mixtures	Water, mole % Calculated	Found
1	Ethanol, diethyl, ether ethyl, tert-butyl ether, water	14.8	13.3, 13.8
2	n-, sec-, tert-, and iso- butanols, water	66.4	66.1
3	Methanol, ethanol, methyl ethyl ketone, water	44.8	44.3
4	Ethanol, acetone, propion aldehyde, isopropyl ether, water	15.7	16.4, 15.6, 16.2
5	Ethanol, n-butanol, acetone, water	99.44	99.46, 99.55, 99.48
		99.86	99.88, 99.87, 99.88
6	Nitrogen-dioxide, water	41.0	39.7
		5.0	5.9, 5.5, 6.0, 8.0, 5.8
		5.0	4.5-5.1
		20.8	19.0-20.8

A method of reducing this memory effect is described by Gifford and co-workers [78]. The second main instrumental problem encountered concerns formation of certain anomalous ions having a specific mass of 19 and an abundance proportional to the square of the pressure in the ion source. It is believed that these ions are H_3O^+ ions which are formed by a collision between H_2O^+ ions and the neutral H_2O molecules. It has been found experimentally [79] that if the ion-repeller voltage is increased, the abundance of these H_3O^+ ions is decreased. This effect is similar to an effect reported by Nier et al. [80]. However, the values of moisture contents obtained by infrared spectroscopy and mass spectroscopy are quite comparable [81].

REFERENCES

The literature on mass spectroscopy is exhaustive. A few selected references [82-91] are given for further study.

REFERENCES

1. R. N. Jones and C. Sandorey, *Chemical Applications of Spectroscopy*, Wiley-Interscience, New York, 1956.

2. R. Mecke, *Z. Phys.*, **81**, 445 (1933).

3. H. N. Nielson, *Phys. Rev.*, **59**, 565 (1941); **62**, 422 (1942).

4. E. O. Hulburt and J. F. Hutchinson, *Carnegie Inst. Wash. Publ.*, **9**, 260 (1917).

5. J. F. Collins, *Phys. Rev.*, **26**, 771 (1925).

6. J. A. Curcio and C. Petty, *J. Opt. Soc. Amer.*, **41**, 302 (1961).

7. E. W. Greenacher and R. Mecke, *Z. Electrochem.*, **23**, 59 (1957).

8. V. P. Vendt, *Dokl. Akad. Nauk, SSSR*, **73**, 689 (1950); through *Chem. Abstr.*, **44**, 10596 (1950).

9. D. Chapman and J. F. Nacey, *Analyst*, **83**, 377 (1958).

10. M. Van Thiel, E. D. Becker, and G. C. Pimentel, *J. Chem. Phys.*, **27**, 486 (1957).

11. A. W. Process, *Can. J. Chem.*, **32**, 956 (1954).

12. L. A. Sayce, *Endeavour*, **12**, 210 (1953).

13. G. D. Dew, *J. Sci. Instrum.*, **30**, 229 (1953).

14. Van Der Maas and J. H. Sadtler, *Basic Infrared Spectroscopy*, Res. Labs., Philadelphia, 1969, p. 108; *Chem. Abstr.*, **72**, 127194h (1970).

15. G. Kemmner, *Infrared Spectroscopy; Principles, Applications*, Vol. 5, *Chemical Monographs*, Franckh, Stuttgart, 1969, p. 125; *Chem. Abstr.*, **73**, 40369r (1970).

16. J. E. Stewart, *Infrared Spectroscopy; Experimental Methods and Techniques*, Dekker, New York, 1970, p. 656; *Chem. Abstr.*, **73**, 114911k (1970).

17. F. Scheinmann, ed., *An Introduction to Spectroscopic Methods for the Identification of Organic Compounds*, Vol. 1: *Nuclear*

Magnetic Resonance and Infrared Spectroscopy, Pergamon, Elmsford, N. Y., 1970, p. 201; Chem. Abstr., 74, 19166h (1971).

18. N. L. Alpert, W. E. Keiser, and H. A. Szymanski, *IR, Theory and Practice of Infrared Spectroscopy*, 2d ed., Plenum, New York, 1970, p. 380; Chem. Abstr., 74, 105582x (1971).

19. H. Hediger, *Infrared Spectroscopy — Principles, Uses, Interpretation* in *Methods of Analysis in Chemistry*, Vol. 11, Akad. Verlages, Frankfurt, Germany, 1971, p. 250; Chem. Abstr., 75, 13425r (1971).

20. K. E. Stine, *Modern Practices in Infrared Spectroscopy*, Beckman Instruments, Fullerton, Calif., 1970, p. 642; Chem. Abstr., 75, 13429v (1971).

21. M. Avram and G. D. Mateesch, *Infrared Spectroscopy — Applications in Organic Chemistry*, Dunod, Paris, France, 1971, p. 642; Chem. Abstr., 75, 28155b (1971).

22. S. F. D. Orr, *Infrared Spectroscopy*, Spectroscopy, 32 (1969); Chem. Abstr., 73, 19836f (1970).

23. R. S. McDonald, *Infrared Spectrometry*, Anal. Chem. (Annual Reviews, April, 1972), 44 (5), 241R (1972).

24. W. Kaye, Spectrochim. Acta, 6, 257 (1954).

25. Wheeler, Chem. Rev., 59, 629 (1959).

26. R. F. Goddu, *Advances in Analytical Chemistry and Instrumentation*, Vol. I, Wiley-Interscience, New York, 1950.

27. B. F. Rudko, N. L. Vasziljeva, and N. A. Gozsenko, *Proceedings of the IMEKO Symposium on Moisture Measurement*, Hungary, 1971, p. 208.

28. G. Herzberg, *Infrared and Ramanspectra*, Van Nostrand, Princeton, New Jersey, 1956.

29. J. Bauman, *The Absorption of Infrared Radiation*, in *Advanced Analytical Chemistry* (Meites and Thomas, eds.), McGraw-Hill, New York, 1958, Chap. 9.

30. Lord and Miller, Appl. Spectrosc., 10, 115 (1956).

31. Lord, McDonald, and Miller, J. Opt. Soc. Amer., 42, 149 (1952).

32. A. Pande, Lab. Pract. (London), 18, 287 (1969).

33. Lecomte, Cah. Phys., 17, 1 (1943).

REFERENCES

34. H. Handroff, *Appl. Spectrosc.*, **8**, 131 (1954).

35. Stimpson and O. Donnell, *J. Amer. Chem. Soc.*, **74**, 1805 (1952).

36. *Handbook of Chemistry and Physics*, 28th ed., Chemical Rubber Publishing Co., Cleveland, Ohio, 1944.

37. Beckman Instrum. Co., Inc., *Bull. 763*.

38. J. Fahrenford, *Spectrochim. Acta*, **17**, 698 (1961).

39. L. L. Pytlewski and V. Marchesani, *Anal. Chem.*, **37**, 618 (1965).

40. R. K. Metzler, *Anal. Chem.*, **36**, 2378 (1964).

41. W. R. Brode, *J. Opt. Soc. Amer.*, **41**, 658 (1951).

42. R. D. Weaver, G. C. Whintnack, and E. C. Ganiz, *Anal. Chem.*, **28**, 329 (1956).

43. H. F. Cordes and C. W. Tait, *Anal. Chem.*, **29**, 484 (1957).

44. A. F. Benning, A. A. Ebert, and C. F. Irwin, *Anal. Chem.*, **19**, 867 (1947).

45. F. J. Versagi, *Chem. Anal.*, **44**, 48 (1955).

46. G. Matsuyama, *Anal. Chem.*, **29**, 197 (1957).

47. J. Mitchell, Jr. and D. M. Smith, *Aquametry, Application of the Karl Fischer Reagent to Quantitative Analysis Involving Water*, Wiley-Interscience, New York, 1948, p. 134.

48. E. A. Coulson, J. L. Hales, and E. F. G. Herinton, *J. Chem. Soc.*, 2125 (1951).

49. R. Dalmon and R. Freyman, *Compt. Rend.*, **211**, 472 (1940).

50. W. L. Kinsey and J. W. Ellis, *Phys. Rev.*, **36**, 603 (1930).

51. W. L. Kinsey and J. W. Ellis, *Phys. Rev.*, **51**, 1074 (1937).

52. W. Kaye, *J. Opt. Soc. Amer.*, **41**, 658 (1951).

53. L. Cahn, *Anal. Chem.*, **28**, 141 (1956).

54. L. White, Jr. and W. J. Barrett, *Anal. Chem.*, **28**, 1538 (1956).

55. M. L. Moberg, W. P. Knight, and H. M. Kindsvater, *Anal. Chem.*, **28**, 412 (1956).

56. S. Bruckenstein, *Anal. Chem.*, **28**, 1920 (1956).

57. W. C. Eichelberger and V. K. Lamer, *J. Amer. Chem. Soc.*, 55, 3633 (1933).

58. H. Brandenberger and H. Bader, *J. Amer. Chem. Soc.*, 33, 1947 (1961).

59. K. H. Norris and J. R. Hart, *Proc. International Symposium on Humidity and Moisture*, 4, 19 (1965).

60. E. R. S. Jones, *J. Sci. Instrum.*, 30, 132 (1953).

61. A. Elliot, W. E. Hanby, and B. R. Malcolm, *Brit. J. Appl. Phys.*, 5, 377 (1954).

62. K. T. Hecht and D. L. Wood, *Proc. Roy. Soc.*, 235A, 174 (1956).

63. F. W. Karasck and E. C. Miller, *Ind. Eng. Chem.*, 46, 1374 (1954).

64. S. T. Abrams and V. N. Smith, *Anal. Chem.*, 34, 1129 (1962).

65. H. S. Knight and F. T. Weiss, *Anal. Chem.*, 34, 749 (1962).

66. W. M. Tripeer, *Humidity and Moisture*, 4, Reinhold, New York, 1965, p. 79.

67. M. Greenberg, Paper presented at International Symposium on Humidity and Moisture, Washington, D.C., 1963.

68. D. M. Gates, *Natl. Bur. Stand. Tech. News Bull.*, 47, 124 (1963).

69. A. Pande, *Modern Hygrometry, Somaiya Publ.*, Bombay, India, 1970.

70. J. Gaunt, *Analyst*, 79, 580 (1954).

71. J. Gaunt, *Spectrochim. Acta*, 8, 57 (1956).

72. E. H. Woodhull, E. H. Siegler, and H. Sobcov, *Ind. Eng. Chem.*, 46, 1396 (1954).

73. A. Savitzky and D. R. Bresky, *Ind. Eng. Chem.*, 46, 1382 (1954).

74. W. A. Morgan, G. Jernakoff, and K. P. Lanneall, *Ind. Eng. Chem.*, 46, 1404 (1954).

75. W. H. Bennet, *J. Appl. Phys.*, 21, 143 (1950).

76. H. W. Washburn, C. E. Berry, and L. G. Hall, *Anal. Chem.*, 25, 130 (1953).

REFERENCES

77. R. C. Taylor, R. A. Brown, W. S. Young, and C. E. Headington, Anal. Chem., 20, 396 (1948).

78. A. F. Gifford, S. M. Rock, and D. J. Camaford, Anal. Chem., 21, 1026 (1949).

79. B. W. Thomas, Anal. Chem., 22, 1476 (1950).

80. A. O. Nier, C. M. Stevens, and B. Rustad, Mass Spectrometer for Routine Hydrogen Isotope Analysis, U.S. Atomic Energy Commission, Report AECD-2767.

81. A. M. J. Mitchell and G. Philips, Brit. J. Appl., 7, 67 (1956).

82. A. L. Burlingame, ed., Topics in Organic Mass Spectrometry, Wiley-Interscience, New York, 1970, p. 471.

83. G. W. A. Milne, ed., Mass Spectrometry — Techniques and Applications, Wiley-Interscience, New York, 1971, p. 521.

84. C. E. Melton, Principles of Mass Spectrometry and Negative Ions, Dekker, New York, 1970, p. 313.

85. A. Quayle, ed., Advances in Mass Spectrometry, Vol. V, The Institute of Petroleum, London, 1971, p. 763.

86. P. H. Dawson and N. R. Whetton, in Advances in Electronics and Electron Physics, Vol. XXVII, Academic, New York, 1969, p. 59.

87. H. E. Duckworth, in Recent Developments in Mass Spectrometry (K. Ogata and T. Hayakawa, eds.), University of Tokyo Press, 1970, p. 26.

88. D. M. Desiderio, Jr., in Mass Spectrometry — Techniques and Applications (G. W. A. Milne, ed.), Wiley-Interscience, New York, 1971, p. 11.

89. A. L. Burlingame, in Recent Developments in Mass Spectroscopy (K. Ogata and T. Hayakawa, eds.), University of Tokyo Press, 1970, p. 104.

90. K. Biemann, in Topics in Organic Mass Spectrometry (A. L. Burlingame, ed.), Wiley-Interscience, New York, 1970, p. 185.

91. J. P. Boullard, C. Jonnet, J. Maragnon, and P. Tauveron, in Advances in Mass Spectrometry (A. Quayle, ed.), Vol. V, Institute of Petroleum, London, 1971, p. 344.

Chapter VII

NUCLEAR METHODS AND TECHNIQUES

1 NUCLEAR MAGNETIC RESONANCE METHOD
OF MOISTURE DETERMINATION

1.1 General

Nuclear magnetic resonance (NMR) is a new nondestructive method of moisture measurement in which the nuclear magnetism of the hydrogen atom is utilized. The nuclear magnetism of hydrogen is a useful property for the identification and quantitative analysis of hydrogen-containing compounds in liquids or solids. The NMR method of moisture measurement is quite unique in the sense that it is based on nuclear properties of the hydrogen atoms in water rather than on properties of the water molecule itself. The detailed characteristics of the NMR phenomenon are influenced by many features of the nuclear environment. It has proved possible to use nuclei of known and favorable magnetic properties as probes to investigate the areas around the nucleus. The NMR technique has a number of applications in industry and research connected with product identification in chemical analysis, as well as the measurement of the moisture content of hygroscopic materials. The application of NMR to moisture measurement is an excellent effort to meet the long-sought industrial requirement for a quick, accurate, and nondestructive method of measurement and control of moisture of raw materials and finished products. However, it may be mentioned that the NMR technique has much wider applications, and its use for moisture measurement forms a very small part of such applications.

The nuclear magnetic resonance phenomenon has been described in a number of interesting publications [1-17]. The technique of NMR was discovered in 1946 simultaneously by two groups of physicists, one with Purcell [18] at Harvard, the other with Bloch [19] at Stanford. These researchers used different techniques, one being of induction type, and the other of absorption. Prior to this, methods were available for measuring the magnetic properties of nuclei; however, since atomic or molecular beam methods are difficult and complicated, the physicists were interested in simpler and also more accurate means of observing the nuclear magnetism. The great advantage of Purcell's and Bloch's work was that it enabled precise observations to be made very readily on ordinary bulk samples.

Though NMR technique is considered to be another form of spectroscopy, it is classified here as a nuclear method because of the fact that it is the spin property of the nucleus which is utilized to indicate the number of certain types of nuclei present in a substance, as, for example, the determination of the number of protons gives an estimate of H_2O in a particular sample. In NMR instead of the energy levels of electrons we are considering the study of energy levels in nuclei. Only certain nuclei with the correct spins are subjects for study; protons are fortunately one of the best and easiest to study and give some of the most informative results. The present discussion involves only proton magnetic resonance. The theory of NMR entails detailed mathematical treatments; however, attempts are made in this chapter to develop the subject in a descriptive manner as far as possible. For a more rigorous and detailed treatment of the subject, the reader is referred to the original publications [1-17].

1 NUCLEAR MAGNETIC RESONANCE

1.2 Nuclear Magnetic Resonance Phenomena

1.2.1 Nuclear Spin. Most nuclei possess in addition to mass and charge the extra characteristic of spin. The most common atoms are those of hydrogen, deuterium, tritium, helium, lithium, boron, carbon, nitrogen, phosphorus, chlorine, etc. This spin property of the atom is the basis of the phenomenon of nuclear magnetic resonance. The nucleus can thus be thought to be rotating, the spin of the nuclear mass producing an angular momentum p directed along the axis of rotation, and the motion of the charge associated with the mass, which is equivalent to an electric current, producing a magnetic field, symmetrical about the axis of rotation. This field is conveniently expressed by its dipole moment μ, which is the product of the magnetic pole strength and the separation between the two poles necessary to reproduce the field. Since both the μ and p are generated by the same motion, the magnetic moment μ and the angular moment p have the same direction and are related by the following equation:

$$\mu = \frac{ge}{2mc} p \qquad (7.1)$$

where c is the velocity of light, m is the mass, e is the charge of the nucleus; and g is the constant of proportionality, a dimensionless number of the order of unity, which is a characteristic quantity for each nuclear species. Usually the nuclear angular momentum p is expressed in the units of h* where h* = $h/(2\pi)$ and h is Planck's constant.

1.2.2 Nuclear Magnetic Energy Level. When no magnetic field is present the nuclear magnet has fixed orientation. When it is placed in an external magnetic field H_0 the magnetic dipole experiences a torque which acts to align it, and if the magnetic field has a static and uniform value H, in the region of the nucleus, the interaction between the two produces a potential energy of

$$E = -\mu_H H_0 \qquad (7.2)$$

where μ_H is the component of the vector μ along H_O. The behavior of a nuclear magnet in an applied magnetic field H_O is illustrated in Fig. 7.1.

For a classified system, Eq. (7.2) predicts a continuous range of energies between μH_O and $+\mu H_O$; however, nuclei have a discrete set of magnetic energy levels. Quantum mechanics requires that the nuclear angular momentum I be quantized along this direction. The allowed components of I along H_O are defined by the nuclear magnetic quantum number n which takes values of I, I - 1, and I - 2, giving a total of 2 I+1 stages; I, the nuclear spin, has a particular integral or half-integral value of each nuclear species, and values extending from 0 to 7 have been found. Because of the proportionality between μ and I, the quantization of I leads to a similar quantization of the magnetic moment, which is given as

$$\mu H + g \left(\frac{e}{2mc}\right) h_n^* = h^* g \mu_O \tag{7.3}$$

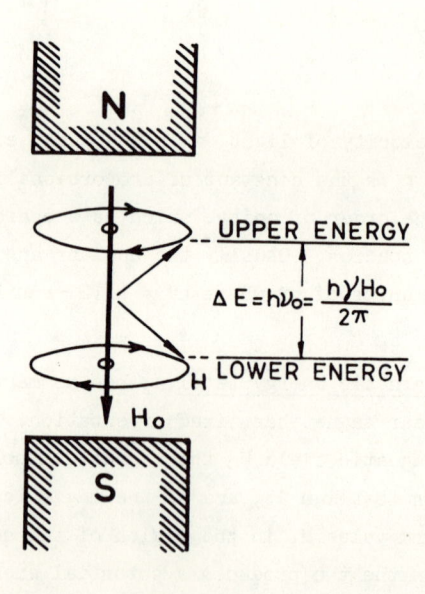

FIG. 7.1. Behavior of a nuclear magnet in a magnetic field.

1 NUCLEAR MAGNETIC RESONANCE

where the nuclear magneton $eh/2mc$ is denoted by μ_0. Upon substitution of this result for μ_H in Eq. (7.2), the magnetic energy becomes

$$E = -ng\mu_0 H_0 = n\gamma h^* H_0 \qquad (7.4)$$

which summarizes the set of $2I+1$ nuclear orientations and energy levels; γ is used to express the nuclear magnetogyric ratio in units of g/h, which is often convenient.

The selection rule for transition among the nuclear levels is given as

$$\Delta n = \pm 1 \qquad (7.5)$$

that is, the magnetic number n changes by -1 or $+1$ so that

$$\Delta E = \pm g\mu_0 H_0 \qquad (7.6)$$

Now from Bohr's frequency condition

$$\Delta E = h\nu \qquad (7.7)$$

and hence we find the frequency ν_0 corresponding to allow changes in n to be

$$\nu_0 = g\mu_0 H_0/h \quad (Hz) \qquad (7.8)$$

or in angular frequency W_0 is given as

$$W_0 = 2\pi\nu_0 = \frac{g\mu_0 H_0}{h} = \gamma H_0 \qquad (7.9)$$

This is known as the resonance condition.

In the picture of an atom described by the quantum-mechanical theory, there are two possible orientations of the nuclear spin axes (for hydrogen nuclei) around the magnetic field direction. These correspond to two discrete energy levels. Transitions between these levels are caused by the application of an oscillating magnetic field of frequency ν_0 such that the resonance condition is satisfied:

$$E = h\nu_0 = \frac{h\gamma H_0}{2\pi} \tag{7.10}$$

where E is the difference between energy levels, h is the Planck's constant, γ is the gyromagnetic ratio (unique for each isotope), H is the field strength of magnetic field applied, and ν_0 is the frequency of radiation required for transition.

This equation gives the energy absorbed from the oscillating field by each proton which undergoes a transition to the upper energy state. Therefore, the net energy adsorbed by a collection of protons is related to the number of these nuclei. Thus we have shown that when a substance is placed in a strong uniform magnetic field, it can adsorb electromagnetic energy at discrete frequencies which are determined by the nuclear magnetic properties of the various atoms present. The interaction between the strong external magnetic field and the very weak magnetic moment of the atomic nuclei results in the establishment of magnetic energy levels corresponding to various orientations of the magnetic moments with respect to the direction of the applied magnetic field. Transitions between these energy levels can be induced by the adsorption of radiant energy having a frequency corresponding to the energy difference. Because these energy differences are so small, the frequency of the radiant energy which can induce the transitions lies in the familiar radio communications band. The basic principles are essentially the same as in other forms of spectroscopy, except that oscillators and receivers are employed instead of light sources and phototubes.

It may here be mentioned that absorption of energy takes place not because the probability of absorption is greater than that of

1 NUCLEAR MAGNETIC RESONANCE

emission. In fact, they are equal, so that if the nuclei in a sample were equally distributed among the energy levels, there would be no net absorption or emission of radiation. However, the equilibrium populations of the levels are not equal, being governed by the Boltzmann distribution law. Thus the relative equilibrium populations of two adjacent levels are given by the ratio of their Boltzmann factors:

$$\frac{N(n_I + I)}{N(n_I)} = \frac{e^{(\mu H_0)}}{KT} \tag{7.11}$$

The lower level, characterized by $n_I + I$, has the larger population. Thus a net absorption of energy from the radiation field occurs.

Taking the case of proton resonance, consider a proton with $I = \frac{1}{2}$ and $\gamma = 0.2675 \times 10^4$ Oe^{-1} sec^{-1} in a magnetic field H, say = 10,000 Oe. In such a case,

$$\frac{N(1/2)}{N(-1/2)} = \frac{e^{(\mu H_0)}}{KT} = 1 + \frac{2\mu H_0}{KT} = 1 + 7 \times 10^{-6} \tag{7.12}$$

This means that for each 1,000,000 protons in the upper level, there are only about 1,000,007 in the lower level. These 7 protons in each 2,000,000 may be responsible for the net absorption of energy from the radiation field. This number will give some indication of the magnitude of the detection problem involved in the case of proton resonance.

1.3 Relaxation Processes and Relaxation Times

The various types of radiationless transitions by means of which a nucleus in an upper spin state returns to a lower state are called relaxation processes. Relaxation processes are of paramount importance in the theory of nuclear magnetic resonance for not only are they responsible for the establishment and maintenance of the absorption condition but they also control the lifetime expectancy of a given state. The uncertainty principle tells us that the "natural" width of a special line is proportional to the reciprocal of the average time the system spends in the excited state. In ultraviolet and infrared spectroscopy, the natural linewidth is seldom, if ever, the limit of resolution. At radio frequencies, however, it is quite possible to reach the natural linewidth, and we shall, therefore, be very much concerned with the relaxation processes which determine this parameter. Relaxation processes are divided into two categories, namely, spin-lattice relaxation and spin-spin relaxation.

In spin-lattice relaxation the energy of the nuclear spin system is converted into thermal energy of the molecular system containing the magnetic nuclei and is therefore directly responsible for maintaining the unequal distribution of spin states. Either or both processes may control the natural linewidth. Spin-lattice relaxation is also called longitudinal or thermal relaxation as well. The term lattice requires definition. The magnetic nuclei are usually part of an assembly of molecules which constitute a sample under investigation, and the entire molecular system is referred to as the lattice irrespective of the physical state of the sample. In the latter process a nucleus in its upper state transfers its energy to a neighboring nucleus of the same isotope by a mutual exchange of spin. This relaxation process therefore does nothing to offset the equalizing of the spin-state populations caused by radio-frequency absorption and is not directly responsible for maintaining the absorption condition.

The effect of spin-lattice relaxation can, as other exponential processes, be expressed in terms of a characteristic relaxation time T_1, which in effect is the half-life required for a perturbed system of nuclei to reach an equilibrium condition.

A large value of T_1 indicates an inefficient relaxation process. The value of T_1 will depend on the gyromagnetic ratio (or ratios) of the nuclei in the lattice and on the nature and rapidity of the molecular motions which produce the fluctuating fields. Because of

1 NUCLEAR MAGNETIC RESONANCE

the great restriction of molecular motions in the crystal lattice most highly purified solids exhibit very long spin-lattice relaxation times often of the order of hours. For liquids and gases the value of T_1 is much less, being of the order of 1 sec for many organic liquids. The term spin-spin relaxation, sometimes called transverse relaxation, usually embraces two processes which result in the broadening of resonance lines. One of these processes is a true relaxation in that it shortens the life of a nucleus in any one spin state, whereas the other process broadens a resonance line by causing the effective static field to vary from nucleus to nucleus. A second relaxation time commonly called the spin-spin relaxation time or phase-memory time arises because of the interaction between two nuclei whose spins are antiparallel along the magnetic field. One of them eventually flips to the other side; i.e., the exchange of spins occurs. The lifetime of a nucleus in any one orientation, i.e., energy level, is thus limited by such a process. The lifetime is described by the spin-spin relaxation time, T_2. The broadening, δE, of the energy level occurs which is given by the uncertainty principle as follows:

$$T_2 \delta E \geq h^* \tag{7.13}$$

A consideration of the two relaxation processes corresponding to T_1 and T_2 enables us to predict what effect the physical state of a substance will have on the observed absorption line. Many solids may be considered as more-or-less rigid assemblages of nuclei in which random movement of the lattice components is negligible. For this reason spin-lattice relaxation times may be very long. On the other hand, local fields associated with spin-spin interactions are large and result in low values of T_2 with the result that absorption lines of solids are usually very broad. Thus the relaxation time affects the width of the absorption bands, very short relaxation times do limit the ultimate resolution one gets in a particular sample. There is a particular relationship between the relaxation time and the amount of radio-frequency power with which one irradiates the sample. One must obtain spectra under conditions of nonsaturation by this power in order that the areas are accurately proportional to the number of hydrogen nuclei present. We must be careful at all times to ensure that we are operating in the nonsaturation region. The difference in relaxation time between liquids and solids is quite substantial and all high-resolution work should be done with liquids alone.

Besides the relaxation processes described above, which are responsible for broadening of the NMR spectral lines, there are a few additional factors which affect or cause the spreading or broadening of the line. These factors are as follows:

1. Natural width due to spontaneous emission
2. Magnetic dipole broadening
3. Electrical quadrupole effects
4. Magnetic field inhomogeneity broadening

The detailed discussion of the contributions of these factors to the broadening of spectral lines is beyond the scope of the book.

1.4 Chemical Shift and Nuclear Magnetic Shielding

The most important single parameter to be derived from the NMR spectrum is the chemical shift. Since the NMR signals of nuclei of different elements in a fixed magnetic field normally occur in very different regions of the spectrum, we are ordinarily concerned only with chemical shifts between nuclei of the same element. So far in our discussion of nuclear magnetic resonance we have more or less assumed that the resonance frequency of a nucleus is simply a function of the applied field and the gyromagnetic ratio of the nucleus. If this were indeed the case, nuclear magnetic resonance would be of little value to the organic chemist. It turns out, however, that the resonance frequency is to the same degree dependent on its molecular environment. This is because the extranuclear electrons magnetically screen the nucleus so that the magnetic field felt by

1 NUCLEAR MAGNETIC RESONANCE

the nucleus is not quite the same as the applied field. Naturally, we might expect the efficiency of this shielding by the extranuclear electrons to bear some sort of relationship to the type of chemical bonding involved. Thus naively we might predict that electron withdrawal from a given nucleus would decrease the shielding of that nucleus. To the extent to which this is true we can regard the magnetic nucleus as a tiny probe with which we may examine the surrounding electron distribution. Although, as we shall see presently, the nuclear resonance picture of electron distribution is not nearly as simple as the one drawn above, it has been found that nuclear resonance frequencies, when properly determined, are remarkably characteristic of molecular structure.

We shall be principally concerned with the nuclear magnetic resonance of the hydrogen nucleus, that is, with proton magnetic resonance, and a preliminary idea of the effect of structure on proton resonance frequencies can be gained by reference to Fig. 7.2. We see that protons in the usual types of organic environments have relative frequencies spread over about 400 Hz at a field strength of 9365 G for which resonance frequency of the hydrogen nucleus (νH) is 40×10^6 Hz. Although this spread is only equivalent to about 10 ppm, relative values for proton signals can be readily determined with an accuracy of ±1 Hz. The separation of resonance frequencies of nuclei in different structural environments from some arbitrarily chosen line position is generally termed the chemical shift. In finely divided metals and alloys a large magnetic shielding was first observed by Knight [20]. The resultant resonance shift has become known as the Knight shift. The shielding results from the enormous local magnetic susceptibility due to the large probability density of conduction electrons near the nuclei. If the arbitrary line position is that of a bare proton, the chemical shift is equal to the screening constant which measures the difference between the applied field and the actual field felt by the nucleus. The chemical shifts of protons are among the smallest for all nuclei but, as both carbon (^{12}C) and oxygen (^{16}O) do not possess magnetic moments,

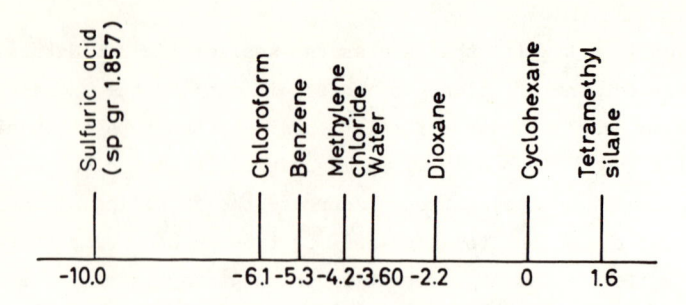

FIG. 7.2. Observed chemical shifts of some liquids giving single-proton signals.

the major application of nuclear magnetic resonance spectroscopy to organic chemistry involves the study of proton shifts.

Early NMR experiments revealed that the resonance condition for a given nuclear species was different in different chemical compounds. These chemical shifts can be measured by observing the difference in resonance frequency, keeping the magnetic field fixed, or by observing the difference in the applied magnetic field, at a fixed radio frequency. The chemical shifts are relatively small for the lighter nuclei. These cannot be measured accurately, unless the linewidths are small compared to the shifts. However, chemical shifts for the heavier nuclei are larger. This chemical effect, or magnetic shielding, has been discussed theoretically, but the complexity of the calculations permits their application only to the simplest molecules. Chemical shifts of resonance lines are field dependent and arise because the magnetic field at the nucleus is in general different from the applied external magnetic field due to either intermolecular or intramolecular effects or both.

1.5 Nuclear Magnetic Resonance Spectrometers

1.5.1 General. The simplest experimental arrangement for observing nuclear magnetic resonance absorption is illustrated by means of Fig. 7.3. The magnetic moments of the nuclei in the sample tend to orient in the direction of the field giving rise to a resultant

1 NUCLEAR MAGNETIC RESONANCE

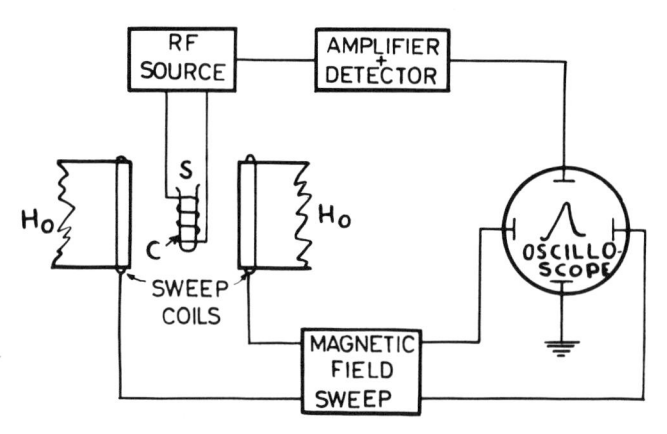

FIG. 7.3. Single schematic diagram for the measurement of NMR absorption.

macroscopic magnetic moment. The effect of the magnetic field H_0 is to cause a precession of the magnetic moment about the direction of the field, with an angular frequency $w_0 = \gamma H_0$. If now a small coil C, connected to an rf signal generator, is wound around the sample so that the axis of the coil is at right angles to the direction of the applied field, there is introduced a small alternating magnetic field of strength H_1 which tends to tilt the direction of the moment away from the H_0 direction as the radio frequency is brought closer to the precession frequency. These transitions correspond to some of the nuclear magnets changing their orientation in the field. The energy absorbed in this process produces a drop in the rf voltage in the tuned circuit containing the oscillator coil and the voltage drop is detected, amplified, and fed into the vertical deflection plates of an oscilloscope. In practice, the radio frequency of the signal generator is fixed and the applied field H_0 is varied near the value at which resonance occurs. This is accomplished by winding sweep coils around the pole pieces of the magnet so that the field strength of the magnet may be varied continuously over a small range. These coils sweep the field with an amplitude of a few gauss at some low frequency (about 50 Hz). The same sweep signal is fed into the horizontal deflection plates of an oscilloscope, and the recurring absorption signal is displayed on the screen.

The size of the pole pieces must be large enough compared to the field passing through the sample to be homogeneous, otherwise the intensity of the absorbed signal will not be proportional to the number of nuclei present in the sample. A permanent magnet having a field strength of 1750 G and poles of 10-in. diameter with a 2-in. air gap was used by Conway et al. [21]. Shaw and co-workers [22] used a **magnetic** field of 6300 G, and Rubin [23] has described an apparatus in which a 1750-G magnetic field is used for hydrogen nuclei whose corresponding precession frequency is 7.4 MHz. The sample container is inserted in the radio-frequency coil which is part of the resonant circuit; the assembly containing the rf amplifier and detector is located inside the magnet yoke. The magnetic field at the sample is swept linearly with time across the **nuclear** resonance values by a small current applied to the sweep coils from the sweep generator.

It is important to note that there are two basic types of NMR spectrometers: one with high resolving power for narrow lines, and the other with high stability for wide lines. The high-resolution type is mainly applied to fluid samples wherein the fine details of electron shielding and nuclear spin coupling are studied. These are subtle phenomena and they are quite important in structural determinations. The wide-line instrument, of which the NMR analyzer is an example, examines spectra in which fine-detailed phenomena are absent. Instrumentally it is better, for reasons concerned with noise and stability, to obtain the derivative absorption curve. This is accomplished by modulating the magnetic field sweep frequency by an audio-frequency square wave, and by demodulating the output of the rf amplifier in phase with the modulation voltage. Both the absorption and derivative curves are shown in Fig. 7.4. Wide-line spectra (as depicted in this figure) are generally obtained from solids, highly viscous liquids, and absorbed fluids.

1.5.2 Constructional Features of an Experimental Nuclear Magnetic Resonance Spectrometer. The experimental apparatus developed by Leane et al. [24] is described here. The apparatus (Fig. 7.5) consists essentially of four units:

1 NUCLEAR MAGNETIC RESONANCE 423

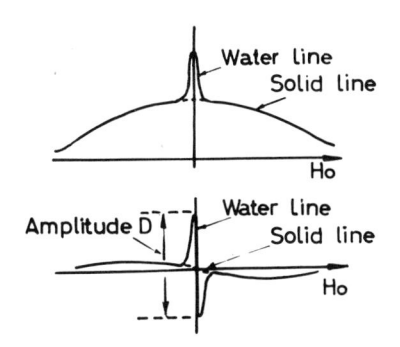

FIG. 7.4. Typical absorption and derivative NMR curves of a material containing both solid and liquid.

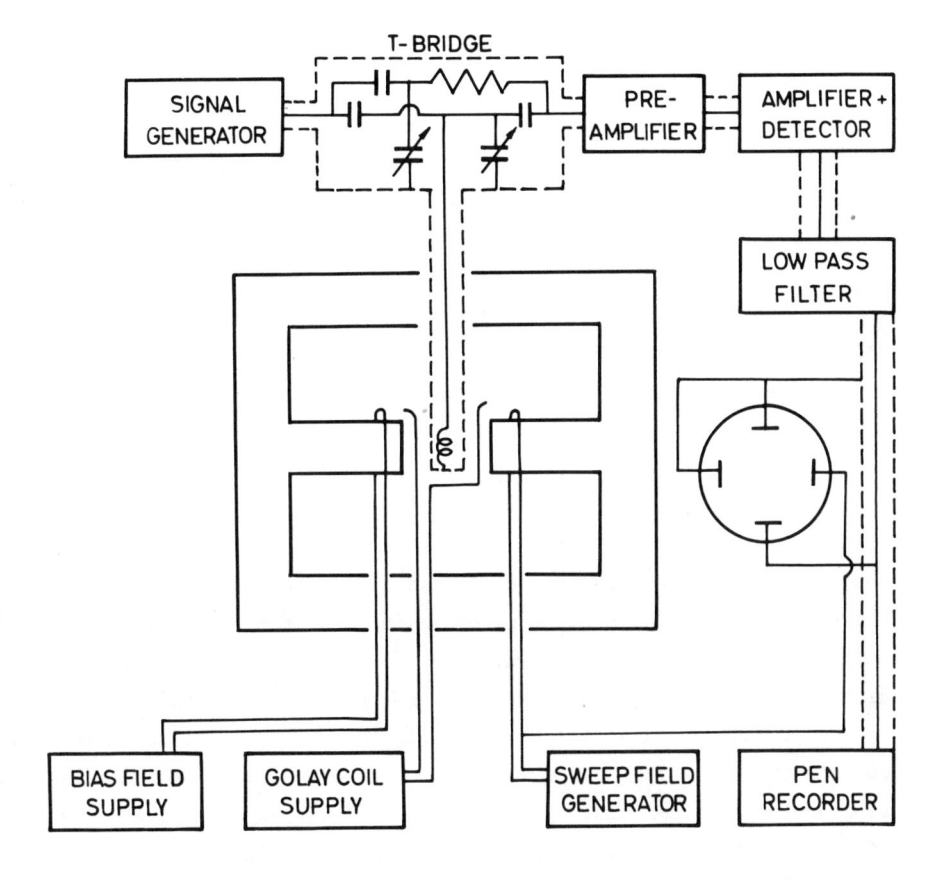

FIG. 7.5. Block diagram of an experimental NMR apparatus using T bridge circuit.

1. A magnet capable of producing a very strong homogeneous field
2. A means of continuously varying the magnetic field over a very small range
3. A radio-frequency oscillator
4. A radio-frequency receiver or detector

The magnet: Both permanent and electromagnets are employed in nuclear magnetic resonance spectroscopy. Each has certain advantages and disadvantages. The particular choice of one or the other depends among other things on the intended application. Leane et al. [24] used a permanent magnet of conventional design having a magnetic field of 7000 G. The magnet had a square yoke of large dimensions to minimize the effects of external magnetic disturbances. The gap was adjusted after the magnet had been magnetized. The temperature of the poles was maintained almost constant at 27°C. The region between the pole faces should have a highly homogeneous magnetic field of the order of 1 in 10^8. It is desirable that the strength of this field should be as high as is practically possible, because the chemical shifts are proportional to field strength, the higher the field strength the better is the dispersion of the spectrum. High field strength gives rise to stronger absorption signals.

Magnetic field sweep system: The precessional frequency of the nucleus can be effected by varying the strength of the applied static magnetic field whereas the rotational frequency of the rotating magnetic field can be determined by varying the frequency of the rf oscillator. The sweeping or scanning of the static field may be accomplished in two ways. First, it is possible to apply direct current to coils wound on the two pole pieces of the magnet. In the second method a direct current is fed to a pair of Helmholtz coils which flank the sample with their axes parallel to the direction of the static field. Either method allows the effective value of H_0 to be varied over a small range without detriment to the homogeneity of the field. Scan time was varied from 6.1 sec to 45 min

1 NUCLEAR MAGNETIC RESONANCE

by Leane et al., and the range of scan was kept from 5 mG to 5 G. The precise points at which the scan starts and stops can be preset and kept constant to a few hertz over a period of several hours.

Radio-frequency oscillator (generator): In order to induce a nuclear transition it is necessary to provide a rotating electromagnetic field, the magnetic component of which moves in a plane perpendicular to the direction of the applied magnetic field. Although the production of such a rotating field is feasible it is more convenient to use a linearly oscillating field. This is possible because such a field may be regarded as being the resultant of two components rotating in phase but in opposite directions. One of these components will be rotating in the same sense as the precessing nuclear field with which it will interact when the frequencies are the same. The other component will have no effect on the nuclei and need not be considered further. Linearly polarized rf radiation is generally used in radio communication. The source of radiant energy is merely a radio-frequency generator or oscillator capable of generating a signal of constant frequency but variable power. A GT-cut 100-kHz quartz crystal maintained at a constant temperature is used. This signal is fed to a coil situated in the pole gap of the magnet, with its axis perpendicular to the direction of the magnetic field. Such an arrangement provides for a magnetic component of the electromagnetic field to rotate in a plane at right angles to the main field direction.

Radio-frequency receiver or detector: The passage of radiation through the magnetized sample is associated with two phenomena, namely, absorption and dispersion. The observation of either dispersion or absorption enables the determination of resonance frequency. In practice it is usually easier to interpret an absorption spectrum than the corresponding dispersion spectrum. Basically the function of the detector is twofold: First, it must separate the absorption signal from the dispersion signal; and second, it must separate the absorption signal from that originating from the rf oscillator. This second function is necessary because although the amplitude of the applied rf signal remains constant, it is very much larger than the amplitude of the absorption signal. There are two principal methods of detection. The first involves the measurement of the effect of the absorption and/or dispersion signals at the oscillator coil of the rf generator. This requires the use of a radio-frequency bridge which functions as a Wheatstone bridge. The bridge network balances out the oscillator signal and allows the absorption or dispersion signal to appear as an out-of-balance electromotive force across the bridge. The out-of-balance signal can be amplified and rectified, and recorded or displayed on an oscilloscope. In order to suppress the unwanted dispersion signal advantage is taken of the fact that the absorption and dispersion signals differ in phase by 90°.

There are more than a dozen types of nuclear magnetic resonance detectors which give a signal proportional to the values of nuclear susceptibilities. However, all of these techniques can be considered in one of two categories: (1) nuclear magnetic resonance absorption or (2) nuclear magnetic resonance induction. In the absorption techniques, the rf rotating magnetic field is supplied by the same coil from which the signal is taken. Therefore, they are sometimes labeled the signal-coil systems. The induction techniques utilize two coils. One supplies the rf rotating field, say, along the x axis. The other is placed in quadrature with the first coil and the steady magnetic field, and lies along the y axis. This arrangement is labeled as a crossed-coil system. Besides these a pulse method of detection is also employed.

A twin-T bridge circuit of detection (Fig. 7.5) has been used by Leane and co-workers [24]. The bridge is extremely easy to adjust and rarely shows any drift except at very high rf levels. A cascade preamplifier is followed by four stages of gain at the operating frequency of 29.9200 Hz followed by a diode detector. The overall voltage gain is about 10^5. The amplifier is driven from stabilized

1 NUCLEAR MAGNETIC RESONANCE

low- and high-tension supplies and is left on permanently. The amplifier can be tuned with slugs in the tuning coils, and it is a simple matter to retune it to the resonance frequency. The dc output from the detector passes through an RC network to limit the bandwidth, and the standing out-of-balance voltage is backed off with a small dry cell. The signal voltage is then applied to an oscilloscope or to a potentiometric recorder.

The nuclear resonance is detected [25-27] in the single-coil bridge nuclear magnetic resonance apparatus (Fig. 7.6) by changes in the impedance of a tuned circuit. In the induction method two coils at right angles are used. The receiver coil is wound around the sample with its y axis perpendicular to both and axes of the oscillator coil x and the direction of the field z. In this arrangement the signal picked up by the receiver coil is due to the absorption of energy by the nuclei. This signal is thus isolated from the background signal by a geometrical arrangement of two coils, whereas in the bridge method isolation is accomplished by balancing two electrical circuits. The cross-coil nuclear induction apparatus (Fig. 7.7) developed by Bloch et al. [28] employs a permanent magnet of field strength 1826 G which for proton resonance corresponds to a fixed radio frequency of 7.76 MHz. The resonance signal (after amplification) is displayed by sweeping the field at a frequency of 60 Hz. As in the bridge method, for detection of weak signals a narrow band amplifier and balanced mixer are used after the rf amplifier-detector system. However the coils are seldom completely balanced in the induction method.

Torrey [29] and Hahn [30] have investigated NMR signals when the rf field is applied not continuously but in the form of pulses. Torrey's method [29] is concerned with the transient decaying oscillations of the signal during the time the pulses are applied, whereas Hahn's method [30] is concerned with the transient behavior in the time interval between the pulses. In the off-period, the single coil acts as a receiver and in the on-period it acts as an oscillator. When intense rf pulses are used, a bridge circuit is employed to

428 VII. NUCLEAR METHODS AND TECHNIQUES

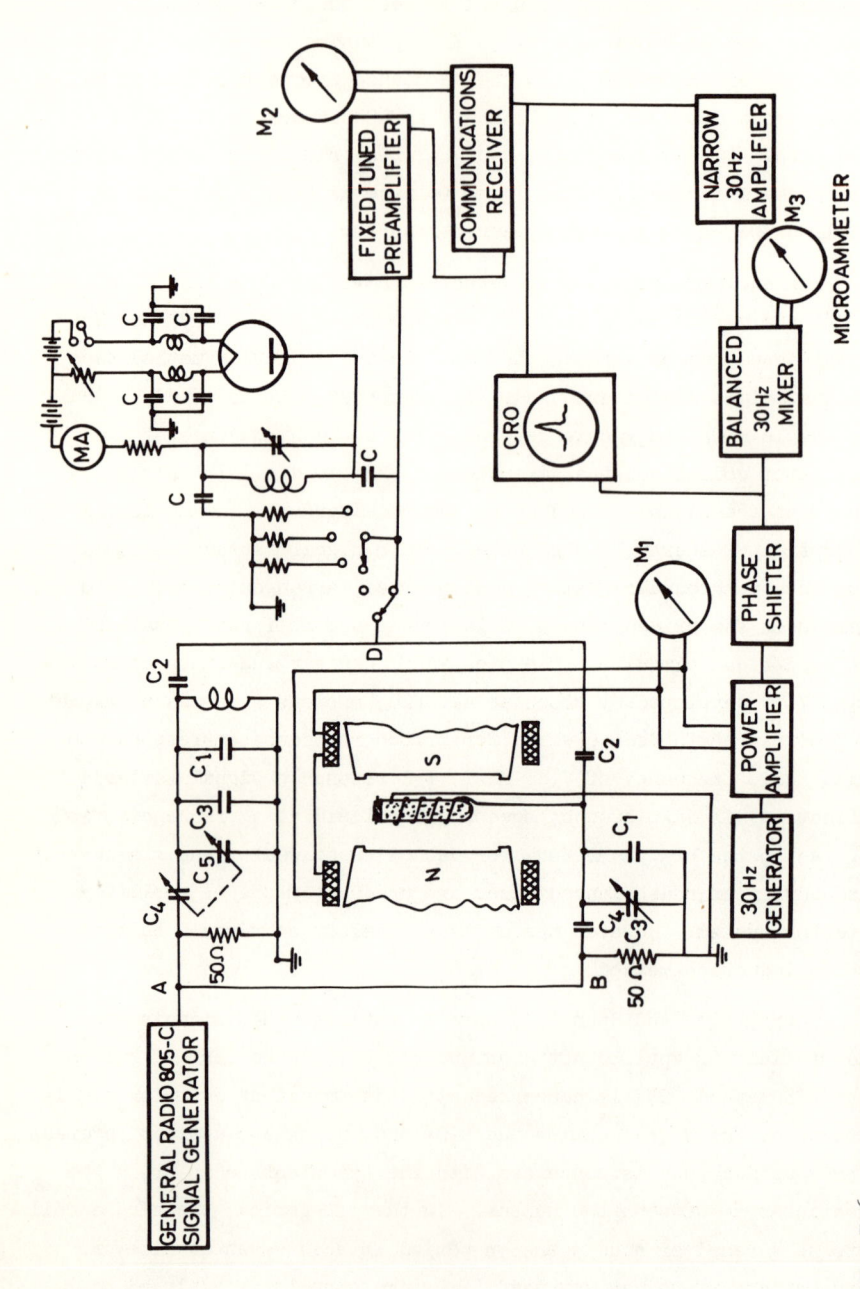

FIG. 7.6. Schematic diagram of a single-coil bridge spectrometer.

1 NUCLEAR MAGNETIC RESONANCE   429

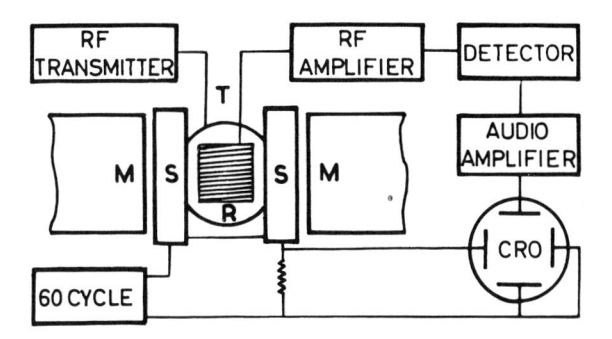

FIG. 7.7. Schematic diagram of a double-coil block (induction) spectrometer.

prevent overloading of the receiver during the on periods. In the precession and spin-echo experiments of Hahn, the response to a pulse or series of pulses is displayed directly on an oscilloscope. The simplest echo experiment is to observe the signal (at time intervals of 2T) in response to a pair of pulses at time zero and T. For purposes of interpretation, it is necessary to find the amplitude of the echo as a function of T. This is conveniently done by taking a multiple-exposure photograph of the echoes obtained for a series of values of T, each successively increased by a small amount. The echo envelope obtained in this way gives the amplitude as a function of T. These spin-echo methods are found useful in the determination of relaxation times.

1.6 High-Resolution Nuclear Magnetic Resonance Spectroscopy

The term high-resolution NMR spectroscopy is now generally applied to nuclear-resonance measurements under conditions of resolution such that the chemical shifts of nonequivalent nuclei in the same molecule can be distinguished [31]. Fine-structure splitting of the resonance signals due to spin-spin interaction is also usually observed. Nuclear-resonance spectra of most solid samples, on the other hand, give rise to characteristic broad signals due to the direct dipole interaction of nuclear spins; they are referred to as broad-band or wide-line spectra.

All high-resolution spectrometers commonly use the bridge or the induction-type detector. The receiver should introduce as little noise as possible so that a high signal-to-noise ratio is obtainable, and the rate of change of the magnetic field (sweep rate) must be sufficiently low so that conditions of slow passage through resonance are established. Furthermore the sweep rate should be low enough so that transient effects are reduced as much as possible, consistent with low enough rf power so that saturation is avoided. The rf oscillator, usually of the Meacham [32] crystal bridge type, has stability of one part in 10^9. A receiver preamplifier of the Wallman [33] type is satisfactory. The necessary sweep fields produced in the auxiliary bias coils are derived from a sawtooth signal generator, the output of which is practically linear, and the sweep rate can readily be varied over the ranges required.

In order to obtain resolution of the order of one part in 10^8 or better, the time stability of the magnetic field and of the rf oscillator must be of high order. Since high homogeneity over the sample volume enclosed by the rf coils is required, better resolution can be obtained with smaller samples. The effective homogeneity in the magnetic field can be further improved by spinning the sample.

The first instrument capable of high resolution gave the three-line spectrum for ethyl alcohol reported by Arnold et al. [31] and by Packard and Arnold [34]. A complete description of an improved spectrometer (Fig. 7.8) using this technique has been given by Arnold [35]. It is of the cross-coil type in which the necessary high field homogeneity and stability are obtained with a permanent magnet. The magnet, with pole faces of $12\frac{1}{2}$-in. diameter and an air gap of $1\frac{1}{2}$ in. has a field strength of about 7000 G. The preamplifier is of the Wallman [33] cascade design. An induction head, or probe, is so constructed that the dominant geometry has cylindrical symmetry about the y direction (the direction of the axis of the receiver coil). Provision has been made for paddle control of the u and v modes and also for spinning the sample holder by means of an air turbine rotor. The resolution achieved with this spectrometer is about one part in 10^8.

1 NUCLEAR MAGNETIC RESONANCE   431

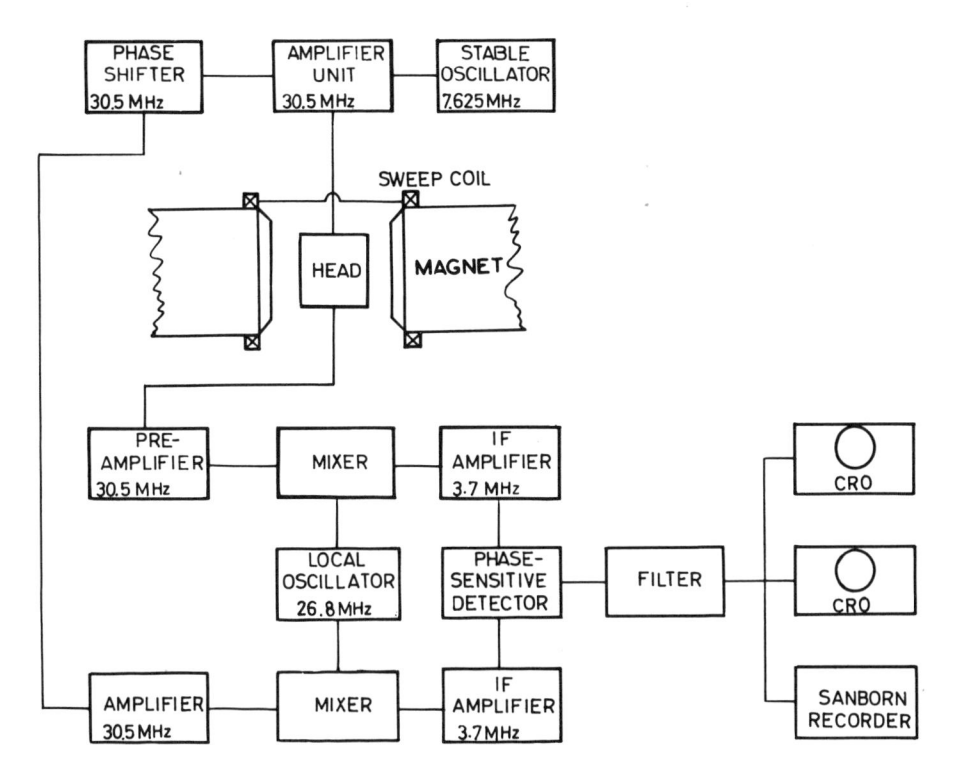

FIG. 7.8. Schematic diagram of a cross-coiled high-resolution spectrometer.

Kozlov and Paneleava [36] have described an NMR apparatus constructed by them which can be used for experimental determinations of the moisture content of many types of hygroscopic materials. The sensitivity of the apparatus is ±0.2 mg H_2O in a volume of 160 cm^3. Accuracy obtained is ±1 to 1.5%. An industrial-scale apparatus for continuous moisture control can be constructed on the basis of this instrument.

1.7 Commercial Instruments

An increasing number of commercial instruments are being used in both academic and industrial laboratories. The best known of these are those manufactured by Varian Associates. All the Varian NMR spectrometers use an electromagnet as a source of magnetic field.

They also employ the Bloch type of probe (double coil) exclusively. The high-sensitivity models contain a variable-frequency rf oscillator, sweep and modulation units, and radio-frequency and lock-in amplifier, together with an oscilloscope, recorder, and all associated electronic equipment. A high-resolution model will normally incorporate one or more very stable oscillators to give one of more fixed frequencies, a sample spinner, radio-frequency amplifier, a sweep generator, an oscilloscope, and a recorder, together with all the required electronic gadgetry. For analysis that will require the highest magnetic field stability (resolution of the order of one part in 10^8) a field stabilizer and a slow sweep unit are available.

A high-resolution NMR spectrometer with some novel features is manufactured by Trub-Tauber and Company, Zurich, Switzerland. This instrument utilizes a permanent magnet with a gap of 25 mm and a field strength of about 5000 Oe. Special current shims are employed to improve the homogeneity of the field. Bias coils for changing the field strength by ±50 Oe are provided. An oscillator controlled at 25 Hz by a quartz crystal is normally provided but oscillators to give any frequency between 1.5 and 30 Hz can be obtained.

Separate oscillator and receiver coils with their axes perpendicular to one another are used, but the "leakage" between them is adjusted electronically rather than mechanically by means of paddles, as in the Bloch system. The resonance signal is amplified conventionally and then fed to an rf phase-sensitive detector. A field stabilizer with linear and sinusoidal sweep generators is included. The instrument is capable of a resolution of 1 in 10^8. However, in practice a resolution of 2 or 3 in 10^8 is obtained with the sample contained in a spherical cavity (2.5 mm diameter) in a spinning cylindrical tube 3 mm in diameter. Other sample configurations can be used.

One of the important commercial instruments for moisture measurement is the Schlumberger NMR analyzer. This instrument (Fig. 7.9) consists of the following major constituent units:

1 NUCLEAR MAGNETIC RESONANCE 433

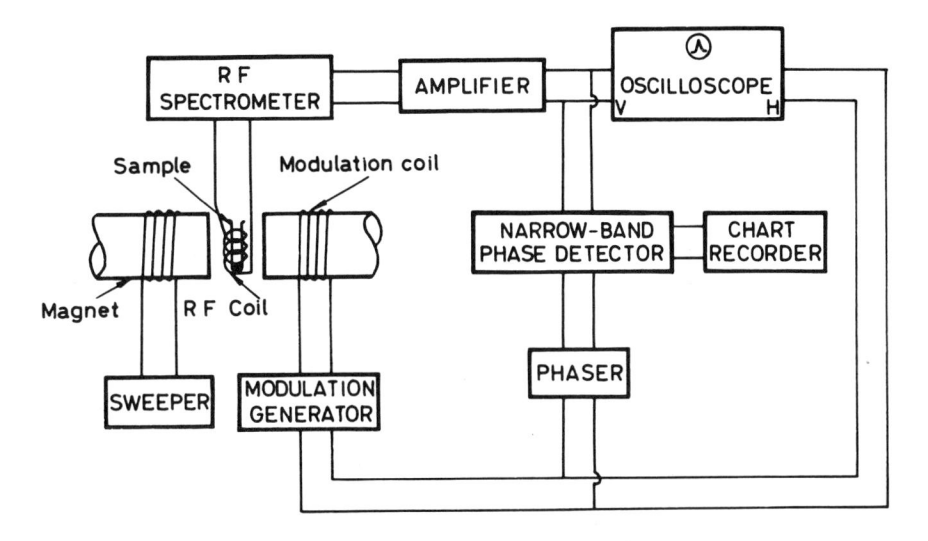

FIG. 7.9. Block diagram of Schlumberger NMR analyzer.

  1. The 1717-G permanent magnet unit with associated coils
  2. The sweep generator and amplifier
  3. The audio modulator
  4. The rf oscillator
  5. Audioamplifier
  6. Demodulator or detector
  7. Recorder
  8. The integrator which computes integral-mass ratio automatically feeds data to the recorder

In operation, the sample container is inserted in the rf coil of an electrically resonant circuit, in the gap of the magnet. The rf coil is then tuned by adjusting the parallel condenser to give maximum reading on the rf level meter. The mass of the sample is set on the integrator controls. A switch on the front of the console automatically starts the sweep cycle. During this cycle, the magnetic field is slowly changed by current fed to the sweep coils from the sweep generator and amplifier. It is simultaneously modulated at 33 Hz by the audio-oscillator to the tank circuit creating a radio-frequency voltage whose audiomodulation is proportional to the energy absorbed by the sample. This rf signal is amplified and the audiomodulation is isolated by the rf amplifier and detector. The audiosignal is then amplified by the audioamplifier, and the NMR signal is recorded.

During the complete cycle, the integrator stores the information being recorded. At the completion of the cycle, the integrator instantly computes the area under the recorded curve divided by the mass of the sample, and automatically records the result directly on the strip chart recorder. The Schlumberger wide-line NMR analyzer records the absorption by a sample at each level of applied magnetic field. The signal, whether it be a derivative, absorption, or integral, is influenced by the amount of rf power supplied to the sample. In the Schlumberger analyzer sufficiently low levels are available so that signal amplitudes are unaffected by rf saturation. As rf power is increased, the signal amplitude is reduced in direct proportion to the mobility of the nuclei being detected.

Japan Electron Optics Laboratory has developed the JNMC-60 NMR analyzer, which is a high-resolution NMR instrument for measurement of proton magnetic resonance. It is a compactly designed single unit (Fig. 7.10) containing the spectrometer system and the electromagnet. The pole gap of the electromagnet, in which the sample is placed, is located at the center of the unit. In this instrument very high homogeneity and stability of the magnetic field is obtained by providing an NMR control field stabilizer to exclude undesirable fluctuations and to ensure very high stability, which enables us to record precise spectrum on the standard recording chart. The NMR control stabilization is the most advanced technique to control the field intensity. It uses the NMR signal itself as the error signal which is negatively fed back to satisfy the resonance condition constantly.

This apparatus utilizes the bridge type of detector circuit. The detector unit is fixed in the pole gap of the electromagnet and

1 NUCLEAR MAGNETIC RESONANCE

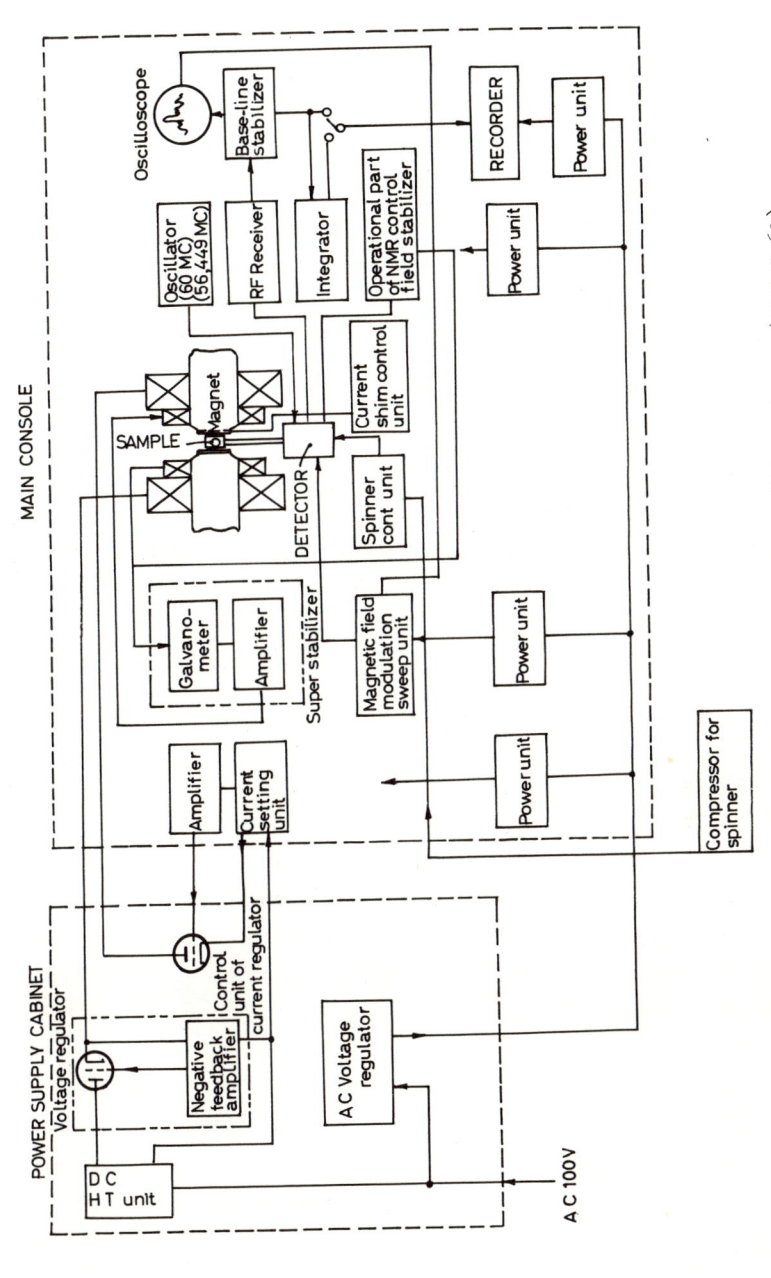

FIG. 7.10. Block diagram of Japan Electron Optics Laboratory NMC analyzer (JNM-C-60).

detects the NMR signal of the sample. The sample is placed and fixed exactly at the center of the magnetic field. There is a provision for spinning the sample by using an air compressor which rotates the sample whenever required. A radio-frequency oscillator is used for observing NMR signals of hydrogen at 60 Hz. Output of the rf oscillator creates a variable magnetic field in the sample coil. The receiver amplifies the NMR signal detected by the NMR detector and feeds it to either a recorder or an oscilloscope. The base-line stabilizer included in the receiver stabilizes the base line of the NMR spectrum, which can be observed on an oscilloscope under rapid-field sweep conditions. This is very helpful for preliminary confirmation of the range where the spectrum will appear for identification of the spectrum, or adjustment of resolution.

For recording the NMR spectrum by the JNM-C-60 calibrated standard recording charts are used. It is therefore possible to read the chemical shift in parts per million. The use of the standard recording charts simplifies the procedures of analysis of the spectrum and of filing the recorded spectra. The movement of the drum-shaped recorder is synchronized with the magnetic field sweep; in other words, the magnetic field is swept simultaneously with the movement of the recorder. Therefore it is possible to record only a part of the spectrum or to record the magnified spectrum at the desired place on the chart. The magnetic field in increasing or decreasing direction can be swept. The sweep width and the sweep time for the full width of the chart are changeable in four stages. A suitable sweep rate can be selected by choosing both the sweep width and the sweep time.

1.8 Sensitivity, Resolution, and Calibration of Nuclear Magnetic Resonance Spectrometers

The detectability of the voltage associated with the rf nuclear magnetization depends [19] on its magnitude as compared with the background of random electrical fluctuations, i.e., the "noise."

1 NUCLEAR MAGNETIC RESONANCE

The ratio of signal to noise determines how readily the nuclear signal can be detected. When this ratio becomes small and approaches unity the detection limit is reached. It can be shown that the magnitude of the NMR absorption is increased by increasing the volume of the coil, the fraction of the coil volume filled with sample, the Q of the sample circuit, and the concentration of nuclei. The sensitivity of the apparatus is improved by decreasing its band pass and its noise figure. The minimum number of protons that can be detected under favorable conditions at room temperature comes to 5×10^{16} the equivalent of 10^{-3} mg of H_2O.

Improvement in signal-to-noise ratio may be obtained by decreasing the bandwidth of the detector. Conventional methods for narrowing the bandwidth consist of sharply tuned audioamplifier of the phase-sensitive variety, and an integrating network of adjustable time constant. The bandwidth of the system is determined by the time constant T of the circuit and is approximately $1/T$. Typical time constants are from 1 to 100 sec, and the corresponding narrow bandwidths are 1 to 10^{-2} Hz, which increase the signal-to-noise ratio accordingly.

Where only water and solid materials are involved, calibration of the NMR analyzer to measure percentage water content is very simple, and a linear relationship between percentage of moisture content and integrator reading in millivolts for a number of solids can be obtained (Fig. 7.11). The range of measurement can be from 100% down to some very low percentage. The calibration for each material may, however, be different as the instrument primarily measures free water. Also calibration ceases to be linear in the lower range of moisture content. This occurs because the binding of water to the solid so broadens the linewidth that the signal no longer is completely overmodulated. For the obtaining of quantitative data, quantitative measurement of chemical shifts is required. The resonance is recorded or displayed under standardized calibrated conditions.

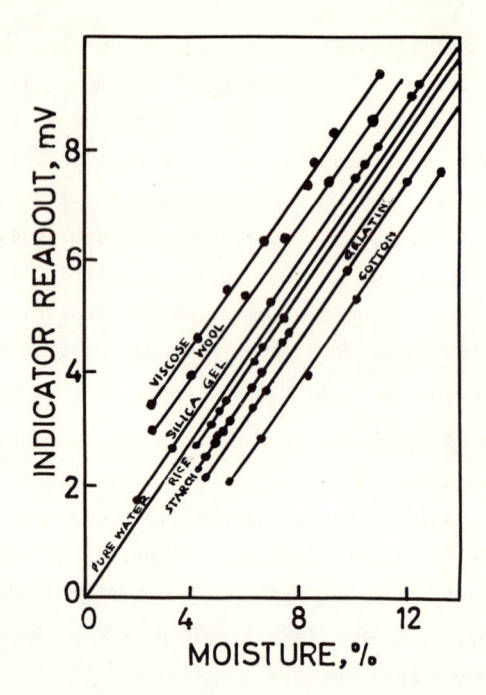

FIG. 7.11. Calibration curves of NMR analyzer for moisture contents in various materials.

1.9 Standardization of Nuclear Magnetic Resonance Spectra

For an accurate quantitative analysis in different molecular species, it is necessary that appropriate procedures for standard line-resonance comparisons be adhered to. One objective in chemical analysis is, of course, to be able to standardize very small differences from one molecular species to another. Both internal and external standardization procedures have been widely used for several years.

An internal standardization procedure amounts to dissolving a small amount of the known reference standard in the sample. There are two specific advantages of using an internal reference standard:

1 NUCLEAR MAGNETIC RESONANCE

1. Simultaneous sweeping of the field or frequency spectrum for the unknown sample and the reference is obtained.
2. The susceptibility corrections are presumably common to both the reference and sample molecular systems.

If a small amount of the reference standard can be dissolved into the system without affecting intermolecular interaction and intermolecular chemical shift of either the reference or unknown species, it would be satisfactory. However, this is not generally a valid assumption, and molecular association effects can, in many instances, contribute to effective chemical shift variations in a magnetic field by as much as several parts in ten millions. A common example of this effect is observed when using water as an internal standard in ethyl alcohol. The position of the internal water line with respect to the hydrogen atoms of the ethyl group varies as a function of the concentration of water. This chemical shift of the water line in comparison with pure water can vary as much as 2.6 mG. From this it would appear that so long as one uses small concentrations (10% by volume) of water as an internal reference standard, such a procedure would be satisfactory.

The use of internal reference standard permits simultaneous sweeping of the field or frequency spectrum for the reference standard and unknown sample, and makes susceptibility corrections presumably common to both the reference and sample molecular systems. However, errors as large as several parts in 10^7 in chemical shift values for intermolecular hydrogen nuclei can arise from intermolecular effects. Hence, internal standardization methods should be used with extreme caution. Chemical shift measurements, without quantitative corrections for molecular interaction effects, can lead to erroneous interpretations of the data.

External reference standard measurements of pure monomolecular systems can be made without polluting the pure system, and without introducing intermolecular effects arising from the presence of the reference standard compound. Various methods of external standardization have been used by NMR investigators. Most of the reported measuring techniques have involved obtaining independent sweeps of the spectra of the reference and unknown samples. With sufficient data for a proper statistical analysis, this procedure has been widely used for chemical shift measurements. The lack of a technique for simultaneous sweeping of reference and unknown samples does seriously limit the accuracy of line separation measurements; nevertheless, a few laboratories have reported accuracies to within 1 part in 10^7 by this method.

The principle of the simultaneous sweep has been utilized recently. The basic problem is to be able to have both the reference and unknown samples in the same field at the same time. The obvious advantage of simultaneous sweep is to be able to use side-band modulation techniques of the spectra by superposing the side band of one resonance upon the fundamental of another resonance. Chemical shifts can, in principle, be measured to an accuracy of a few parts in 10^9. Some investigators have approached this condition of placing both the reference and unknown samples in the same field by separating the sample and the reference compounds by a thin glass membrane across a 5-mm Pyrex glass tubing sample holder.

Zimmerman and Foster [37] have been able to perfect a spinning external standardization procedure which encompasses simultaneous sweeping of reference and unknown samples. Any sharp line reference standard may be used. Side-band modulation techniques of the system are utilized, and the ultimate limitations of accuracy of this system are determined by the width of the resonance lines, the field sweep rate, and the accuracy of the modulating audio oscillator. The mechanism of this method is simply a spinning coaxial system of two precision glass tubes. The sample to be studied is placed in the inner tube and the reference standard is placed in the annular region between the outer diameter of the inner tube and the inner diameter of the outer tube. Such a procedure can be dependable only if proper precautions are taken for averaging the asymmetric flux fields in the sample and reference regions. Both theoretical and experimental evaluations of this external standardization procedure have been completed successfully.

1.10 The Sample

One of the limiting factors in high-resolution measurements is the heterogeneity of the applied magnetic field. It was pointed out by Bloch [19] that the effective homogeneity of the field can be improved in a rather simple way by providing a motion of the substance within the sample under investigation. For this procedure to be effective, it is necessary that the rotational frequency should be in excess of the desired resolution expressed in hertz. Thus 2 or 3 revolutions/sec are adequate if we wish to achieve a resolution of 0.5 Hz. If the spinning frequency is too low, the averaging of the field is incomplete and the main absorption signal is accompanied by side bands. In practice, side bands can also result from uneven spinning of the sample tube so that care must be taken to use tubes which spin smoothly. The spacing of side bands is symmetric about the main band and is equal to the spinning frequency or multiple thereof. Spinning side bands can therefore be identified by comparison of spectra obtained using different spinning frequencies. Very high spinning frequencies can cause the formation of a vortex which may extend into the operative region of the sample. This is to be avoided since it can cause a serious reduction in resolution.

Another method for obtaining optimum condition is approached by reducing the sample volume. The extent to which the sample volume can be reduced is in turn limited by the signal strength required for observation and depends on the signal-to-noise ratio of the particular receiving and recording equipment used. A suitable compromise among these limiting factors must therefore be established for a particular set of conditions. It should be noted, however, that, although the integrated signal intensity is reduced with smaller sample volumes, the signal amplitude is usually not reduced to the same degree since the greater field homogeneity over the smaller regions gives rise to sharper signals. Sample volumes of the order of 0.003 cm^3 have been successfully used in some measurements of proton signals. Depending on the degree of dilution of the particular nuclear species being measured, sample volumes up to 0.5 cm^3 and sometimes larger may be necessary to obtain an adequate signal strength. For proton measurements, solvents such as CCl_4, CS_2, and deuterated compounds are frequently useful. Samples with high viscosity may cause signal broadening which may be overcome by solvent dilution or by increasing the temperature of the sample. Frequently, solid compounds with relatively high melting points are not sufficiently soluble to give adequate resonance signals.

For moisture measurement it is in many cases desirable that the temperature of the sample over a continuous range of both high and low temperatures be kept constant. Such temperature control is desirable in high-resolution experiments not only for observing temperature-dependent rate processes but also for improving the solubility of solids or else to melt them in order that a high-resolution spectrum can be obtained. The design is complicated by the necessity for spinning the samples; this means that for best thermal control the temperature of the air driving the turbine should be adjusted before it enters the probe. Moreover, in some cases the crossed-coil probe is such that the whole assembly cannot be thermostated; furthermore, the probe is sensitive to thermal gradients. This means then that the sample, spinner, and the control device which regulates the sample temperature and prevents heat transfer with the probe must all be contained within the two crossed coils. Nonetheless, at least two devices have been used more or less successfully with the Varian instrument and a commercial version is now available. Except for the sample spinning, the Varian probe poses much the same difficulties in temperature control for solid-state studies. With spectrometers of the crossed-coil type, altering the temperature of the entire probe assembly is impractical, owing to its more complicated construction and the need for proper balancing. Control devices for maintaining sample temperature are

1 NUCLEAR MAGNETIC RESONANCE

thus confined to the space within the receiver coil assembly. Some economy of space is effected by constructing the coil in the form of a small, thin-walled Dewar tube, the receiving coil being wound on the outside of the inner glass wall of the tube. The sample is then preheated or precooled to the desired temperature before it is inserted in the Dewar tube for measurement.

1.11 Proton Magnetic Resonance Spectra of Water in Solids and Liquids

In a liquid, the motion of the molecules is usually so rapid that the local magnetic field is smoothed out to a small average value. As a result, the absorption line is very narrow, and in pure mobile liquids such as water the linewidth will be determined principally by the heterogeneity of the applied magnetic field. This dependence on the physical state of the nuclear environment is demonstrated by a simple experiment which can be performed with ice. The hydrogen nuclear magnetic resonance signal obtained from a completely frozen sample of ice is broad and weak, having a signal width of the order of 50 kHz or more. If one now continuously records the resonance signal as the ice melts, he finds that a sharp intense signal 1 kHz or less in width begins to form on top of the broad pedestal signal. This sharp signal increases in intensity until the ice has completely melted, while the broad weak signal disappears.

In a solid compound of hydrogen, the nuclei are fixed rather rigidly in position with respect to their neighbors and are only capable of restricted movement. Because of this rigidity, any given nucleus may be in a total magnetic field that is several gauss lower or higher than the applied field. Since the nuclei pass through magnetic resonance at widely different values of the applied field, the line width is comparatively broad (of the order of several gauss).

In materials where both solid and liquid are present, the total absorption is the sum of the absorption due to hydrogen nuclei in the solid material and in the water. We take advantage of the difference in linewidths between liquids and solids to measure the moisture in hydrogen-containing substances. It is rather difficult to distinguish between proton signals from water and those from other hydrogen-containing substances in the liquid phase. However, there is a sharp signal from the liquid water superimposed on the broad signal from the solid obtained by a low-resolution apparatus. Either peak-to-peak amplitude or the linewidths of the absorption line can be used as a measure of the water content. The analyzer can therefore detect hydrogen in any state of molecular combination in the sample.

The hydrogen nuclear magnetic resonance signal from water in moist solid is narrow and strong; the hydrogen signals from chemically combined water and from the hydrogen in carbohydrates and other solid constituents are weak and broad. In the case of moist cornstarch, the hydrogen nuclear magnetic resonance signal has two well-defined components consisting of a broad pedestal signal some 35 kHz in width upon which is superimposed a narrow intense signal of a few kilohertz width. The narrow signal was shown [38] to be due to the hydrogen atoms in the sorbed moisture, while the broad signal was found to arise from the hydrogen atoms in the solid constituents. All the hygroscopic substances studied exhibit this type of resonance behavior. The reason for this is that the width of the absorption line is strongly dependent on the molecular motion within the sample. Nuclear magnetic resonance depends on the total effective magnetic field strength at the individual nucleus; the total field is the sum of the applied magnetic field at that point plus the field contributed by neighboring magnetic particles (such as magnetic nuclei).

Figure 7.12 is a recording of the complex signal from a sample of cornstarch [38]. Removal of water from the sample results in a diminution of the narrow absorption. Studies of many hygroscopic materials have revealed an excellent correlation between the magnitude of the narrow absorption and the water content of the material.

1 NUCLEAR MAGNETIC RESONANCE   445

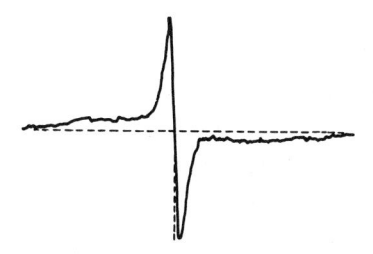

FIG. 7.12. Complex hydrogen NMR signal from moist starch.

In practice, the conditions of operation of the apparatus are chosen so that only the narrow absorption due to the hydrogen atoms in the water is recorded. This is possible because of the relatively large difference in width of the narrow and broad components of the complex line. Figure 7.13 shows the typical recorded line from sorbed water alone. To record this line, the modulation was set approximately equal to the width of the narrow component of the line shown in Fig. 7.12.

The disparity between the linewidths of the hydrogen in a sorbed state and the hydrogen in combination with the solid in which it is

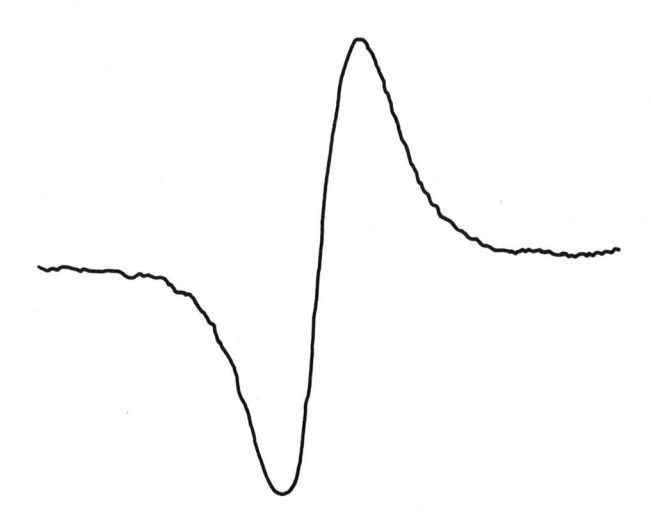

FIG. 7.13. Hydrogen NMR signal from water sorbed on starch.

absorbed or adsorbed thus makes it possible to obtain an accurate measurement of the moisture content of the hygroscopic materials. The analyzer, however, records the derivative of the absorption curve and the peak-to-peak amplitude of this derivative curve is a measure of the moisture content. This derivative curve is obtained by modulating the absorption curve by superimposing on the swept dc field of the pole pieces of the homogeneous magnet a small square wave of constant amplitude and low frequency. The peak-to-peak amplitude has to be plotted against direct moisture values to give a calibration curve. These calibration curves for most of the materials are usually linear above 5% moisture content but below this level greater curvature becomes perceptible. This effect is attributed to greater interaction of the absorbed water with the solid material when only a small quantity of water is present.

Two parameters are ordinarily used to characterize an absorption line (Fig. 7.14). These are D_{max}, the peak-to-peak amplitude of the line, and $\delta\nu$, the width of the line. Both quantities are useful for the determination of water content. In nuclear magnetic resonance, linewidth is defined as the width at half the peak amplitude on the absorption curve which is similar to a resonance curve of a tuned tank circuit excited by a sine wave. As stated earlier absorption linewidth is related to the hydrogen mobility in the sample and the homogeneity of the magnetic field over the volume of the sample. Also the shape of the line is influenced considerably by the chemical and physical states of the hydrogen in the sample. The peak-to-peak amplitude appears to be more reliable since small differences in water content have a greater effect on the amplitude than on the linewidth. In limited ranges where marked changes in linewidth are observed, this may give more accurate results.

A graph showing the variation of D_{max} with water content is presented in Fig. 7.15. To compensate for the small but unavoidable variations in the amount of material in the sample placed in the apparatus the observed values of D_{max} have been divided [39] by W, the weight of the sample. For starch a graph such as the one shown

1 NUCLEAR MAGNETIC RESONANCE 447

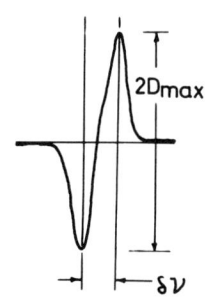

FIG. 7.14. Quantities used to define an absorption line.

in Fig. 7.15 is satisfactory for the determination of the water content over the range of 6%. Below 6% water the narrow line becomes broadened and D_{max} is too small for a precise determination of water. Plots of peak intensity of nuclear absorption, I_p, and water contents, however, give straight lines for samples of wood, starch, pectin, potato, etc. (Fig. 7.11). Also the theory of NMR leads one to expect a linear relationship between I_p and the moisture content, provided the magnetic environment of the hydrogen nuclei is independent of the water content. The source of variation

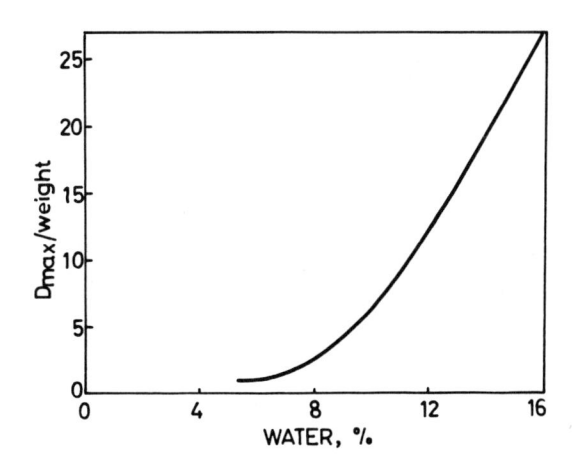

FIG. 7.15. Variation of signal amplitude with moisture content in starch.

from linearity might be the specific orientation of the initial water absorbed.

Since the narrow absorption becomes broadened as the water content decreases, it is also possible to use the linewidth as a measure of water content. It has been observed that the width of the hydrogen absorption varies with the water content of some cornstarch-water systems. It may be of interest to note that the width of the hydrogen absorption line observed for a 0.01-cm^3 sample of water in a very uniform magnetic field is only about 1/600 of the width observed in the equipment ordinarily used for the measurement on starch. If magnets can be perfected so that uniform fields can be obtained over a volume of several cubic centimeters, it is reasonable to expect that the use of the linewidth as a measure of water content can be extended to much higher moisture contents than is possible with the equipment now available.

The use of the linewidth, $\delta\nu$, rather than D_{max}, as a measure of water content offers a singular advantage. When D_{max} is used it is necessary to determine the weight of the sample. If $\delta\nu$ is used, however, the weight of the sample is no longer critical since the linewidth is an intrinsic property of the starch-water system and does not depend on the amount of sample used for the measurement. Low moisture (content) measurements can thus be made by measuring the linewidth of the water signal as an alternative to D_{max} measurement as suggested by Shaw et al. [22].

Shaw and Elsken [40] made measurements of linewidth for starch and egg albumin at 27°C. Their results for starch are summarized in Table 7.1. In these measurements the water content was varied over a range from about 6 to 17 g water/100 g dry solid. By using a high-resolution apparatus it has been possible to differentiate between the free and bound water as shown by Shoolery and Alder [41]. The time required for one analysis is 30 to 60 sec. Most of the apparatus presently in use seem to be suitable for many types of hygroscopic materials, over a wide moisture range (5 to 100%), and have an accuracy of 0.2%.

TABLE 7.1

Relation between Linewidths and Moisture Contents of Starch

Sample no.	Water content (g water/100 g dry solid)	Linewidths (kHz)
1	6.3	2.3
2	8.2	1.3
3	10.2	1.0
4	13.2	0.60
5	15.7	0.45

1.12 Study of Hydrogen-Bonded Systems

In mixtures of water and some organic liquids such as ethyl alcohol, dioxane, and acetone, hydrogen bonds are formed and broken at different concentrations of water. In such systems dependence of the chemical shift of the relevant protons on concentrations of water can be studied. An interesting study of the association of ethyl alcohol and water using NMR has been made by Weinberg et al. [42]. It was found by them that the presence of water in solutions has marked effect on chemical shifts of both ethanol-OH and associated H_2O lines. No appreciable changes in chemical shift, however, occur until molar concentration of 1:1 is obtained in the alcohol and water system. Owing to fast interaction in this region, the OH and H_2O lines rapidly coalesce into a single sharp line, and after coalescence the position of the coalesced line does not show any appreciable shift as water concentration is increased.

In Fig. 7.16 the frequency separation of the OH and H_2O lines from the CH_3 line of alcohol is plotted as a function vol % water in the mixture. At low water concentration the H_2O and OH lines are separated from the CH_3 line by 136 and 167 Hz, respectively. The resulting coalesced line is 146.5 Hz. If rapid exchange between the hydrogen of the H_2O and OH groups is assumed, then the mole

450

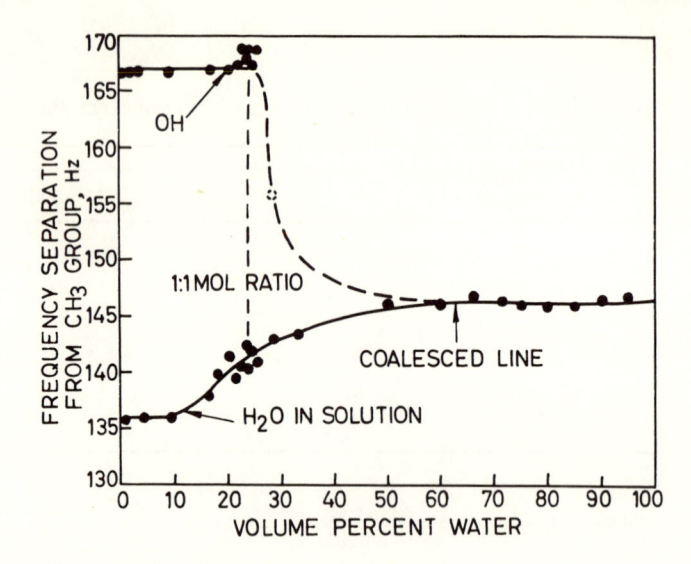

VII. NUCLEAR METHODS AND TECHNIQUES

FIG. 7.16. Curve showing the relationship between frequency separation due to chemical shift and the volume percent of water from CH_3 group.

fraction ratio necessary to obtain coalescence at 146.5 Hz is $N_{H_2O}/N_{OH} = 1$ within 2%.

In order to make a comparison of a free water line with either the H_2O line in alcohol solution or the coalesced line, it is necessary to make proper corrections due to bulk diamagnetic susceptibility of differences between pure water and pure alcohol. In order to make this correction, a shift of the CH_3 line of alcohol was obtained by Weinberg et al. [42] with respect to an external standard (acetone). In Fig. 7.17 a plot of the frequency shift of the CH_3 line relative to the acetone standard is made over the limits of concentration. The total diamagnetic shift was found to be 12.5 Hz.

The results obtained by Weinberg and Zimmerman [42] are summarized in Fig. 7.18. From this figure it can be observed that with a sample of pure alcohol, the free-water external standard line is 7.5 Hz from the OH line. With a correction of 12.5 Hz for diamagnetic susceptibility, the free-water line, if placed in the pure alcohol field, would have a 26-Hz shift from the OH line. Hence,

1 NUCLEAR MAGNETIC RESONANCE

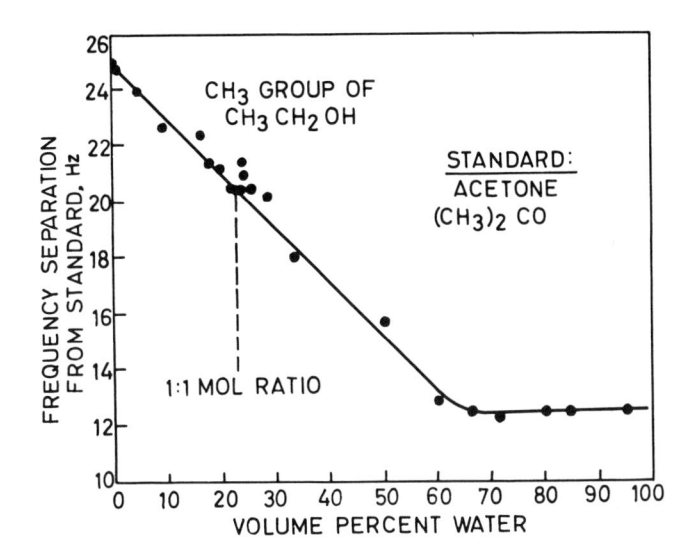

FIG. 7.17. Curve showing the relationship between frequency separation due to chemical shift and the volume percent of water from acetone standard.

with proper corrections for susceptibility, the coalesced line is observed to have the same resonance position (within 0.5 Hz) as pure water. Also without extrapolation, the effect of differential hydrogen bonding in free water as compared with a low concentration of water in alcohol amounts to a chemical shift of 11 Hz.

Dharmatti et al. [43] have studied the phenomenon of hydrogen bonding in water-acetone and water-dioxane mixtures and found the relationship between the chemical shift of water protons and the concentration of water in acetone and dioxane solutions. The results are plotted in Fig. 7.19. A linear relationship between chemical shifts and water concentration is obtained from which the amount of water present can be precisely determined. Both the curves in this figure show that the chemical shift of water protons moves continuously toward a higher field with dilution.

A number of research workers have studied the water-dioxane mixture by various physical methods such as refractometry, dielectric

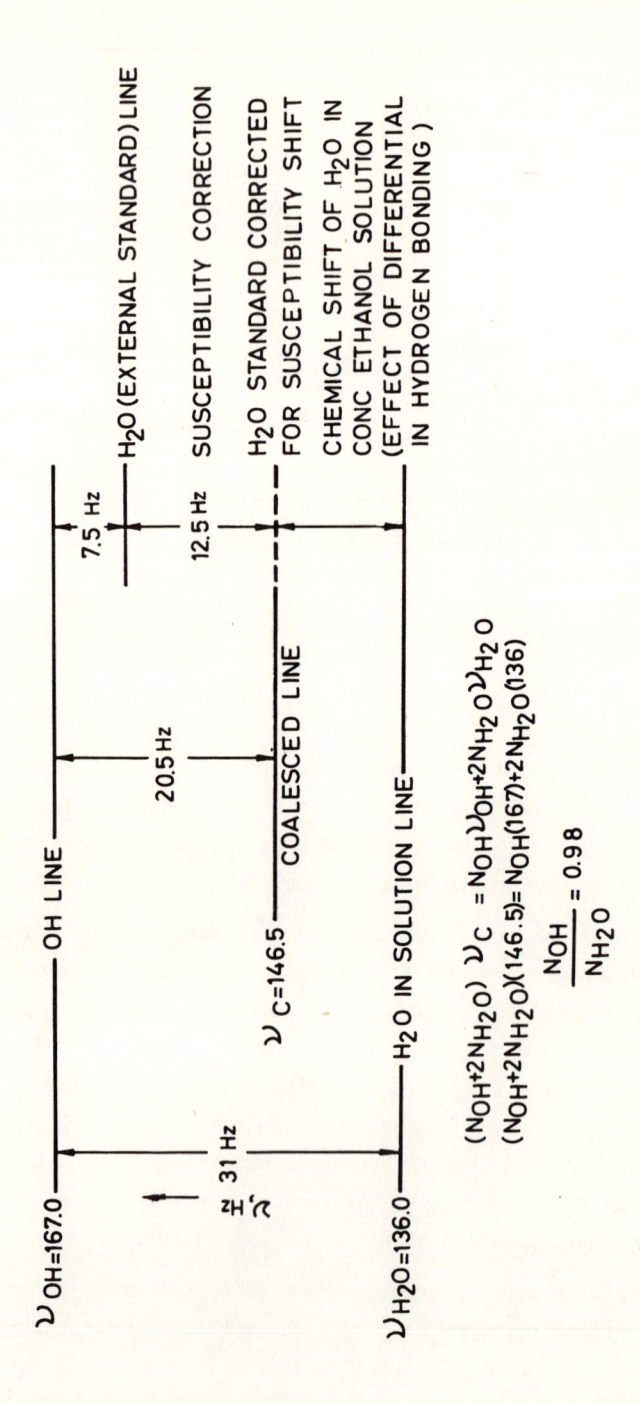

FIG. 7.18. Chart showing the summary of the data of chemical exchange in water-ethanol mixture.

1 NUCLEAR MAGNETIC RESONANCE   453

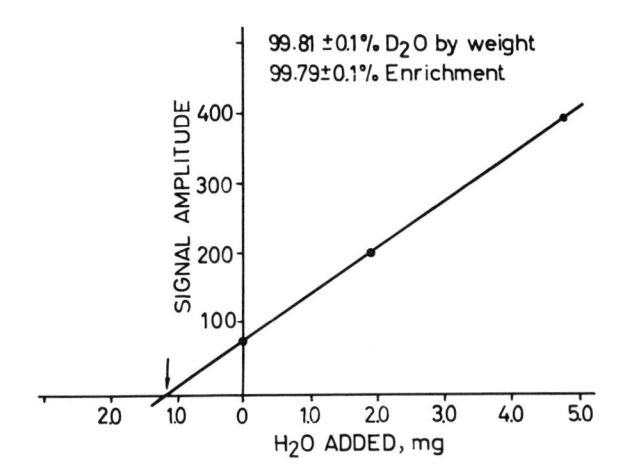

FIG. 7.19. Graph showing the relation between the NMR signal amplitude and the quantity of water added.

constant measurements, viscosity, and X-ray diffraction. All of them have observed a remarkable change in the behavior of these mixtures at a concentration of about 0.8 mole fraction of water. The curve for water-dioxane mixtures obtained by Dharmatti et al. [43] (Fig. 7.19) also shows a change in slope at 0.82 mole fraction of water. The change in slope cannot be attributed to complete depolymerization of water at this concentration because it has been already observed that water is associated even at infinite dilution.

1.13 Applications of Nuclear Magnetic Resonance Methods to Moisture Measurement

The application of nuclear magnetic resonance to the determination of moisture is based on the absorption of radiofrequency energy by the nuclei of hydrogen atoms. Each proton in the molecule contributes one unit of intensity to the resonance signal, so that the relative number of equivalent protons can be obtained from intensity considerations. It is this property of proton magnetic resonance which is utilized for quantitative analysis by measurement of the intensity of the absorption at resonant frequencies characteristic of the particular atomic species of interest. A most attractive aspect of this new technique from the analytical chemist's point of view is the fact that nearly all substances are readily permeable to electromagnetic waves so that measurements can be made on opaque liquids and solids.

Applications of NMR to moisture determinations in solids are virtually unlimited. These include wheat, oats, rice, sugar, starch and its derivatives, candy, corn, cheeses, all types of cereals, nylon, wool, cotton, tobacco, pure organic compounds, silica gel, soap chips, and other solids. Paper, pulp, and wood also lend themselves to rapid moisture analysis with the instrument.

A promising field for the technique lies in food and agriculture because of the economic motivation for moisture determination. Restrictions based on government specifications, losses due to spoilage, and variations in handling properties are all vitally tied up with moisture content. A number of investigations [38, 44] on cereal products have been made as part of a food study. The results are very encouraging and are leading to wide recognition. It is difficult to estimate the lower limits of sensitivity because the signals depend on the binding energy of water to the material, and this varies considerably. Moisture contents of a few hundredths of a percent can be detected in products such as sugar, whereas highly polar materials such as gelatin bind water so tightly that moistures in the vicinity of 10% give small signals. Calibration curves for wheat flour and types of wheat grain, and for rolled oats, converted rice, and tapioca showing linear relations have been obtained [38]. In addition to these, moisture in candies, sugar, gelatin, pure inorganic solids, dextrins, gluten meal, starch derivatives, and whole corn, etc., has been investigated accurately by some researchers [22, 40].

As a test of the precision obtainable in a specific case, measurements on a sealed sample of starch (containing 13.6% water) were made [38] daily over a period of several months. It was found

1 NUCLEAR MAGNETIC RESONANCE

that the 95% confidence limits for a single measurement were ±0.10% water absolute. This corresponds to a relative error of about 0.75% and compares favorably with oven analyses performed on a routine basis. From the results obtained O'Meara and co-workers [38] have given a few general statements regarding the applicability of the method of moisture measurement to these materials.

1. Substances having the same general molecular structure and similar water-binding capacities fall on a single calibration curve.

2. If there is a change in the relative amounts of mobile and nonmobile water in the materials, they do not fall on the same curve.

3. Simple sugars and low-molecular-weight polysaccharides do not fall on the same calibration curve as the high-molecular-weight polysaccharides.

4. Particle size and the manner of packing in the sample container do not affect the calibration curve. Identical results are obtained with powdered and granular unmodified starches.

5. In the limited number of materials studied, wide variations in the ash content do not appear to alter the calibration curve. This has been found to be true for unmodified starches having a fivefold variation in ash content.

6. Some fairly pure protein-water systems are expected to fall on the same general calibration curve as the starches.

The application of this method to wholegrain corn and to product feeds and meals appears to be somewhat limited at the present time because of interference from the fat and oil contained in these products. Since fat and oil are essentially liquid under the conditions of measurement, the hydrogen atoms in such compounds also give a narrow nuclear magnetic resonance signal and thus add to the signal obtained from sorbed water. If the fat content of such products varies appreciably, that variation is superimposed upon the calibration curve for moisture, and the present techniques are unable to resolve completely the contributions of the two substances. However, recently a few methods [38] and techniques [21, 44] have been devised for the separation of oil or fat and water contribution in the instrument required for the measurement of one or the both of them together.

Conway et al. [21] have used the NMR technique for the moisture determination of a number of confectionary products and found that the method gives reliable results as compared with those obtained by other techniques.

The study of the chemical shifts accompanying hydrogen bonding in tributyl phosphate has been made by Murray and Axtmann [45] who have utilized the phenomena for the estimation of water in this chemical. Their method involves the measurement of the chemical shift of the water proton resonance with respect to the methyl proton resonance in tributyl phosphate, and hence it requires no external standard. A number of investigators [46-48] have studied the chemical shift accompanying hydrogen bonding in systems other than tributyl phosphate and water. In every case the breaking of the hydrogen bonds is accompanied by a shift of the proton resonance to higher fields. For water infinitely diluted in a solvent with which is does not interact, e.g., benzene, the shift from the position of the pure water resonance divided by the applied field or frequency is approximately 4.0×10^{-6}. The dilution results in nearly all of the hydrogen bonds being broken.

It was found by Murray and Axtmann [45] that the proton signal from water, extrapolated to infinite dilution in tributyl phosphate, is displaced from the pure water signal to higher fields by 2.0×10^{-6}. This small shift is interpreted to mean that, in contrast to the benzene-water system, the water does react with the solvent, but that the resultant bonds are somewhat weaker than the water-to-water hydrogen bonds. Typical tributyl phosphate spectra are displayed in Figs. 7.20 and 7.21 wherein the large, sharp peak at the extreme right of the recording trace is due to the methyl protons. The broad, partially resolved hump to the left of this peak arises from most of the methylenic protons, while the quartet at the left of the trace comes from those methylenic protons that are attached to the carbon atoms immediately adjacent to oxygen atoms.

1 NUCLEAR MAGNETIC RESONANCE

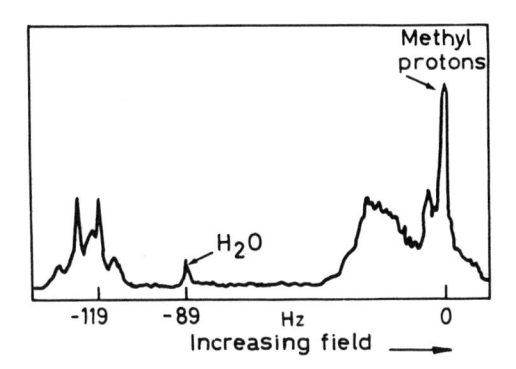

FIG. 7.20. Nuclear magnetic resonance spectrum of tributyl phosphate containing 1.7% water.

The water peak occurs approximately midway between the two methylenic proton groups (Fig. 7.20) in tributyl phosphate containing 1.7 wt % water. Similarly, the spectrum for nearly saturated (6.2 wt % water) tributyl phosphate shows (Fig. 7.21) the water proton signal coincident with one line of the quartet. In this case the signal has increased in intensity and, as well, shifted to a lower field strength. The chemical shift of the water proton resonance with respect to the methyl peak from tributyl phosphate was measured for 11 samples whose water concentrations ranged from 0.44 to 6.3 wt %. At least five determinations were made on each sample.

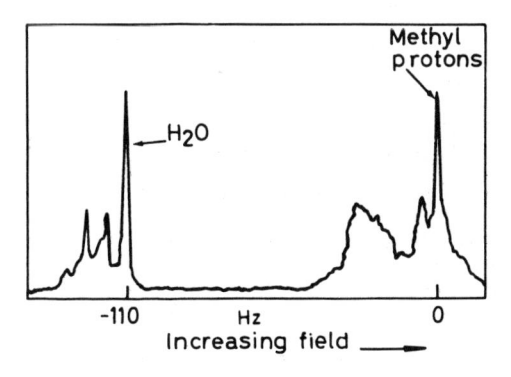

FIG. 7.21. Nuclear magnetic resonance spectrum of tributyl phosphate saturated with water.

The result, when plotted, shows a linear relationship between the chemical shift and the concentration of water, with a slope of 4.9 Hz for 1% water. The precision of individual measurement was 0.65 Hz which is equivalent to 0.13% water by weight.

1.14 Continuous Measurement of Moisture Content by Nuclear Magnetic Resonance Method

An NMR apparatus for the measurement of moisture content of various hygroscopic materials free from environmental interaction has recently been developed by Rollwitz [49-51] in which the moisture measurement can be accurately made even in the presence of oil or fats or other materials containing hydrogen, whose contributions to spectra could be either eliminated or separated.

In this method the linewidth of the moisture signal is plotted as a function of the moisture level for water in starch and a linear relationship is obtained. The decrease in linewidth means an increasing relaxation time as the moisture levels increase. This is because at the lower levels, the water molecules are held more firmly by the starch and there is less relative motion of the hydrogen nuclei, resulting in a wider linewidth. The higher moisture levels are held less firmly, giving more motion and a reduced linewidth. The decreasing linewidth with increasing moisture content makes the peak-to-peak first harmonic amplitude vs moisture curve nonlinear rather than a straight line. It was found, however, that a calibration curve could be obtained for various starches which would permit a measurement of moisture content to 1% accuracy. With some materials it may be advantageous to measure both the first harmonic amplitude and the absorption-curve amplitude.

For the moisture measurements on flowing samples Rollwitz [49] has developed a technique for passing the whole stream through the rf coil and the magnet (Fig. 7.22). If the system is completely stabilized, a continuous measure of moisture can be obtained (Fig. 7.23). The continuous flow measurement run is shown in Figs. 7.24 and 7.25 and repeatability is shown in Fig. 7.26. As can be seen

1 NUCLEAR MAGNETIC RESONANCE   459

FIG. 7.22. Continuous-process stream NMR analyzer.

from Fig. 7.26 the density of the material in the sampled volume makes large deviations especially when the material first flows.

Rollwitz [51] has also developed another NMR equipment which uses the variation in linewidth with moisture level instead of the variation in amplitude. Therefore, the system does not require consistent packing density since it only requires sufficient signal to obtain a measure of linewidth. The system is fully automatic and has an accuracy of 1%. It has been estimated from measurements that the accuracy can be maintained for filling factors of 0.3 to 1.0. Therefore large voids will not cause errors. The moisture meter developed by him can be used on both batch samples and continuous flow.

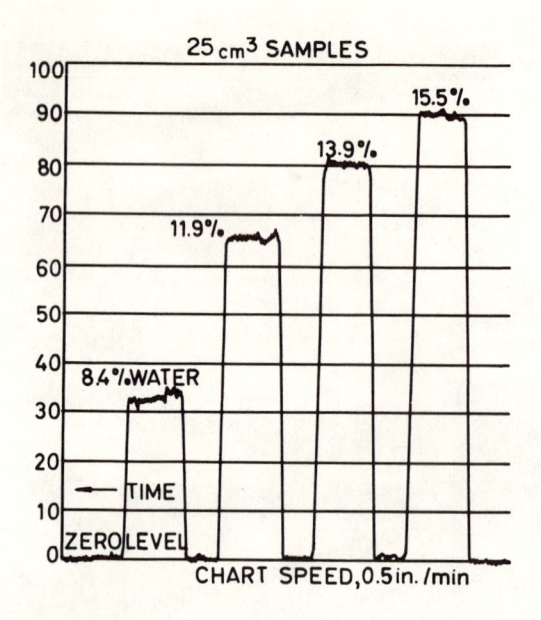

FIG. 7.23. Nuclear magnetic resonance absorption peaks of milo maize at different moisture levels.

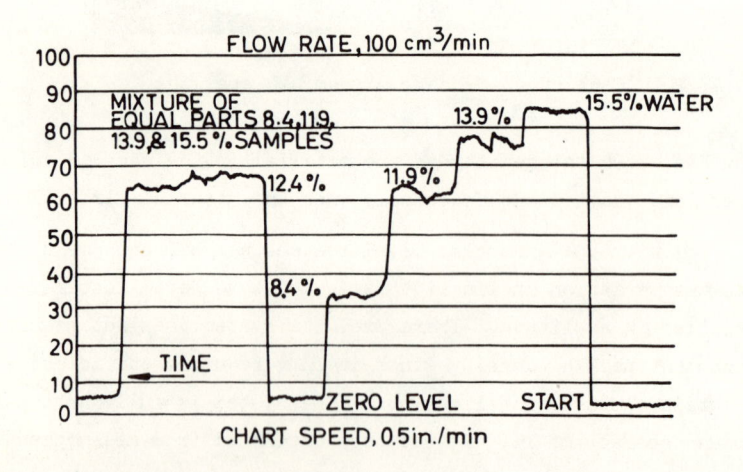

FIG. 7.24. Signals of flowing milo maize at four moisture levels and for a mixture of all four.

1 NUCLEAR MAGNETIC RESONANCE

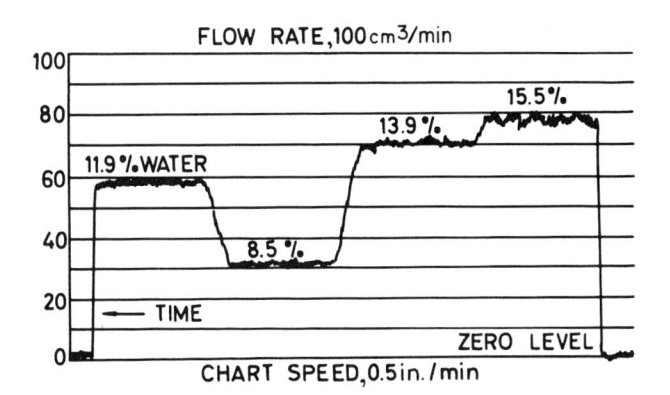

FIG. 7.25. Nuclear magnetic resonance signals for continuous flow of milo maize wherein the grains of various moisture levels were present.

On a batch sample meter a standard sample will pop up into the same coil when the unknown sample is removed and be depressed out of the sample coil when the unknown sample is inserted in order to keep the servomechanism locked in. On continuous flow measurements, there should always be enough sample in the sample tube of sample coil to permit this locking in. The measurement of percentage mois-

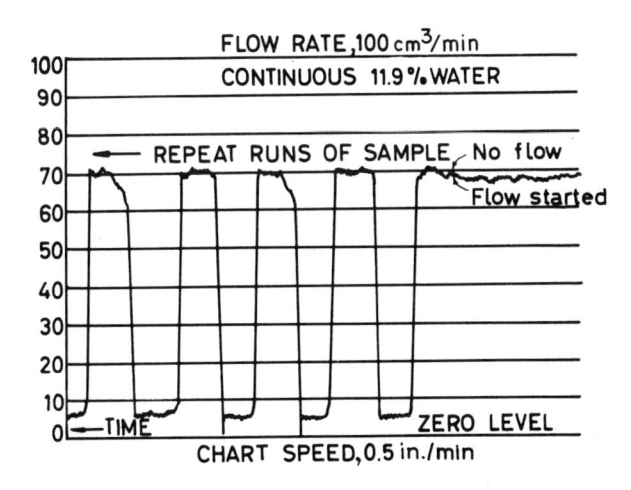

FIG. 7.26. Peaks showing repeated continuous runs of the same sample.

ture will be independent of the amount of sample as long as enough sample is present to give error signals greater than the noise. At moisture levels around 10% in starch, it is estimated that the "filling factor" can be as low as 30%. The measurement requires no special skills on the part of the operator since there are only two operating controls. The sample on the batch sample measurement requires no special preparation or weighing. The only requirement is that the sample contain enough material to give a signal large enough to permit locking in. The moisture measurement is almost instantaneous. The only time lag involved is the time required for the servomotor to reach the zero point of the error signal. This time lag is less than 1 sec. The indication is an above-zero reading on both or either the recorder or meter and is made from a very high signal-to-noise ratio signal. Therefore, the accuracy will be limited only by the accuracy of the meter and the recorder and by the signal-to-noise ratio of the error signal, and should be better than 0.5%.

The second harmonic moisture analyzer developed by Rollwitz [51] does not measure the amplitude of the absorption signal but measures only the modulation required for the maximum of the peak second harmonic. The unit requires few operating controls since it is locked in at all points by servomechanisms. This NMR analyzer is capable of measuring the moisture content of liquids and gases in addition to that of solids. However, moisture in gases can be measured if the number of hydrogen nuclei have a concentration greater than 10^{14} cm^3.

Gallbraith et al. [52] have used a modified version of a broadline spectrometer for moisture measurements of coals, cokes, and iron ore. In their apparatus a permanent magnet of approximately 3750 G provides the steady field across a gap of 1.5 in. A perpendicular oscillating field was derived from a quartz crystal oscillator, which fed a simple resonance circuit through a high impedance. The sample coil was formed from 14 turns of 24 SWG copper wire wound upon a thin Teflon former and in parallel with the coil was a 150 rf variable condenser. The level of rf power at the sample

1 NUCLEAR MAGNETIC RESONANCE

coil was varied, but there was no evidence of saturation effects with either the wet or dry coal. Two sets of magnetic coils were wound directly over the magnet pole pieces; the inner set provided 390-Hz modulation of the steady magnetic field, and the outer set enabled it to be varied for displaying the resonance line. The current necessary for this was supplied by a circuit which made it possible to sweep backward and forward every few minutes through the magnetic field required for resonance (field sweep approximately 5 G/min). Ladner and Stacey [53, 54] have successfully applied this technique for measuring moisture in moving coal feed. The accuracy of measurement is ±1% over a range of 5 to 14% of moisture content.

Nuclear magnetic absorption by protons may be used to measure water content over the range encountered in natural and dehydrated biological materials. A linear relation was found by Shaw and co-workers [22] between the height of the proton absorption line and water content for typical vegetable tissues. Recent work in the low-moisture region has shown departures from linearity for some materials, e.g., apple tissue and starch. A recording rf spectrometer was used together with a 4600-G permanent magnet modulated by 1 G. The lines observed at 25°C for a number of protons and carbohydrates containing 5 to 2% water are similar and consist of a line 0.7 G wide superimposed symmetrically on a line about 1 G wide.

Mitchell and Philips [55, 56] have designed an equipment capable of continuously monitoring the amount of light water in a light/heavy water mixture. Such an equipment is found useful for monitoring heavy water in nuclear reactors and in the manufacture of heavy water by enrichment from ordinary water. Nuclear magnetic resonance absorption is induced in protons contained in mixtures of light and heavy water. The magnitude of the power absorption is used as a measure of the concentration of light water present and samples of known concentrations are used to standardize the absorption. Two techniques for inducing the absorption have been developed by these researchers; one method is appropriate for H_2O concentration in the range 7 to 100% and the other for low H_2O concentrations. In both cases the signal output from the equipment rises almost linearly with H_2O concentration. Using the first method, a signal-to-noise voltage ratio of 20 is obtained with a 7% concentration. A similar ratio is obtained from samples with 0.2% H_2O by using the second technique. The effect of flowing low-concentration samples through the apparatus has been studied. The signal output falls with flow rate and at 40 ml/sec is half that obtained at zero flow.

The absorption method as developed by Pound [57, 58] and Watkins [59] has been employed by Mitchell and Philips [55, 56] as it offers a number of practical advantages. In this method the sample is contained in a coil forming part of the tank circuit of an oscillator. Nuclear magnetic resonance is detected by the drop in rf voltage across the coil as power is absorbed by the protons in the sample. The amount of power absorbed depends on the particular way the resonance condition is brought about.

Both static sample and flowing sample experiments were performed. The light water used was purified by an ion-exchange process and was not air free. The heavy water was of approximately 99.8% purity. The concentration of heavy water in the mixtures was measured by an infrared absorption method (HOD band at 3 µm) developed by Gaunt [60]. The NMR method relies ultimately on comparison with a standard, the concentration of which is measured by a specific gravity technique. For experiments with static samples, sealed glass tubes approximately 11-mm outer diameter by 8-cm long containing known concentrations of heavy water were supplied. In the flowing sample method the mixture of H_2O and D_2O was allowed to circulate through the rf coil assembly system. In the static sample experiments, the variation of signal amplitude against concentration of H_2O in D_2O was found to have a linear relation as shown in Fig. 7.27.

The nuclear resonance signals to be obtained from H_2O/D_2O mixtures flowing through the rf coil assembly were investigated. In particular attention was directed [55] to the study of D_2O with low H_2O content as this was of immediate practical interest. The liquid

1 NUCLEAR MAGNETIC RESONANCE

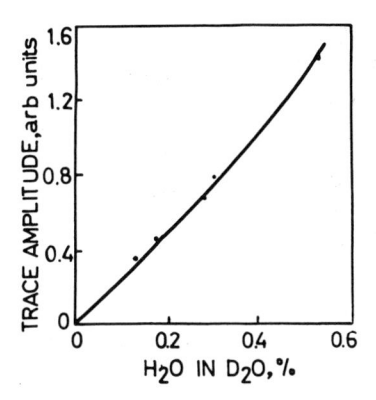

FIG. 7.27. Nuclear magnetic resonance absorption trace amplitude vs percentage H_2O in D_2O (static samples).

under examination in the work reported was D_2O with 0.3% H_2O concentration, in a similar way as for static samples, and the main concern was with the effect of flowing the liquid through the rf coil. The technique used was to sweep the main field H back and forth through the resonance value at 0.013 G/sec and to modulate the field with a 50-Hz ripple as before. In searching for the optimum signal amplitude at a particular flow rate, the radio-frequency field amplitude was held constant and the amplitude of the 50-Hz ripple varied. The optimum field modulation amplitude for the flowing liquid was three times that for the static sample but was not critical. The signal trace amplitude is plotted against flow rate in Fig. 7.28 for two values of the rf field. It will be noted that the signal falls off as the flow rate increases.

The techniques employed by Mitchell and Philips [55] cover the range of H_2O concentrations of practical interest (0.2 to 100% H_2O in D_2O) with adequate sensitivity. Using the rapid transient method a static sample containing 1% H_2O gives proton signals with a signal-to-noise ratio of 3:1. This indicates the minimum detectable H_2O concentration, and the method is suitable up to 100% H_2O. Static or flowing samples (up to 40 ml/sec) containing 0.3% H_2O yield signals of at least 20:1 signal-to-noise ratio. Measurements have been made on samples from 0.13 to 0.53% H_2O concentration.

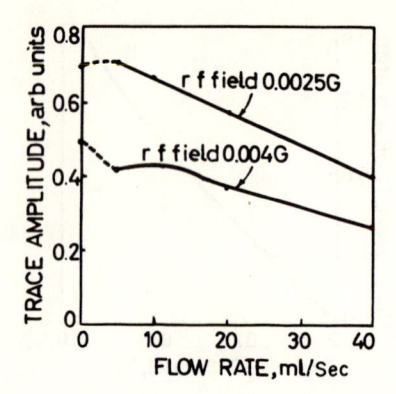

FIG. 7.28. Nuclear magnetic resonance trace amplitude vs rate of flow of 0.3% H_2O sample (flowing samples).

Experiments for the estimation of H_2O in mixtures of H_2O D_2O have been conducted by Ferret and Seymour [61] utilizing the NMR spectroscopy technique similar to the one described above. The experiments of Ferret and Seymour [61] were conducted on proton resonance, which gives strong signals, and, although their experimental accuracy was limited by the field inhomogeneity and oscillator stability, they were able to get good accuracy of 1 to 3%. The efficiency of deuterium detection is 9.64×10^{-3} times that of proton detection and with a natural abundance of deuterium of about 1.6 parts in 100,000, it is even more difficult to detect deuterium in water unless the spectrometer is extremely sensitive and the field highly homogeneous. Figure 7.29 shows the signal-to-noise ratio and reproducibility of the H_2O in high-purity D_2O. In this case the relaxation times are sufficiently similar from sample to sample so that the amplitude is a measure of the amount of H_2O present. Although the uniform sensitivity of NMR to the number of hydrogen nuclei present, regardless of the compound in which they are located, can be a detriment in trace analysis, it is definitely an asset in mixtures containing several substances in high concentrations. In such cases, no single substance will swamp the others as would be the case if the sensitivity to different compounds varied widely.

1 NUCLEAR MAGNETIC RESONANCE

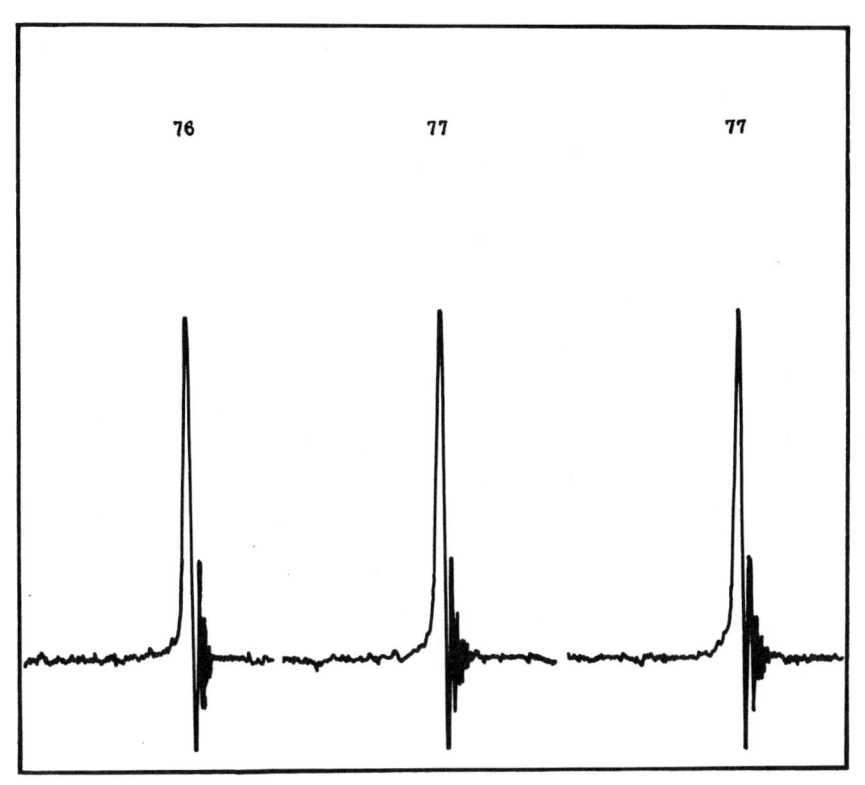

FIG. 7.29. Nuclear magnetic resonance signal amplitude for three successive recordings of residual H_2O resonance in high-purity D_2O.

1.15 Study of Adsorption of Water by Nuclear Magnetic Resonance Method

Nuclear magnetic resonance techniques have successfully been employed in recent years to study the adsorption of water. Nuclear relaxation processes arise from the magnetic interactions between the nucleus under study and its ambient field. The high-frequency components of the local field determine the spin-lattice relaxation time (T_1), and the linewidth parameter (I/T_2) arises from the interactions with the low-frequency spectrum of the local field and from a broadening associated with the lifetime of the spin state. T_1 is the longitudinal and T_2 the transverse relaxation time, respectively. If the nuclei of a system do not all enjoy the same average local field interactions during the time of relaxation measurements, then such a system is defined as a multiphase nuclear system. The multiple-phase nuclear system technique has been used extensively for the determination of moisture content in proteins and starches [40]. In this instance the resonance linewidth of the hydrogen of the solid chemical structure is extremely broad, whereas the linewidth of the adsorbed water is (in comparison) very narrow. Tanaka and Yamagata [62] have reported the observation of a multiphase system in adsorbed water on carbon. In this instance a distinction was made between the water adsorbed in and that adsorbed above the monomolecular layer by observing a sharp resonance line superposed on a broad resonance line.

Zimmerman et al. [63] have used nuclear magnetic resonance pulse (spin-echo) techniques for adsorption studies. Their studies of adsorbed water vapor on silica gel by means of nuclear magnetic resonance spin-echo technique have demonstrated in no small way the future role this physical tool may play in probing the phenomena of molecular sorption of solids.

Using the spin-echo technique, the coexistence of two absorbing phases of water vapor on silica gel surface has been directly observed [63] by nuclear magnetic relaxation measurements. In specific instances where two adsorbing phases have been observed to exist, it has been possible to evaluate the relative number of molecules associated with each adsorbing phase. A simple calculation for an adsorption shows that the number of water molecules associated with the stronger adsorbing phase is remarkably close to the theoretically calculated monomolecular coverage. In a more refined experimental investigation of the nuclear magnetic resonance relaxation phenomenon of water vapor adsorbed on silica gel, the two-phase behavior for both longitudinal and transverse relaxation time measurements is observed to exist simultaneously. The two adsorbed phases in longitudinal relaxation data are shown to be identical with the corresponding two phases in transverse relaxation data. The adsorption at low coverage is identified only with the short relaxation time

1 NUCLEAR MAGNETIC RESONANCE

component and the coverage at which the second adsorbed phase begins can be determined.

1.16 Miscellaneous Applications

The NMR method has been recently employed for the measurement of moisture contents in such diverse materials as coal [64], pesticides [65], barbiturates [66], and various pharmaceutical products [67, 68].

1.17 Advantages of the Method

The nuclear magnetic resonance method of determining moisture in many types of materials is rapid, nondestructive, and presents the results in the form of an electrical signal which conceivably can be used to control automatically driers or blenders in the manufacturing plant. Important advantages of the technique lie in its ability to make measurements which generally do not depend on particular size, compaction, or on the presence of moderate amounts of nonparamagnetic electrolytes. Finely powdered materials and whole grains can be handled with equal facility. These variations usually interfere with other electromagnetic methods of moisture analysis. This is not the case with nuclear magnetic resonance because the nuclear characteristics being measured do not vary with the above-mentioned conditions. No special precautions are thus required for the preparation of the sample for measuring and the method of packing is not critical, and since no part of the sample is in direct contact with the sensing element, hermetically sealed samples can be used and the measurement can be repeated as often as desired.

Because of the wide range of instrument parameters available and the unique approach of analysis, it can shed light on various related phenomena. The method appears to be applicable to a very large number of water-sorbing materials. Slow time-dependent processes which involve changes in water distribution and mobility may be studied. Among these are aging, water migration, and the effect of processing upon water binding. At present studies are being made on materials containing oil and water, and it appears that many products will be analyzed for both these components. The method is unique among electrical methods in that it is useful over the entire moisture range of a few percent to 100% water. Considerations of sensitivity make its use for high-moisture materials most attractive. A question often asked concerns the possible use of nuclear magnetic resonance for continuous measurement on stream installations. At present most of the instruments are designed for batch sampling. The use of an analyzer on a moving stream is physically feasible and this method has been recently employed for continuous measurements. However, a particular material and process would require tailor-made sampling devices as shown by Ladner and Stacey [53, 54] who have applied this technique for continuous measurement of moisture in coal. Some indications of how NMR might be used in control circuits have been published by Aikman et al. [69].

1.18 Disadvantages of the Method

On the debit side one must point out that the present cost of the equipment is relatively high compared to that of other devices for measuring water content. Even in production quantities, the equipment required for moisture measurement will cost an appreciable amount. Moreover the method as presently used does not give a single standard curve for all types of materials. It appears that separate calibration curves will be required for substances differing widely in composition. The method in its present form is not quite applicable to materials having a variable fat or oil content. The instrument is complex and requires skilled electronic technicians for its operation and maintenance.

1.19 Present Status of the Method

The basic principles of the nuclear magnetic resonance method have been well established, but as pointed out further evaluation

1 NUCLEAR MAGNETIC RESONANCE

will be necessary before its full potentialities can be realized in practice. It is expected that the analytical studies using the NMR instruments developed in the last decade will contribute the additional experimental data required to fully evaluate the NMR method for moisture measurement on many types of materials. Measurements on a wider variety of these substances will also establish the degree to which physical and chemical modifications of their structure may effect the calibration curves obtained by this method. In addition, it appears that further studies of linewidths should be made on these materials since the linewidth data obtained to date have been limited to a few substances. As has been shown the linewidth can be related directly to water sorption properties, and it may therefore offer better possibilities of obtaining a standard curve that would be valid for most moisture-absorbing solids.

Further work on the absorption of systems containing both fat and water appears to be warranted. Although both fat and water do contribute to the NMR signal, the characteristics of the radiofrequency absorption process for the two materials are sufficiently different so that it appears to be within the capabilities of the method to resolve the two contributions. The possibility of a single measurement technique which would measure nondestructively both the fat and water content of a substance is sufficiently important to merit more effort in this direction. The instrumentation and techniques developed so far for the measurement of moisture by NMR have emphasized stability, reliability, and simplicity of operation. There are some advantages associated with the rf spectrometer circuitry and methods for recording the nuclear resonance signals which may lead to practical systems that would offer more flexibility and consequently wider applications. The extension of this technique to the measurement of moisture content on a continuous flow basis is the logical result of this development and it is hoped that an investigation of continuous-flow methods will be used in the near future. The feasibility of continuous-flow measurements on liquids has already been demonstrated and it is expected that continuous-flow measurements on solid materials will not present any basic difficulties.

2 NEUTRON-SCATTERING METHOD OF MOISTURE MEASUREMENT

2.1 Introduction

The neutron-scattering method of measuring soil water content is founded upon the physical principles concerning the interaction between neutrons and the medium. The neutron was discovered in 1931 by Chadwick [70] as a result of its readily detectable and strong interaction with a material rich in protons, in this case, paraffin. Similar effects were also obtained with water and oil. Thus the principle of a method using neutrons to measure the presence of a proton-rich material such as water in substances relatively free from protons was indicated by this early work. Specific application to the detection of moisture in soil was described 20 years later by Belcher et al. [71]. Since then an increasing number of reports and papers have been published and various forms of commercial instruments are now available to make routine measurements of the moisture content of soils as well as of other similar materials.

2.2 Principle of the Method

The phenomenon of neutron scattering and neutron interaction with matter has been discussed in a number of publications [72-77].

The neutrons interact with matter in a number of ways; the interactions that are of interest are scattering and capture. Scattered neutrons are deflected from their path by atomic nuclei and lose energy. In capture, the neutron ends its existence. This reaction is often the basis of detection. As a generalization, we may say that scattering is the principal interaction with matter for fast neutrons, whereas capture occurs to an appreciable extent with slow neutrons. The scattering process of fast neutrons leads to the

2 NEUTRON SCATTERING

existence of slow neutrons by what is usually called moderation. On the other hand, the capture of slow neutrons is involved in their detection and thus forms the basis of measurement. The collisional cross section of the slow neutrons is about 2000 times that of fast neutrons. It has been observed that the energy loss is much greater in neutron collisions with atoms of low atomic weight and is proportional to the number of such atoms present in the material. Hydrogen, which is the principal element of low atomic weight, is largely contained in the molecules of the water in materials such as soils. It has been established experimentally that among the common elements, hydrogen is most effective in slowing down neutrons. Hence, if fast neutrons are projected into a moist material, a slowing down of neutrons takes place, depending upon the quantity of hydrogen present, which in turn is proportional to the moisture content. Holmes [78] has derived a linear relationship between slow-neutron density and moisture content.

Due to the large collisional cross section for hydrogen the slowing-down length for hydrogen will be very small compared to that of other common soil elements. Therefore, if a counter to detect slow neutrons is placed near a source of fast neutrons in soil, the percentage of counts registered will be a function largely of the amount of hydrogen (water) present in the soil. Other elements will have comparatively very little effect. The counter, as stated, should be near the source. If the counter is placed far from the source, the counting rate will be smaller for hydrogen than that for other elements. It is now considered best practice in soil moisture measuring experiments to place the neutron counter as close to the fast-neutron source as possible.

2.3 Instrumentation

Belcher et al. [71] and Spinks et al. [79] demonstrated that it was practicable to determine soil moisture by using the neutron-scattering method and developed experimental equipment for this purpose. Consequently, Gardner and Kirkham [80], Sharpe [81],

Van Bavel and co-workers [82], Gueron [83], and Knight and Wright [84] elaborated the technique of measurements and interpretation of the data obtained. The instrumentation required for measuring moisture content of soils and similar materials by means of the neutron-scattering method consists of four main units: (1) probes containing a source of fast neutrons, (2) a detector for slow neutrons, (3) an instrument to determine the count rate from the detecting device, and (4) a suitable standard to verify the performance of the equipment.

2.3.1 Probes and Fast-Neutron Sources. Many types of geometry have been employed in the design of moisture probes. Some of these have been summarized by Van Bavel and co-workers [82]. Such studies have shown that the geometry employed in the design of the neutron probe is very important since the operational characteristics of a probe depend greatly on this factor. Sharpe [81] considered that the best geometry of source to counter was to have the source 5 cm below the bottom of the counting tube and on the same axis. Holmes [78], however, found it preferable to place the source in the midplane of the sensitive volume of the counting tube and as close to it as possible. Two types of probes, known as the surface type and the depth or insertion type (Figs. 7.30 and 7.31), respectively, are usually employed. The insertion type has a counting geometry of 4 in., while the surface type is limited to a counting geometry of 2 in. Graphite is used as a reflector in surface-type probes. The insertion-type probe head is lowered into a 2-in. diameter vertical hole in the soil by means of an aluminum probe cylinder for the measurement of moisture content at different depths, whereas the surface-type probe is placed on the surface of the soil or concrete. Several fast-neutron sources have been devised, but only a few have been found practical in connection with neutron moisture measurement. All of these are mixtures of alpha emitters and beryllium. It has been shown by Van Bavel [85] that for many practical purposes and for the usual design of moisture detectors, sources from 1 to 2 mCi in strength are sufficient. Radium-beryllium sources as ordinarily

2 NEUTRON SCATTERING   475

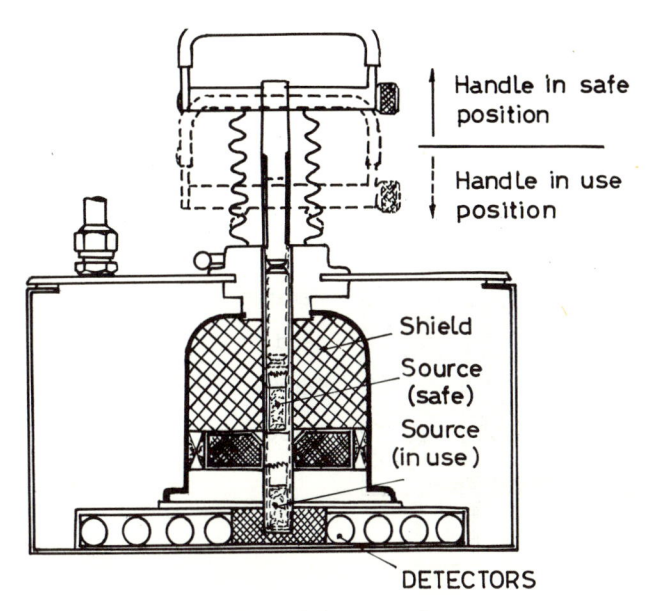

FIG. 7.30. Neutron surface moisture probe.

available yield 18,000 neutrons/sec and per mCi of radium. Gardner and Kirkham [80] have devised a compact unit containing a mixture of polonium and beryllium (contained in a metal cylinder 17 mm in length) as a source of fast neutrons. The mixture has a half-life of 140 days.

2.3.2 <u>Methods of Detection</u>. Many possibilities for the detection of slow neutrons have been discussed by Curtiss [86] and Allen [87]. Lane et al. [88] used the foil-activation method for detecting slow neutrons for moisture measurement purposes in which together with a fast-neutron source a foil of indium was inserted into the soil. The fast neutrons emitted by the neutron source lose their energy by collision with the hydrogen atoms in the water molecules in the soil, and become slow neutrons which are absorbed by the stable indium, which is made radioactive. Subsequently this foil is removed and its activity is determined. In the method developed by Belcher et al. [77] the foil was positioned around a Geiger counter

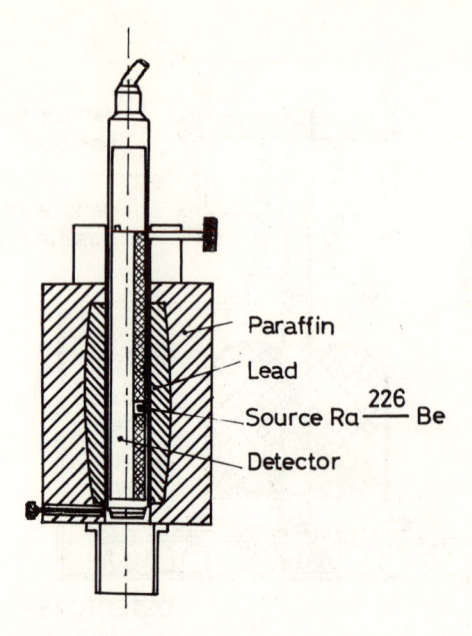

FIG. 7.31. Neutron depth moisture probe.

which detected the induced radioactivity. In later work, foil counting was not found practical because of the time required for the radioactivity to subside before a new measurement could be made. Impurities in the foil and various radioisotopes produced by continued exposure to the neutron flux also create problems. Some researchers have used soil scintillators together with photomultipliers for the purpose of detecting slow neutrons. However, the use of scintillation techniques appears to be limited by the demands of stability required of field equipment, and also because of the insufficiently selective response of scintillators to neutrons in the presence of a strong gamma field.

The method which is presently being used by a large number of investigators for detecting slow neutrons in soils makes use of a gas-filled BH_3 counter or a B^{10}-lined counter. Although construction and filling details differ, most of these counters have in common the fact that they operate at voltages between 1200 and 1400 V and that they produce neutron pulses of the order of magnitude of 1 mV. Thus it is generally necessary to have an impedance converter located at the counting tube to permit counting of pulses at some distance from the detecting device. The drawback of the BF_3 counter is that, in order to give a sufficiently high counting rate, it must occupy a sizable volume. Thus, moisture detectors that use BF_3 tubes are relatively bulky and require a large hole or access pipe to locate the device at the desired position.

A boron trifluoride slow-neutron counter is used to measure the slow-neutron density. This counter is cylindrical with a diameter of 5 cm and a length of 35.5 cm, and is filled to a pressure of 40 cm. The counter is placed immediately on top of and is maintained concentric with the source of fast neutrons. The counter is operated at 3500 V. This high voltage is derived from a high-voltage power supply unit with a maximum output of 4000 V dc. The pulses from the counter are fed through a Bell-Jordan linear amplifier into a count recorder.

Application of the neutron moisture meter have been extended to field problems in which measurements are required to be made by placing the equipment on the surface of the soil and concrete. Unlike the earlier neutron meters, which had their probes immersed inside the wet material, the probe in this case lies on the surface of the material. This tends to reduce the volume that is effective in slowing down neutrons, and hence makes the instrument less sensitive. To overcome this deficiency a thick cast-iron U-shaped reflector was placed around the detector, i.e., boron trifluoride (BF_3), in order to reflect some of the neutrons that otherwise would have escaped. By this device neutron count is increased two to three times. It is found that improved boron trifluoride counters are better suited for measuring slow neutrons directly in both soils and concrete.

2.3.3 <u>Count Rate Meters</u>. The device that is used to determine the count rate must be capable of three things: First, it must be able to handle the very large number of gamma and neutron pulses that are coming in without saturation or pile up in the amplifiers. Second, it must be able to discriminate, by a suitable input sensitivity regulation, between the gamma-induced and the neutron-induced pulses. Finally, the device should be able to determine the neutron-induced count rate without appreciable coincidence loss. Generally, slow-neutron count rates as determined with the usual equipment range up to 25,000 counts/min. Most laboratory-type equipment used for counting radioactivity-induced voltage pulses can easily handle the indicated requirements. However, the neutron method is inherently a field method and the measurement or count rate must be made with a device that is portable and compact and yet has all the required features listed above. The count rate, usually expressed as counts per minute, may be found directly with a rate meter or indirectly by a combination of a scaler and a timer. In principle, there is no difference between these two methods, the inherent precision in the case of a rate meter being determined by the readability and accuracy of an indicating meter, and in the case of a scaler by the accuracy of a timer. In both cases, however, the count rate as determined is subject to random statistical fluctuations caused by the random decay of the radium. Well-constructed rate meters and scalers are capable of obtaining a precision that is commensurate with the random fluctuations of the count rate and with the accuracy with which a calibration relation can be ascertained.

For evaluating counting performance in a moderating medium, a number of different standards have been proposed. Some of these consist of a limited volume of water or a limited volume of paraffin. Limited volumes of a moderating substance have the advantage of portability. It is questionable whether the use of small volume is justified because small changes in the relative position of probe and standard might affect the neutron count rate. Furthermore, considerable evidence indicates that paraffin standards are subject to changes due to change in ambient temperature. Most investigators now agree that a water standard close to infinite size is the preferable method of standardizing the equipment. The possible drawback is that such a standard is rather heavy and bulky because it would have to contain approximately 200 liters of water. Neutron meter standards have also been proposed that would correspond to varying soil moisture contents.

2.4 Portable Neutron Soil Moisture Meters for Field Operations

The neutron method for measuring moisture content is primarily a field method although instances of its use in greenhouses are found. For those who wish to use the neutron-scattering method of measuring moisture in the soil in the field, a portable instrument is required which needs as few manipulative controls as possible. A number of field instruments have been described in the literature, the first being that of Van Bavel and co-workers [82]. The sensitivity and the stability of this instrument were found to be sufficiently good for it to have much appeal to the users. Another such portable apparatus has been described by Stone et al. [89]. This is a portable proportional counting apparatus, which uses dekatron tubes in the scaler section of the unit and employs ^{10}B-enriched boron-lined counter tubes, requiring an HT supply which is obtained from dry cell batteries.

A portable neutron soil moisture meter similar to that of Stone and co-workers [89] and suitable for field use has been developed by Holmes and Turner [90]. Its power supply is a 6-V accumulator from which it draws current during operation. The total counts recorded are displayed on dekatron tubes, and the overall resolving time of the apparatus is about 120 sec. Using a 5-mCi radium-beryllium neutron source and a 12EB-40 slow-neutron detector tube, the counting rate with the probe in water is 24,000 counts/min. The calibration curve with respect to soil water content is approximately linear. Burn [91] has developed a portable neutron moisture meter for measuring moisture content changes in natural soils.

In this apparatus (Fig. 7.32) a depth probe was constructed

VII. NUCLEAR METHODS AND TECHNIQUES

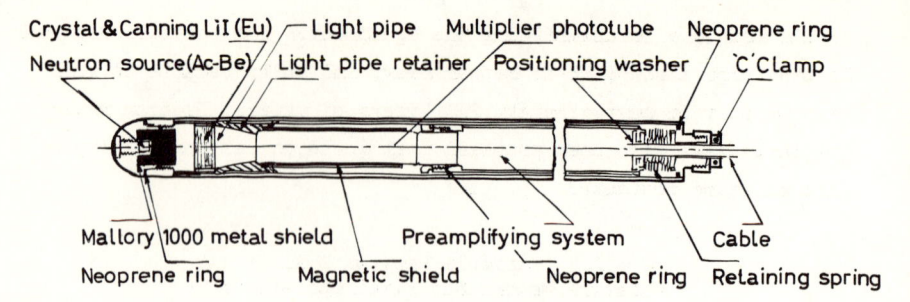

FIG. 7.32. Cross section of neutron moisture meter probe.

using a scintillation type of detector for use with a portable battery-operated scaler. The probe was designed with a scintillation detector and its geometrical arrangement was dictated by the desire to have it slip inside an aluminum access tube with an outside diameter of 1 1/2 in. and a wall thickness of 1/16 in. A source of actinium and beryllium emitting 10^5 neutrons/sec is located at the lower end of the probe and separated from the ^{6}LiK scintillation crystal by a shield of alloy of a specific gravity of 16.9. A Lucite light pipe funnels the light activity from the crystal to the window of the photomultiplier tube, and this is followed by a preamplifier which produces the signals that drive the battery-operated scaler.

Two assumptions are made in the design of the neutron meter.

1. All hydrogen atoms detected are chemically bonded to oxygen atoms in the form of water.
2. No other process is involved except the mechanical one of elastic collisions with neutrons emitted from a constant source.

It seemed a simple matter to conform to these basic assumptions, and it was considered, with some justification, that a neutron moisture meter, once calibrated, could be used in different soil types. However, this aspect has been further studied and laboratory and field calibrations have been carried out to obtain more accurate results.

2 NEUTRON SCATTERING

Recently Rozsa and Toth [92] have developed a portable neutron-scattering moisture meter and applied it for continuous measurement of moisture content of coal feeds, in ceramic industry, in ore processing, and in the sand mills of foundries. Toth and Pazmandi [93] have applied a neutron moisture meter for continuous monitoring of moisture content in a coal drier plant in the range 6 to 30% with an accuracy of ±1%. They have employed the most suitable geometry configurations. Neutron moisture gauges and radioisotope instruments have been described in the literature [94, 95].

2.5 Commercial Instruments

Besides the experimental neutron-scattering equipment described above, a few commercial instruments have been developed and are marketed. These are (1) Moisture and Density Analyzer developed by Nuclear Enterprises (GB) Ltd., Scotland and (2) Qualicon 507 Bulk Moisture Gauge, developed by Nuclear Chicago, Illinois. The constructional and operating features of these instruments are described in the manufacturer's literature, and the reader is referred to them.

2.6 Calibration of the Neutron-Scattering Analyzer

2.6.1 Introduction. As it is not possible to compute accurately the relation between slow-neutron counting rates and moisture content, it is necessary to obtain this experimentally. There are significant disturbing effects related to the chemical composition and the density of the soil that render the idea of a universal calibration relationship impracticable. The method of measuring water content of soil by the neutron-scattering method should therefore be supplemented with convenient techniques for calibration. The calibration of the instruments, expressed as counting rate vs water content, has been attempted empirically by measuring the counting rate in samples of known water content. It is, of course, important that a sufficient amount of the sample be taken to represent an infinite medium, and the calibration curves obtained by a number of researchers [71, 82, 79] satisfy this requirement. They have shown too that the calibration is unaffected by the nature of the material, sand or soil, giving points which belong to the same curve. This implies that the water contained in the soil contributes very largely to the slowing down and diffusion of the neutrons and that to a certain degree of accuracy, all other constituents may be neglected when considering the physical process.

2.6.2 <u>Laboratory Calibration</u>. Of greater usefulness and accuracy is a calibration obtained with prepared homogeneous volumes of soil set up in the laboratory. In the preparation of such standards it is necessary that they be of sufficient size. Van Bavel et al. [82] showed that a 1-m^3 sample is about the minimum required for a count rate independent of the volume. This figure applies to low moisture contents and requirements would not be that high at moisture contents, say, over 0.20 volume fraction. The sample should be as homogeneous as possible with regard to both the density and moisture content, and the measurement of the moisture content by volume should be made on the sample in its entirety. However, if this is not possible, large subsamples should be used. With the aid of this technique, well-defined relations between count rate and moisture content can be obtained, as shown by Marais and Smit [96] and Lane et al. [88]. It was pointed out by them that besides moisture content, density should also be carefully controlled in calibration procedures.

The neutron-scattering instrument was calibrated by Burn [91] in the laboratory by preparing samples in 55-gal steel drums which had previously been found to be of adequate size for this purpose. Readings were obtained with the probe positioned at every inch or two of depth, and only those values that were unaffected by the upper and lower limits of the sample were averaged for making the calibration curve. All actual values of the readings were related to readings obtained with the probe positioned in a wax standard. The values of these ratios were used in the construction of the laboratory calibration curve (Fig. 7.33). McGuinness et al. [97] evolved calibration procedures by simulation for which mixtures of

2 NEUTRON SCATTERING 483

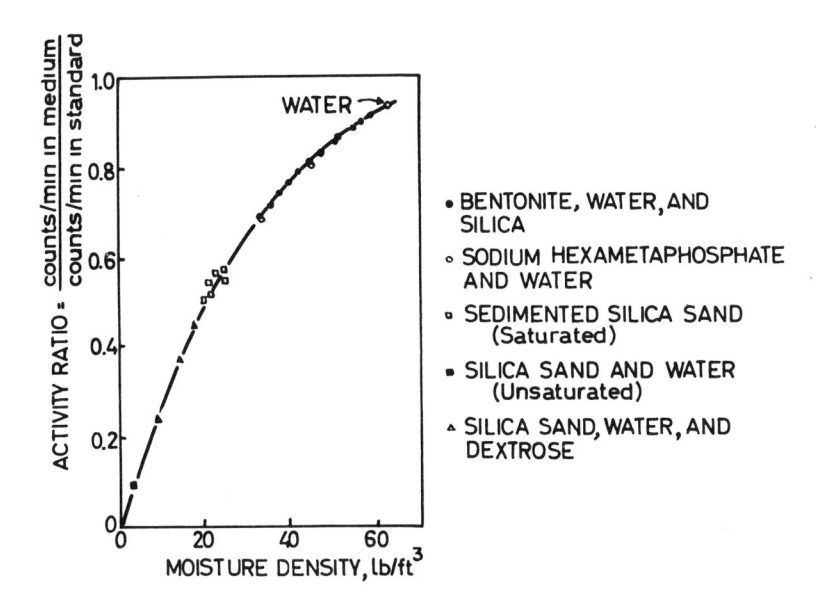

FIG. 7.33. Laboratory calibration curve of neutron moisture meter.

alum and sand in large barrels were used to correspond to certain known moisture contents. Standards of paraffin and sand were proposed by Hauser [98] and liquid standards containing either boric acid or cadmium chloride were investigated by Van Bavel et al. [82]. The most easily constructed standards are probably boric acid solutions. However, they are limited to a useful range of about 8 to 35% moisture content by volume. Solid standards involve more labor in construction, but are also more permanent. The use of simulating standards can only be made when used in relation to a known calibration relationship in soil; they cannot take the place of an actual calibration. However, they are useful in verifying easily the behavior of the neutron moisture meter on a continuing basis.

2.6.3 Field Calibration. The use of neutron moisture meters is usually based on field calibration, that is, a relationship between counting rate and moisture content obtained by installing access tubes in natural soils. Samples of the soil at the depth of insertion of the detecting device are taken. This procedure would be without objection if soils were homogeneous and if unbiased samples of the volumetric moisture content were easily obtained. Unfortunately, both conditions are rarely met. Thus, the values for the moisture content found by direct sampling in a medium that is not expressly prepared for the purpose often have large uncertainties or errors. A calibration curve based on such data necessarily carries this uncertainty with it. It is therefore desirable to specify the method of calibration while giving data of moisture measurement.

As the laboratory calibration does not give correct values of moisture contents of soils when applied in field operations, field calibration was carried out by Burn [91]. Samples of high sensitive clay from deep excavations were obtained and thoroughly remolded until they could be made to flow easily into a container by means of a small vibrator. Three samples at different water contents were prepared. Readings of neutron activity in the media compared with that in the wax standard were determined in the same manner as was used to establish the calibration curve. Moisture contents were determined by oven-drying the samples and calculating the densities. The results obtained fell well below those obtained in the laboratory. Further correlative values of neutron activity vs moisture density were found by obtaining samples from vertical bore holes in the vicinity of a 12-ft deep access tube. These bore holes were all located no further than 3 ft and no closer than 1 ft from the access tube. Samples and readings were taken on the same day periodically during the summer months as the soil at this test site gradually dried.

In plotting the calibration curve great importance was given to the data obtained in the laboratory and to those determined for the test trench samples [91]. It was found that a natural variation in water content exists in the soil; samples from auger borings only 3 1/2 ft apart showed differences as large as 10% for the same depths. He also compared [91] the laboratory curve (Fig. 7.33) with the field calibration curve (Fig. 7.34) and showed that there was a difference between the two. The two curves appear to be parallel with a difference in activity ratio of 11%.

2 NEUTRON SCATTERING 485

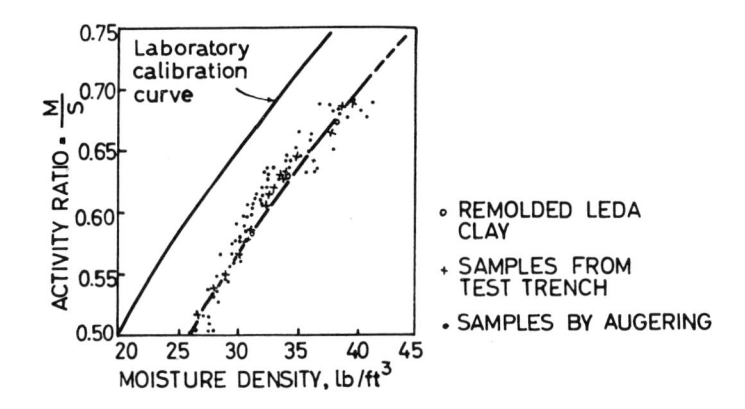

FIG. 7.34. Field calibration curve for neutron moisture meter.

In a typical field experiment for calibration described by Lane et al. [88], a series of holes of 6-ft depth and 2-in. diameter were drilled at various levels on the banks of the South Saskatchewan River to get a variety of soil types, densities, and moisture contents. The soil types encountered in these holes ranged from sandy silts to medium plastic alluvial clays. The holes were drilled with a 2-in. auger and lined with 2-in. diameter aluminum pipe (0.050 in. thick). Three readings for moisture content at each depth were averaged to give a mean value. In Fig. 7.35 is shown the average moisture content as a function of the counts per minute. The density used for this purpose was the average density in the same region determined with the use of standard oil displacement method and measuring volumes. A linear relationship is found to exist between counts per minute and pounds of water per cubic foot. The equation for this line is

$$x = 0.02y - 2.5 \qquad (7.14)$$

where x represents pounds of water per cubic foot of soil, and y represents counts per minute.

The readings obtained with the neutron-moderating moisture meter reflect the moisture per unit volume of soil. Conversion of meter

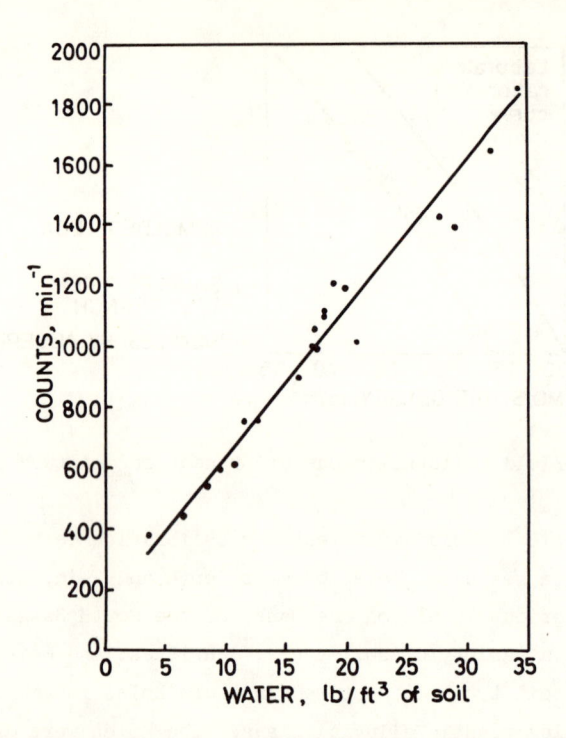

FIG. 7.35. Calibration curve for moisture meter using a 50-mCi radium-beryllium source.

reading to percentage of dry weight is easily made for comparison with results of oven drying:

$$W = \frac{W_v}{Y - W_v/100} \qquad (7.15)$$

where W is the classical moisture content of the soil defined as the ratio of the weight of water present in the soil to the dry weight of the solid soil particle; W_v is the volume moisture content of the soil; and Y is the wet density of the soil.

The use of gamma-ray density meters permits accurate density measurements on all organic or inorganic materials. The determination of soil density by the nuclear method is based on the known

2 NEUTRON SCATTERING

interaction of gamma rays and the orbital electrons of atoms. Since the density probes give the wet density Y_h of the examined soil, the dry density Y_s is obtained by merely subtracting the volume moisture content as determined with the moisture probes.

For the comparison of the neutron-scattering method with the standard oven-drying method the samples of the soil were taken by Lane et al. [88] every 6 in. during excavation of the holes. Density variations at each hole site were determined from an auxiliary 4-in. hole about 1 ft away, using the standard oil displacement method of measuring volumes. Densities were determined for consecutive 6-in. layers. Two or three readings for moisture content of each depth were averaged to give a mean value.

This is plotted against the average measured moisture content in the bed 6 in. above and below the source, since the zone of influences of the source is primarily a sphere of about 6-in. radius. The comparison of neutron and gamma-ray meter with actual oven-drying values is shown in Fig. 7.36 in the case of a vertical hole.

In order to study the effects of flooding on the comparative efficiency of the neutron moisture meter Lane et al. [88] carried out a field test which consisted of drilling several 2-in. holes in a 12-ft^2 area to a depth of 10 ft. Moisture content determinations were made by oven drying soil samples taken during the drilling of the test holes, to serve as a check on neutron meter readings. Prior to flooding, a series of moisture content and density determinations were made at 6-in. intervals of depth using the neutron meter and the previously obtained calibration curves. The area was then completely flooded and allowed to stand for 12 hr, after which moisture content determinations were again made with the neutron meter. This procedure was prepared three times. At the conclusion of flooding, further soil samples were obtained by drilling holes close to the original cased holes. Water content determinations were run on these in the conventional way with the last set obtained with the neutron meter. The results of these two comparisons for

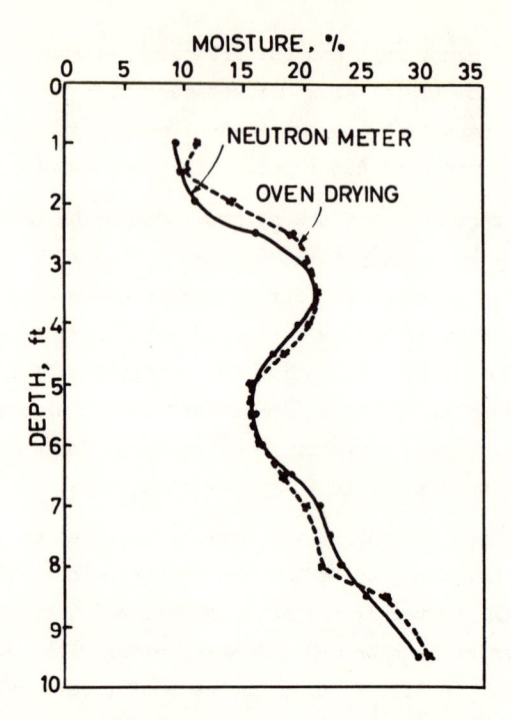

FIG. 7.36. Moisture profile comparison between standard oven-drying method and neutron meter.

one typical hole are shown in Fig. 7.37. These indicate that the neutron meter can be used to detect moisture content variation in a mass of flooded soil.

All determinations agreed within 3% moisture and most were within 2% moisture or less in the range 0 to 100% water content. Some of the soils, however, gave very different values from those obtained by the oven-drying method. This was attributed to the presence of large amounts of organic and inorganic materials which would upset the calibration curve. In the earlier development of the neutron-scattering method by Belcher et al. [71], Gardner and Kirkham [80], and Van Bavel et al. [82], indications were obtained that a universal calibration relation might hold. Later on it was shown by Holmes and Jenkinson [99], Mortier and De Boodt [100], and in particular by Marais and Smit [96] that only in the first approximation can a universal calibration be applicable.

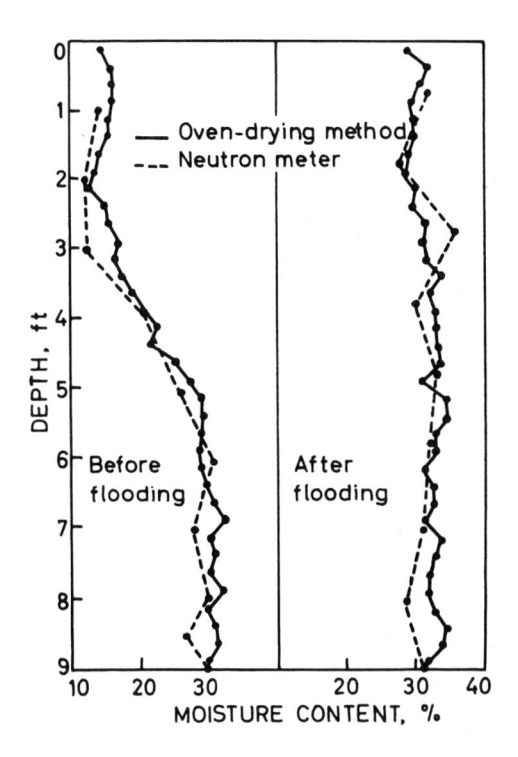

FIG. 7.37. Moisture profile comparison between standard and neutron methods for a field flooding test.

Another explanation of the variation of the calibration curve is the effect of the dry density of different types of soils on neutron count rate. This interpretation is mainly based upon the effect of nonwater hydrogen that would be present in more-or-less concentrated fashion, depending on the bulk or dry density of the soil material. However, the effect of other soil elements besides hydrogen may be involved. At any rate, the bulk density of the soil has a measurable and predictable effect upon the calibration.

The counting rate in water is a convenient normalizing measurement to be used to correct field readings for changes in the apparatus as well as to convert them to a standard level of counting rate. It may also be used to check the apparatus for proper functioning according to the well-known method of determining the standard deviation first from a number of individual counts, and then independently from the total number of counts recorded.

The dependence of counting rate on the soil water content is measured for a range of water contents and materials, and the resulting calibration curve is drawn. In order to eliminate variation from one instrument to another, the calibration curve has been referred to a standard count rate of 22,000 counts/min with the probe in the polythene tube in water. Each measurement is adjusted for the following variables: (1) background counting rate, (2) resolving time of the apparatus, and (3) normalizing counting rate in water. If these three adjustments are made to the observed counting rate, then the calibration curve should be applicable to all instruments. The calibration curve refers to the probe being placed far enough below the surface of the soil for the medium to be effectively infinite; that is, no appreciable number of neutrons must escape through the soil boundary.

It is fortuitous that different soil types appear to give approximately the same calibration curve. Clay materials which retain a large amount of (equivalent) water at the oven-drying temperature usually also contain abundances of elements such as boron and other neutron absorbers that are large compared with the abundances existing in sands or lighter textured soils. It seems likely that there is positive correlation between the amount of neutron absorbers and the amount of loss-on-ignition water possessed by soils, leading evidently to a canceling of their influence on the calibration curve when the latter has the water content determined on the oven-dry weight basis. Figure 7.38 shows the counting rate vs moisture content per unit volume for the following five soils: (1) Clarian, (2) Monona, (3) O'Neil, (4) Putnam, and (5) Wabash, as investigated by Gardner and Kirkham [80]. A single curve can be drawn to cover the whole moisture range from oven dryness to saturation for all the five soils. However, if greater accuracy is desired separate calibration curves for each soil can be drawn as suggested by Holmes [78] who studied some mineral soils and found that their calibration

2 NEUTRON SCATTERING

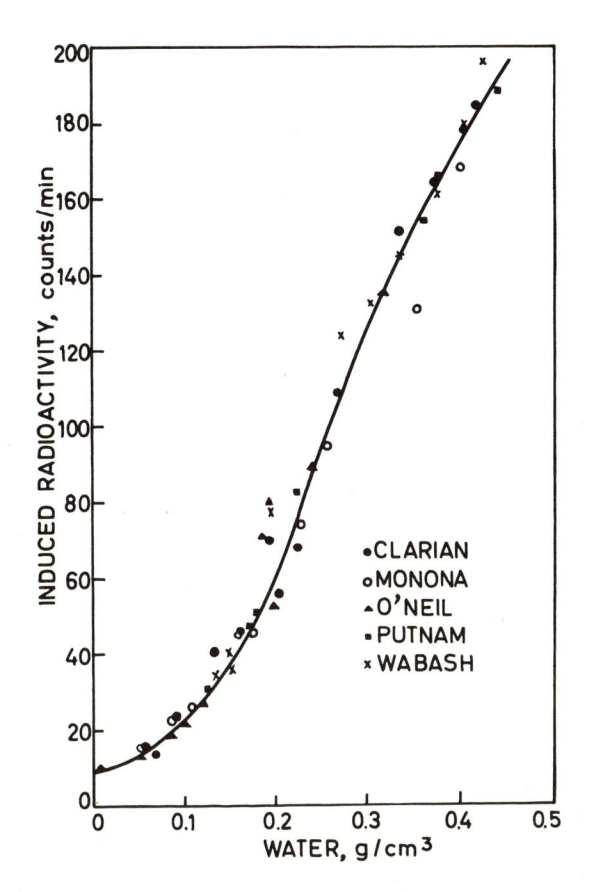

FIG. 7.38. Counting rate of slow neutrons as a function of moisture percentage for several soils.

curves could be best represented separately. Whether a single calibration curve can be used for a number of soils or separate curves should be drawn for each soil depends on the accuracy desired.

2.7 Techniques for Using the Neutron Moisture Meter in the Field

In the practice of soil engineering there is a definite relationship between the maximum density to which a soil can be compacted, the amount of energy applied in the compaction process, and the moisture content of the soil during the compaction. The civil engineer and soil scientists are therefore very much interested in the measurement of moisture content of the soil in the fields. Huet [101] has obtained comparative data of moisture content and dry density using surface and depth measurements technique on a subgrade silty sand. It is interesting to compare the observed divergence between the averages of two sets of moisture content determinations, one of the sets being made by the radioactive method and the other by the oven-drying method. It was observed by Huet [101] that by using the two techniques a mean difference in percentage of the dry weight of approximately 1% exists between the results obtained by the radioactive and the oven-drying methods.

In order to use the neutron moisture meter in the field for depth measurement a suitably lined access hole for the probe must be provided. For this purpose it is preferable to dig a hole of the right diameter and insert a snug-fitting lining. Stolzy and Cahoon [102] used a polyvinyl chloride plastic tube as a lining and found that it had the effect of lowering the counting rate, as compared with the counting rate obtained with an aluminum tube lining, because of the chlorine content of the polyvinyl chloride. Holmes and Jenkinson [99] have used either aluminum as a lining, which has no measurable influence on the counting rate, or polythene tubing, which enhances the counting rate.

However there is no significant difference between the water contents as measured in the aluminum- or polythene-lined holes, and therefore either aluminum or polythene is suitable as a lining. It is important, however, that the access hole diameter be uniform. It may be calculated that the magnitude of soil water content determined from a calibration curve might be in error by a value ranging from 0.008 to 0.002 g/cm^3. However, it is found that the calibration suffers a parallel shift if the polythene wall thickness varies. The measurement of changes in water content of the soil, therefore, is not likely to be affected. The probe should be easily lowered and raised in the access hole. Acentric placement of the probe could lead to a maximum error of about 3% in the counting rate. Precaution should be taken to ensure that during normalization with an access tube in water the probe is centered correctly.

It may be pointed out that this technique of measuring moisture content of soils at different depths will not be suitable for measuring the moisture content at the surface as the distribution of the moisture content, i.e., the profile of the moisture variation and distribution along the depth of the soil varies in an unknown manner. This fact was realized by a number of investigators in the beginning of the development of the neutron moisture meter, and two types of probes were developed, one of which was known as the surface moisture probe and the other as the depth moisture probe, both of which have been described earlier. In the depth measurement the detecting device is lowered in the soil by means of an access tube or pipe made of a suitable material as described above. Access pipes made of aluminum, polyethylene, and steel have been used. Noncorrosive materials that are reasonably rigid and do not contain any slow-neutron-absorbing elements can be used. The access tube and its dimensions are part of the geometry which must be held constant throughout all measurements, and a pertinent calibration must be made. In the surface moisture measurement the detector can merely be laid on the surface. This method was first employed by Van Bavel et al. [103]. However, in earlier work, Belcher et al. [71] suggested that the detector be enveloped in a paraffin shield in order to obtain a greater efficiency and sensitivity. A further report on the utility of a hydrogenous shield for surface measurements is given by Van Bavel [85]. In this report, it was also demonstrated that surface measurements are inherently more sensitive to the disturbing effects of inhomogeneity with regard to moisture content. Accordingly and in comparison with the depth measurement, surface measurements of moisture content by the neutron method are often only approximately correct.

2.8 Applications of the Neutron-Scattering Method

The neutron-scattering method of moisture measurement was developed primarily for the determination of moisture content of soils at different depths and on the surface, as other known methods were not adequate for this purpose. The applications of this method for the determination of the moisture content of soils, sands, and clay minerals have been described in Chapter XII. However, typical applications are discussed to illustrate the scope of the utility of this new technique for solving some of the complex problems of measurement and control of moisture.

The applications of this technique for the measurement of moisture content of materials other than soils are rather limited. Possibilities exist, however, with regard to materials that are predominantly not hydrogenous except for their water content. Examples are moist foundry sand and the moisture content of ores before or during processing. The neutron method, being a nondestructive method, does not have to be a part of the process treatment itself but can be used contiguous to a conveyor or hopper.

A specific application is the use of the neutron method to measure the water content of snow. A report on this subject was recently given by Anderson et al. [104]. At this moment it remains to be seen whether the neutron method can take the place of the conventional snow-gauging methods.

In many industrial applications, knowledge of the moisture content of hydrogenous materials is of the greatest interest. A few examples are grains, plant or seed pulses of various kinds, chemicals, and others. The presence of nonwater hydrogen in these materials means that a considerable background problem exists. Also, in many of these materials the bulk density depends on the moisture content itself, and thus the concentration of the hydrogen per unit volume would not be related simply to the water content. Measurements that were made by Van Bavel [105] in grains showed that, actually, the

3 CONCLUSION

neutron density in dry grain was greater than in moist grain because the bulk density of moist grain was greater, thus offsetting the greater moisture content on a weight basis. Nevertheless, the method responded to differences in moisture content and this principle could possibly be put to good use.

By means of the neutron method, it is possible to distinguish between oil and brine. Again, in view of the varying and unknown compositions of brines and of the porosity of rocks, the neutron method is not a quantitative indicator of the composition of deep strata but only an indication. It must be used in connection with other geophysical exploration methods to draw the correct inferences.

Miyashita [106] has employed the nuclear-scattering method for determining the moisture content of raw materials required for iron-making processes. These materials were coke and iron ore for blast furnace charge. It was found by him that the neutron moisture meter can be used not only to measure the moisture content of these materials but also to control the moisture of their contents. Changes ordinarily occurring in the chemical composition and the grain size distribution of materials do not matter significantly, while changes of the density are serious. It is therefore desirable to keep the density constant or apply density correction.

Squires [107] has developed a nuclear method for accurately measuring traces of light water in heavy water. In his method the transmission of slow neutron through a sample of a mixture of light and heavy water is compared with that through a standard sample. The method gives an accuracy of 0.006% in the heavy water content after 3 hr of counting.

CONCLUSION

Most of the research work on the neutron-scattering method for moisture measurement has been carried out on the measurement of moisture content of soils and sands and similar granular materials.

However, attempts are being made to extend the application of this technique to materials such as ores, coal, and coke for blast furnace charge. Special neutron moisture meters have been developed for measuring moisture content of cornstarch and similar foodstuffs. At present, the application of the method is widespread in the United States, particularly in the field of agriculture, water resources research, forestry, and more recently the construction industry. The chief advantages of this method are accuracy and simplicity. No preliminary treatment of the sample is necessary, and the neutron measurements can be carried out by an unskilled operator. The method can be adapted for continual monitoring supply of a heavy water.

However, the cost and weight of equipment and the lack of proper training of operators and complete reliability of commercially available components are inhibiting a more rapid acceptance of the method; only with time are these difficulties being overcome. The health hazard associated with the use of radioactive materials does not seem to have prohibited the application in any appreciable degree. Use of this method has also been reported from the United Kingdom and several other countries of Europe and the Soviet Union. The Atomic Energy Commission in India has also developed an experimental neutron moisture meter, which is being used on laboratory scale for the measurement of moisture content of soils and similar hygroscopic materials. Other reports of its applications, particularly in agricultural research, have come from South Africa and Australia.

One of the important applications of the neutron meter has been in the study of foundation movements of light buildings on highly plastic clays, a method of detecting moisture variations in the underlying clay without disturbing the original equilibrium conditions. In order to extend the application of the neutron moisture meter to materials other than soils (where it has special advantages over other methods), it is necessary to reduce the most important source of error, i.e., the variability of the calibration relation. Even under carefully controlled laboratory conditions in which the same material is prepared at identical density, the measurement of its moisture content is still subject to an undesirably high error, resulting in values that are seldom more closely defined than 0.3 to 0.5% moisture by volume. A publication by Hewlett et al. [108] gives a further discussion of this aspect.

Berke and Papp [109] have designed a nuclear moisture meter and successfully applied it for in situ measurement of a sand soil moisture over prolonged periods of time. The instrument was calibrated in the laboratory by thermogravimetric method and gave high accuracy both in soils of low moisture content such as sand soils and with the higher moisture contents of biphase system.

According to calculations, the volume of water considered to be the soil moisture amounts to only 0.005% of the entire water supply of the earth; however, due to its importance, ever greater attention is being paid to its investigation. Knowledge of soil moisture and of its changes is of particular significance for the solution of hydrological and of hydrometeorological problems.

The hydrological and hydrometeorological parameters necessary for describing the circulation of water are being systematically measured. Special application is being made for investigating the moisture content of the soil layer above the ground water table, the results being indispensable for the solution of other theoretical or practical problems.

REFERENCES

1. E. R. Andrew, *Nuclear Magnetic Resonance*, Cambridge Univ. Press, New York, 1955.

2. N. F. Ramsey, *Nuclear Moments*, Wiley, New York, 1953.

3. H. S. Gutowsky, *Physical Methods in Chemical Analysis*, vol. III, Academic, New York, 1956, p. 304.

4. G. E. Pake, Magnetic Resonance, *Scientific American*, 1, 1958.

5. J. A. Pople, W. G. Schneider, and H. J. Bernstein, *High Resolution Nuclear Magnetic Resonance*, McGraw-Hill, New York, 1959.

6. J. D. Roberts, Nuclear Magnetic Resonance, McGraw-Hill, New York, 1959.

7. W. O. Statton, J. Polym. Sci., 3, 3-8 (1963).

8. P. L. Corio, S. L. Smith, and J. R. Wasson, Nuclear Magnetic Resonance Spectrometry, Anal. Chem. Annual Reviews, 44, 407R (April 1972).

9. R. Lynden-Bell and R. K. Harris, Nuclear Magnetic Resonance Spectroscopy, Appleton Century-Crofts, New York, 1971.

10. P. Diehl, E. Fluck, and R. Kosfeld, eds., NMR — Basic Principles and Progress, vols. I and II, Springer-Verlag, New York, 1970.

11. B. I. Ionin and B. A. Ershov, NMR Spectroscopy in Organic Chemistry, 2d ed., Plenum, New York, 1970.

12. L. M. Jackman and S. Sternhell, Applications of Nuclear Magnetic Resonance Spectroscopy in Organic Chemistry, 2d ed., Pergamon, New York, 1969.

13. W. W. Pandler, Nuclear Magnetic Resonance, Allyn and Bacon, Boston, Mass., 1971.

14. R. T. Schumacher, Introduction to Magnetic Resonance, W. A. Benjamin, New York, 1970.

15. H. Strehlow, Nuclear Magnetic Resonance and Chemical Structure, 2d ed., Steinkopff, Darmstadt, Germany, 1968.

16. R. J. Abraham, Analysis of High Resolution NMR Spectra, Elsevier, New York, 1971.

17. C. H. Gungan and J. R. Van Wazer, Compilation of Reported NMR Chemical Shifts, 1951 to Mid-1967, Wiley-Interscience, New York, 1970.

18. (a) E. M. Purcell, R. V. Pound, and N. Bloembergen, Phys. Rev., 70, 986 (1946).

    (b) E. M. Purcell, H. C. Torrey, and R. V. Pound, Phys. Rev., 69, 37 (1946).

19. (a) F. Bloch, Phys. Rev., 70, 460 (1946).

    (b) F. Bloch, W. W. Hansen, and M. E. Packard, Phys. Rev., 69, 127 (1946).

20. W. D. Knight, Phys. Rev., 76, 1259 (1949).

REFERENCES

21. T. F. Conway, R. F. Cohee, and R. J. Smith, Food Eng., 29, 81 (1957); Mfg. Confectioners, 27, 27 (1957); Electronics, 31, 51 (1958).

22. T. M. Shaw, R. H. Elsken, and C. H. Kunsman, J. Assoc. Office Agr. Chem., 36, 1070 (1953).

23. H. Rubin, Inst. Soc. Amer., 5, 64 (1958).

24. J. B. Leane, R. E. Richards, and T. P. Schaefer, J. Sci. Instrum., 36, 230-33 (1959).

25. N. E. Bloembergen, M. Purcell, and R. V. Pound, Phys. Rev., 73, 679 (1948).

26. N. Bloembergen, Nuclear Magnetic Relaxation, Nijhoff, The Hague, 1948.

27. R. H. Dicke, Rev. Sci. Instrum., 17, 268 (1946).

28. F. Bloch, W. W. Hansen, and M. E. Packard, Phys. Rev., 70, 474 (1946).

29. H. C. Torrey, Phys. Rev., 76, 1059 (1949).

30. E. L. Hahn, Phys. Rev., 80, 580 (1950).

31. J. T. Arnold, S. S. Dharmatti, and M. E. Packard, J. Chem. Phys., 19, 507 (1951).

32. L. A. Meacham, Proc. IRE, 26, 1278 (1938).

33. H. Wallman, A. B. MacNee, and C. P. Gadsden, Proc. IRE, 36, 497 (1948).

34. M. E. Packard and J. T. Arnold, Phys. Rev., 83, 210A (1951).

35. J. T. Arnold, Phys. Rev., 102, 136 (1956).

36. M. G. Kozlov and L. A. Paneleava, Chem. Abstr., 7439 (1964).

37. J. R. Zimmerman and M. R. Foster, J. Phys. Chem., 61, 282 (1957).

38. (a) J. P. O'Meara, M. T. Shaw, and W. L. Rollwitz, Paper presented before the Amer. Assoc. of Cereal Chem. meeting, St. Louis, Missouri, May 1955.

    (b) J. P. O'Meara and W. L. Rollwitz, Proc. Inst. Soc. Amer., 9, 310 (1954).

39. S. Brunauer, P. H. Emmett, and E. Teller, J. Amer. Chem. Soc., 60, 309 (1938).

40. T. M. Shaw and R. H. Elsken, J. Chem. Phys., 18, 1113 (1950) and 21, 565 (1953), and Anal. Chem., 27, 1983 (1955).

41. J. Shoolery and B. Alder, J. Chem. Phys., 23, 805 (1955).

42. I. Weinberg and J. R. Zimmerman, J. Chem. Phys., 23, 748-49 (1955).

43. S. S. Dharmatti, G. Govil, C. R. Kanekar, and Y. P. Virmani, Extrait du Bulletin Ampere, 9^e Annee, Fasc. Special, 479-494 (1960).

44. W. L. Rollwitz, Humidity and Moisture, vol. 2, Reinhold, New York, 1965, pp. 137-147.

45. B. B. Murray and R. C. Axtmann, Anal. Chem., 31, 450 (1959).

46. J. T. Arnold and M. E. Packard, J. Chem. Phys., 19, 1608 (1951).

47. A. D. Cohen and C. Reid, J. Chem. Phys., 24, 790 (1956).

48. H. S. Gutowsky and A. Saika, J. Chem. Phys., 21, 1688 (1953).

49. W. L. Rollwitz, Humidity and Moisture, vol. 4, Reinhold, New York, 1965, pp. 149-162.

50. W. L. Rollwitz, A Nuclear Magnetic Resonance Moisture Meter, Proc. Natl. Electron. Conf. 12, 113-125, 1956.

51. W. L. Rollwitz, U.S. Pat. 3,045,175 (1962).

52. I. F. Gallbraith, W. R. Ladner, and A. E. Stacey, Humidity and Moisture, vol. 4, Reinhold, New York, 1965, pp. 163-169.

53. W. R. Ladner and A. E. Stacey, Brit. J. Appl. Phys., 13, 136 (1962).

54. W. R. Ladner and A. E. Stacey, Fuel, London, 40, 295 (1961).

55. A. M. J. Mitchell and G. Philips, Brit. J. Appl. Phys., 7, 67-72 (1956).

56. A. M. J. Mitchell, S.R.D.E. Tech. Res. Memo. No. 175 (1958).

57. R. V. Pound, Progress in Nuclear Physics, vol. 21, Pergamon, New York, 1952.

REFERENCES

58. R. V. Pound and W. D. Knight, Rev. Sci. Instrum., 21, 219 (1950).

59. G. D. Watkins, Doctoral Thesis, Harvard Univ., Cambridge, Mass., 1952.

60. J. Gaunt, A.E.R.E., Report C/R 1264 (1953).

61. D. J. Ferret and F. D. Seymour, Isotopic Analysis by Low Resolution Nuclear Magnetic Resonance, A.E.R.E, C/R 2/99 (1957).

62. K. Tanaka and K. Yamagata, Bull. Chem. Soc. Japan, 28, 90 (1955).

63. J. R. Zimmerman, B. G. Holmes, and J. A. Lasater, J. Phys. Chem., 60, 1157 (1956).

64. H. Reinhardt, Bergbautechnik, 20, 29, 88 (1970).

65. L. H. Keith and A. L. Alford, J. Assoc. Offic. Anal. Chem., 53, 1018 (1970).

66. H. W. Avdovich and G. A. Neville, Can. J. Pharm. Sci., 4, 51 (1969).

67. M. Plat, Farmaco, Ed. Prat., 25, 143 (1970).

68. D. M. Rackham, Talanta, 17, 895 (1970).

69. A. R. Aikman, R. S. Cordington, and E. F. Kirchner, Control Eng., 4, 108 (1957).

70. J. Chadwick, Proc. Roy. Soc., Ser. A136, 692-708 (1932).

71. D. J. Belcher, T. R. Cuykendall, and H. S. C. A. A. Sack, Tech. Develop. and Eval. Center Tech. Develop. Rep., 127, 1-20 (1950).

72. L. F. Curtiss, Introduction to Neutron Physics, Van Nostrand, Princeton, N. J., 1959.

73. R. K. Adair, Neutron Cross-Sections of the Elements, Rev. Mod. Phys., 22, 249-289 (1950).

74. J. Cork, Radioactivity and Nuclear Physics, Van Nostrand, Princeton, N. J., 1947.

75. S. A. Korff, Electron and Neutron Counters, Van Nostrand, Princeton, N. J., 1946.

76. R. E. Lapp and H. L. Andrews, Nuclear Radiation Physics, Prentice-Hall, Englewood Cliffs, N. J., 1948.

77. J. W. Baum, Neutron Dosimetry — A Review, Univ. of Rochester Atomic Energy Project, Rochester, N. Y., March 1956.

78. J. W. Holmes, Neth. J. Agr. Sci., 4, 30-34 (1956); Aust. J. Appl. Sci., 7, 45-52 (1956).

79. J. W. T. Spinks, D. A. Lane, and B. B. Torchinsky, Can. J. Technol., 29, 371-374 (1951).

80. W. Gardner and D. Kirkham, Soil Sci., 73, 391-402 (1952).

81. J. Sharpe, Brit. J. Appl. Phys., 4, 93-94 (1953).

82. C. H. M. Van Bavel, N. Underwood, and R. W. Swanson, Soil Sci., 82, 29-41 (1956).

83. J. Gueron, J. Phys. Radium, 15, 65A-75A (1954).

84. A. H. Knight and T. W. Wright, Radioisotope Conference, Oxford, II, 11-22 (1954).

85. C. H. M. Van Bavel, Soil Sci. Soc. Amer. Proc., 26, 405 (1962).

86. L. F. Curtiss, Introduction to Neutron Physics, Van Nostrand, Princeton, N. J., 1959.

87. W. D. Allen, Neutron Detection, Philosophical Library, New York, 1960.

88. D. A. Lane, B. B. Torchinsky, and J. W. T. Spinks, Paper presented at a meeting of Committee D. 18 of the Amer. Soc. of Test Mater., Cleveland, Ohio, 1952.

89. J. F. Stone, D. Kirkham, and A. A. Read, Soil Sci. Soc. Amer. Proc., 19, 419-423 (1955).

90. J. W. Holmes and K. G. Turner, J. Agr. Eng. Res., 3, 199-201 (1958).

91. K. N. Burn, Humidity and Moisture, vol. 4, Reinhold, New York, 1965, pp. 205-211.

92. S. Rozsa and E. Toth, Proc. Imeko Symposium on Moisture Measurement, Hungary, 1971, pp. 299-307.

93. E. Toth and L. Pazmandi, Proc. Imeko Symposium on Moisture Measurement, Hungary, 1971, pp. 211-217.

REFERENCES

94. International Atomic Energy Agency, Radioisotope Instruments in Industry and Geophysics, Bibliographical Series No. 20, IAEA, Vienna, 1966.

95. International Atomic Energy Agency, Neutron Moisture Gauges, Technical Reports Series No. 112, IAEA, Vienna, 1970.

96. P. G. Marais and W. B. Smit, Afr. J. Agr. Sci., 5, 225-238 (1962).

97. J. L. McGuinness, F. R. Dreibelbis, and L. L. Harrold, Soil Moisture Measurements with the Neutron Method Supplement Weighing Lysimeters, Soil Sci. Soc. Amer. Proc., 25, 339-342 (1961).

98. V. L. Hauser, Agr. Eng., 43, 88-89 (1962).

99. J. W. Holmes and A. F. Jenkinson, J. Agr. Eng. Res., 4, 100-109 (1959).

100. P. Mortier and De Boodt, Neth. J. Agr. Sci., 4, 111-113; Trans. 7th Int. Congr. Soil Sci., 1, 321-329 (1960).

101. J. Huet, Humidity and Moisture, vol. 4, Reinhold, New York, 1965, p. 185.

102. L. H. Stolzy and G. A. Cahoon, Soil Sci. Soc. Amer. Proc., 21, 571-574 (1957).

103. C. H. M. Van Bavel, P. R. Nixon, and V. L. Hauser, USDA Reports, 41, 70 (1963).

104. H. W. Anderson, P. M. McDonald, and W. G. Lloyd, U.S. Forest Serv. Res. Note, PSW-11, 1963.

105. C. H. M. Van Bavel, Humidity and Moisture, vol. 4, Reinhold, New York, 1965, pp. 171-184.

106. Y. Miyashita, Humidity and Moisture, vol. 4, Reinhold, New York, 1965, p. 195.

107. G. L. Squires, Proc. Phys. Soc., Section A, 67, 520 (1954).

108. J. D. Hewlett, J. E. Douglass, and J. L. Clutter, Soil Sci., 97, 19-24 (1964).

109. B. Berke and B. Papp, Proc. Imeko Symposium, Hungary, 1971, p. 425.

Chapter VIII

AUTOMATIC CONTROL OF MOISTURE

1 INTRODUCTION

Automatic control of moisture content in industrial processing is part of the broad phenomena of automation. Controlling the amount of moisture in a product or a process is of great significance to many industries such as paper, timber, textiles, chemicals, and agroproducts. For some industries, effective moisture control means a profitable moisture balance in the finished product; for others, it means increased productivity because of fewer rejects or decreased downtime because there are no overwet or overdry pieces to halt an operation. For most of them, it is actually a combination of benefits. In those industries where practically all processing is continuous, periodic moisture determinations with manual resetting of controls are not possible. Only continuous, precise control can bring a process up to its full efficiency.

This chapter contains a brief introduction of the principles of automatic control and their applications in controlling the moisture content in industrial processes. The discussion of automatic control outlined here will prove helpful in the selection, application, and adjustment of automatic control equipment for moisture. The chapter is divided into four main parts. In the first part a nonmathematical introduction to the fundamentals of automatic control in general is discussed. The second part describes the circuits and instruments employed for the automatic control; in the third part, some specific examples of the control of moisture in industrial processing are described; and in the fourth part the economic aspects of automatic controls are briefly discussed.

A detailed discussion on automatic control is outside the scope of this book. For a more advanced discussion of the subject, especially as related to the mathematical and electronic techniques used in solving automatic control problems, the reader is referred to some excellent publications [1-9] on the subject.

2 FUNDAMENTALS OF AUTOMATIC CONTROL

There are two types of control devices; one is known as the open-loop system and the other is known as the closed-loop system. In the open-loop system no check of the output magnitude against the input is made, i.e., no feedback is employed, whereas in a closed-loop system a continuous measurement and control of the parameter of the process is made and out of the error signal obtained from this measuring or monitoring device, feedback is applied to bring the parameters of the process to the desired value. A generator to supply power to a laboratory which is remotely installed with its field rheostat is an example of an open-loop system. In this case the scale of the rheostat is calibrated in-line voltage, but no voltmeter is provided. It is assumed by the designer that the voltage supplied to the laboratory is that indicated by the original calibration of the rheostat. Actually such a calibration would not be reliable since the voltage could be affected by load,

2 FUNDAMENTALS

generator speed, field voltage, and other variables. There is no check on the controlled quantity, and the operation is that of an open-loop system. The fundamentals of a servosystem are illustrated in Fig. 8.1. Control by error, or input-output difference, is the essence of closed-loop control as well as of the feedback amplifier and servomechanism.

An example of a servosystem is shown in Fig. 8.2. The distinction between servomechanisms and regulators is not always clear, and may not be necessary from a fundamental point of view. The definition of a servomechanism is related to position; however, it does explain the usual system analysis in terms of an instantaneous angle as the independent variable. A servomechanism is a particular type of feedback control system in which the controlled variable is a mechanical position.

Figure 8.3 is a block diagram of an open-loop control system. The input to the system is a command and the output is a controlled variable, where the command specifies the desired behavior of the controlled variable. The command is supplied to control elements which manipulate some variable that influences the behavior of the controlled variable associated with a system called the controlled system. In the on-off lamp circuit, the command is the switch setting, the control element is the switch, and the manipulated

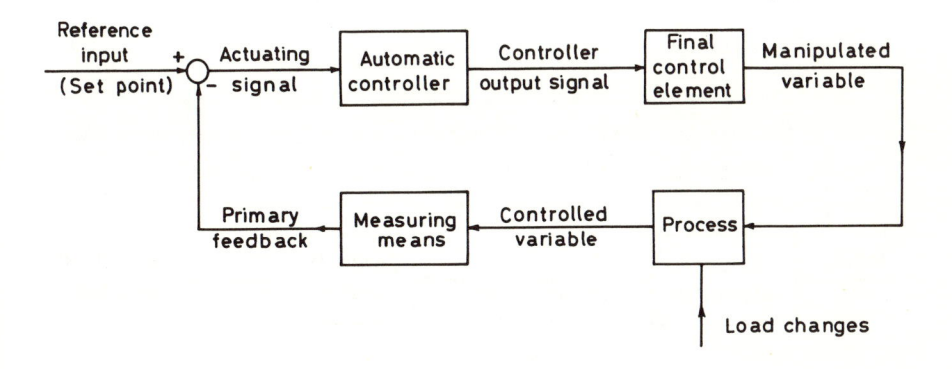

FIG. 8.1. Automatic control system.

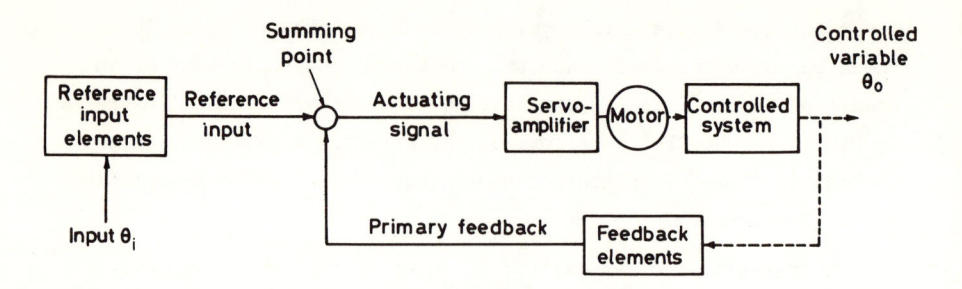

FIG. 8.2. Block diagram of a servomechanism.

variable is the resistance of the switch (which is either infinite for the opened condition or essentially zero for the closed condition). The controlled system is the lamp circuit and the controlled variable is the light emitted by the lamp.

Figure 8.4 is a block diagram of a closed-loop system. Notice that diagrammatically there is a closed loop starting at a summing point, passing through control elements and controlled system, and returning to the summing point. This closed loop is null seeking; that is, it acts so as to reduce the actuating signal to zero. The actuating signal is some function of the difference between the command and the controlled variable. The functional relationship is always such that the actuating signal approaches or becomes zero as the difference between the command and controlled variable approaches zero. Thus, in seeking a null, the closed loop acts to reduce the difference between the command and the controlled variable.

Two important advantages are obtained by making control dependent on the results obtained. A closed-loop system compensates for disturbances in the controlled system, and also compensates for

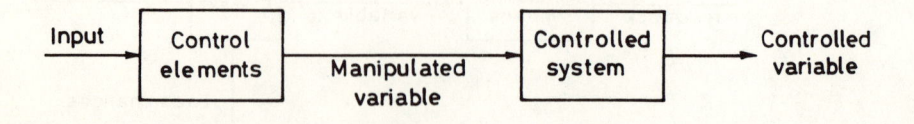

FIG. 8.3. Block diagram of an open-loop control system.

3 AUTOMATIC CONTROL SYSTEM

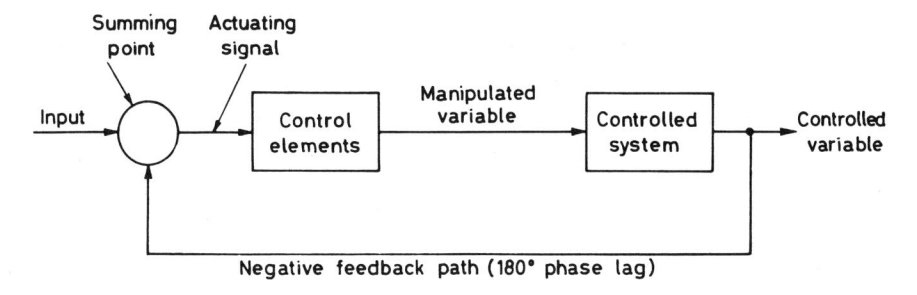

FIG. 8.4. Block diagram of a closed-loop circuit.

variations within the control elements. The closed-loop systems are used where significant disturbances in the controlled system or variations of the control elements are expected. The percentage of variation that is considered significant, of course, depends on the precision with which it is desired to maintain the output variable. In every completely automatic control application, we have a closed loop. The control engineer working in a manufacturing unit or factory with process control must think in terms of closed-loop systems. All factors such as the process, the measurement, the controller, and the final control element, and any auxiliary devices which form a part of the circuit must be considered together.

3 AUTOMATIC CONTROL SYSTEM

3.1 The Basic Units of an Automatic Control System

The automatic control system of a process comprises the following units:

1. Sensing and measuring system
2. Feedback system
3. Controlling and correcting devices

All these units must work in close unison and synchronism with each other to give a perfect automatic control device. The sensing and measuring unit detects and measures the value of controlled conditions (usually physical quantities) in a processing plant. Thus in the case of moisture control, the value of moisture is transmitted to the controlling unit, which automatically compares it with the desired and preselected moisture content. Whenever these values differ, a signal is sent to the correcting unit which alters an appropriate setting of a motor and brings the actual moisture back to the desired value. The quality of process control depends on the accuracy, sensitivity, and speed of response of the measuring units. These instruments must be reliable and robust. The measuring means is, therefore, an important part of the controller. The construction of the measuring device is determined principally by what quantity is to be controlled. A quite common characteristic of measuring devices is that, by the process of measuring the controlled variable, it is converted into a variable more easily utilized in the feedback control loop.

The basis of automatic control is a closed-loop circuit, i.e., one having a feedback. Theoretically two types of feedback systems are possible. The terms negative and positive feedback are commonly used to describe the initial sense of the feedback relative to a transient stimulus; alternative terms are degenerative and generative feedback, respectively. In practice, however, negative feedback is usually employed. A brief description of the negative feedback system is given here; for more detailed and rigorous treatment the reader is referred to the extensive literature available [1-9]. Negative feedback, in its broadest sense, can be said to exist in a structure when, upon applying a disturbance to the structure, influences are invoked which oppose the disturbance and restore the original state in whole or in part. When the feedback is positive, on the other hand, the disturbance is assisted and the system tends to move away from its original state. Thus, in a structure embodying feedback of either sign, a closed loop of dependencies is to be found.

Random fluctuations appear in every feedback system in one form

3 AUTOMATIC CONTROL SYSTEM

or another and indeed many feedback applications are specifically designed to reduce these disturbing effects. Feedback control loops can be either stable or unstable. A feedback control loop is said to be stable when its controlled variable comes eventually to a steady, noncyclic value following a disturbance. The control systems are made with a built-in, 180-angular-degree phase lag so that the correction to process input is opposed to changes in the process output and the desired value is restored. A control loop will be stable if at the frequency of oscillation that gives a total phase shift of 2π around the loop, the gain around the loop is less than one. However, if at the frequency of oscillation that gives the total phase shift, the gain around the loop is one or more, the loop is unstable. Any disturbance causes this type of loop to break into endless oscillations. These oscillations continue because at gains over one, more energy is being added than is being used, and it is being fed back in phase with itself so that the oscillations are self-sustaining, or self-excited. This tendency of self-sustaining oscillation is the greatest limitation to feedback control.

The controlling unit links the measuring unit with the correcting unit. When the measured condition in a process changes from a desired value, this unit automatically transmits a signal to the correcting unit, which takes appropriate action. Modern controlling units may be operated mechanically, hydraulically, pneumatically, or electrically. The pneumatic type is technically the most advanced, and many reliable designs are available. It is thought that more than 90% of the existing units are pneumatic. It has become general practice to install pneumatic or hydraulic controllers because they are simple, inexpensive, and reliable, and do not catch fire. They have some advantages in performance, such as extremely high speeds of response, and they are very convenient for use where signals have to be transmitted over long lines; they are more flexible than other types of controlling units and so are particularly suited to the centralized control of a large plant. Also it is an easy matter to combine electrical units with mechanical or hydraulic units. Controlling units can be made to operate in various ways so as to deal with almost all possible problems.

3.2 Combination of Controls

So far we have considered separately the basic control devices available for automatic control. Their functions can be classified into four fundamental control responses as follows: (1) two-position, (2) proportional, (3) floating, and (4) rate. Two-position control may be used alone or as an auxiliary part of other control equipment for emergency purposes. It is the most commonly used of all control effects. This is natural because of its low initial cost, ease of maintenance, and because in many applications the results obtained with two-position control are entirely satisfactory. In proportional control the signal that determines the rate of corrective action can be directly proportional to the deviation of the measured condition. Proportional control may be used alone provided the load changes are not great and that the offset that results from these changes does not impair the quality of the product being processed. Proportional control will be found in many applications as the sole method of control. Floating control, when used alone, shows performance characteristics similar to two-position control. Rate control is transient and must be combined with proportional. But there are many critical operations in modern high-speed processing which require a more exacting control. The use of a single mode of control, such as two-position or floating with its inherent oscillating characteristics, and proportional control with its inherent offset characteristics, is not satisfactory. Therefore industrial automatic controller combinations which incorporate the benefits of more than one control system are common. The three important controller combinations are: (1) proportional plus reset, (2) proportional plus rate, and (3) proportional plus reset plus rate.

3.3 Modes of Control

The mode of control is the manner in which a controller makes corrections relative to deviation. It is to be noted that the mode of control actually applied to a correction of the process input results from the combined operating characteristics of all functional elements comprising the control system. The control units are made to produce one of the following modes of control:

1. Two-position or on-off
2. Single-speed floating
3. Proportional-speed floating
4. Proportional position (or throttling)
5. Proportional plus reset (or simple reset)
6. Proportional plus rate
7. Proportional plus rate plus reset (three-term control)

Each mode of control has its own characteristics, advantages, and limitations.

Probably the most difficult decision in instrumenting a control process is that of selecting an adequate yet economical mode of control. The solution is usually a compromise between the quality of control obtained and the cost of the control system. The control system must be sufficient to meet the tolerance of the process, but it should not include refinements beyond those required or its cost will be excessive. If there is any doubt, completely adequate instrumentation should be chosen, because the economic loss due to "overinstrumentation" is slight compared to product quality and quantity loss resulting from economy on the control equipment. Processes with very small capacity, notably flow processes, are successfully controlled by proportional-speed floating mode alone or by wide-band proportional control combined with very fast reset.

3.4 Time Lags in Automatic Process Control

There are two types of time lags that occur in the automatic control of a process: one is the process time lag and the other is the control-system time lag. In process control this feature is termed the plant lag or the process lag. Lag, in general, is any deviation from instantaneously complete response to input signal. The control system also displays two other lags: that of the measured value behind the true value, the measurement lag, and that of the control action (i.e., the operation of the regulating unit) behind the measured value which dictates it, which we may call the controller lag. Time lags, in addition to inertia, are caused by three properties of the process, namely, capacitance, resistance, and transportation time. Automatic control systems too have time lags that can have a serious effect on performance of fast-acting control loops. The same kind of lags, i.e., resistance-capacity lags and dead time which are found in a process are also encountered in control systems. Furthermore, the lags found in controllers are caused by the same properties: capacitance, resistance, and transportation.

In general every part of an automatic control system must be designed, selected, installed, and maintained to avoid time lags as much as possible. It must be stressed that a given time lag has just as bad an effect on control-loop stability when it occurs in parts of the automatic control system as when it occurs in the process itself. However, it is possible that some of the lags attributed to controlling systems may be negligible in a particular process, as is the case where electronic controls are used. Here the lag due to transfer of the electronic impulses is far too small to be of any significance, although it does exist.

3.5 Pneumatic Controls

Pneumatic controls are used extensively in industrial processes. The final control element can be operated by a simple flexible diaphragm or bellows and can be accomplished by skilled operators. Another important reason for the widespread use of pneumatic control devices is their explosion-proof characteristics. For many applications such as in oil refineries and in those industries utilizing inflammable materials, it is a requirement that all control equipment must be explosion proof. Pneumatic controls satisfy this prerequisite. The control effects of proportion, reset, and rate covered in the previous sections can be obtained easily in pneumatic circuits. Often the measuring portion, which is the input to the

3 AUTOMATIC CONTROL SYSTEM

controller, is not pneumatic. The input usually takes the form of a physical motion or force imparted to the input element of the controller. The mechanism that accomplishes this part of the closed-loop system is dependent on the variable to be controlled. As a combination of electric and pneumatic devices operate together in closed-loop control systems, transducers find considerable applications.

3.6 Electric Controls

Electric controllers use electric power to actuate the final control elements. These are different from the controllers utilizing pneumatic or hydraulic power for this purpose. Electric controllers are also to be differentiated from electronic controllers. The main distinction between the electric and electronic circuit lies in the use of vacuum tubes, thyratrons, and semiconducting solid-state devices such as transistors, zener diodes, and silicon rectifiers in the latter system. A completed control loop should, if possible, consist of a combination of electric, electronic, pneumatic, or hydraulic elements, thus incorporating the advantages of all. The combination of all these devices is not practicable. However, the electric and electronic control devices are very often coupled together. With electric control systems the final control element can be operated by a reversible electric motor. These motors are comparatively expensive and possess a comparatively great amount of inertia. Electric controllers can be classified in two principal ways:

1. By the type of signal received from the primary element:
    (a) Self-operated
    (b) Relay
2. By the mode of control:
    (a) Two-position
    (b) Floating
    (c) Proportional
    (d) Proportional plus reset
    (e) Proportional plus reset plus rate

In the design of electric control circuits that possess proportional, reset, and rate-type action a close familiarity with the Wheatstone bridge, the potentiometer, and the characteristics of a resistance-capacitance circuit is required.

Electric controllers vary from rather simple devices to relatively complex systems. Accordingly, a wide latitude of choice is available in selecting a controller so that its characteristics are consistent with the requirements of the application. Electric controllers have certain distinguishing characteristics as compared with pneumatic or hydraulic systems. Probably the most outstanding single characteristic of an electric control system is in the matter of transmission. The speed and ease of transmission of electric signals are in marked contrast to those of pneumatic signals.

Electric control systems lend themselves readily to special combinations of equipment where two or more variables may be sensed and enter into the overall control action. Many varied combinations are often desirable, and the ready mixing of electric signals in any desired proportion or combination is easily accomplished in such multielement controls. Often a single controller may be required to operate more than the one final control element, and in such cases drive units may be readily operated in parallel or in any desired sequence; each drive unit has a separately adjusted proportional-band response to suit the characteristics of the particular final control element being operated.

With the development of solid-state devices such as transistors, zener diodes, and thermistors, electrical controllers using these devices are being developed quickly and it is likely that they may eventually replace the conventional pneumatic or hydraulic control devices to an appreciable extent, as they offer considerable advantages in miniaturization, performance, and reliability.

3.6.1 Speed Control of dc Motors. In the control of moisture content in industrial processings, electric motors of high capacity are now used to drive the huge drying machines and the cylinders employed for drying purposes. Under all steady conditions, the torque created by any type of motor will be exactly equal to the resistance torque of the load to which it is coupled. Should the conditions change, the speed of the motor will automatically vary so that new sets of conditions are obtained at which the motor torque is again equal to the load torque. This adjusting action is subject to the limitation that the torque of a motor has a certain maximum or peak value, and, if the load should exceed this value, the motor will come to a standstill. The current taken by a motor increases with the load torque, though not always in direct proportion. As the rate of heat generation in a motor is proportional to the square of the current value, the load should be kept within limits in order to avoid undue heating which would result in increased deterioration of the insulating materials, with the risk of premature failure. In practice, the normal load should be kept well below the maximum or peak torque if the motor is to have a reasonable life, although most motors can drive a momentary high torque without reaching a dangerously high temperature.

In a dc motor, the speed is approximately proportional to the voltage applied to the armature, and inversely proportional to the magnetic field strength. The speed of a dc motor can thus be increased by reducing the magnetic field strength. Figure 8.5 shows that the magnetic field strength is not directly proportional to the field current. This is due to the fact that at high magnetic flux densities the iron parts of the field system tend to become more or less saturated with magnetism, and a very high field current is required for a given increase of field magnetism above this region.

When a shunt-regulating resistance is used to control the speed of a shunt motor the motor should always be started with maximum field strength, otherwise the reduction of starting torque may be such that the motor will not start until the starter has been moved to give the motor a very high armature current. Figure 8.6 shows a regulator which is fitted with a device to ensure that the motor is started correctly. In the regulator is fitted a coil A which creates

518   VIII. AUTOMATIC CONTROL

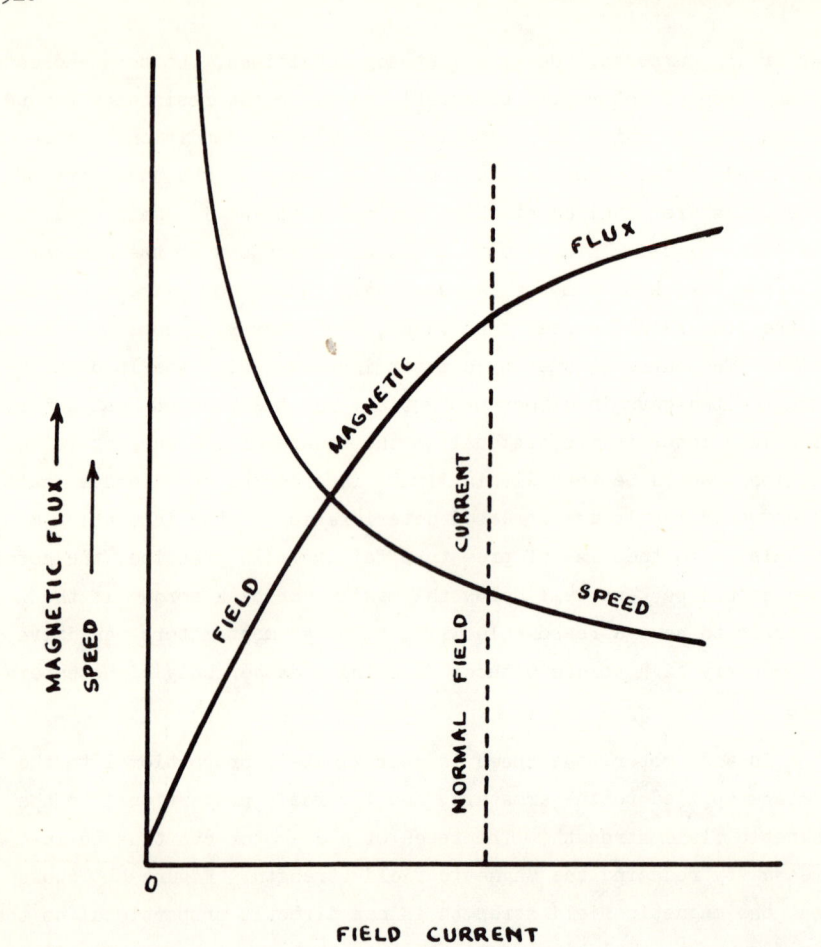

FIG. 8.5. Speed control of a dc motor by changing field current.

sufficient magnetism to hold up the armature F. If the motor should be started with the regulator contact away from the correct full-field position, the armature will not be lifted, and the contacts B will be closed to short-circuit the field-regulating resistance. The speed can only be increased by first moving the regulator arm D to the slow-speed position to open the contacts B and raise the armature. The starter has a no-volt coil N, which is frequently connected in the field circuit, which releases the starter if the

3 AUTOMATIC CONTROL SYSTEM

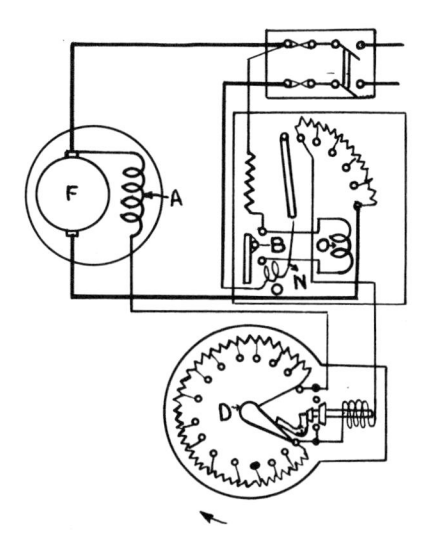

FIG. 8.6. Connections of field regulator with shunt motor.

supply is cut off. This coil is also deenergized to trip the starter if there is an overload, and the resulting excessive armature current through the overload coil O causes this to attract an armature to close contacts connected across the no-volt coil. The speed of a shunt motor, which has field windings of high resistance connected in parallel with the armature, may be increased by connecting a resistance in the field circuit to reduce the field current.

    The speed of a shunt motor may also be increased, within limits, by feeding the armature at a higher voltage. It is not advisable to supply the shunt fields at higher voltage, unless a resistance is connected in the field circuit to limit the field current to its normal value, otherwise the field windings are likely to overheat and burn out. If the field current is maintained correctly the speed and safe full-load horsepower will be practically proportional to the armature voltage, and the safe full-load torque practically unchanged, although it may be possible to obtain some increase of torque without overheating if the ventilation is much improved at the higher speed. The remarks regarding shunt motors apply equally to compound machines, although the effects obtained will be modified slightly due to the series field windings.

For the control of large shunt and compound motors which require to be run at variable speeds, the Ward-Leonard system is usually employed, although it involves a considerable capital outlay. This system enables a wide range of economical operating speeds to be obtained, and also reduces to a minimum the waste of power which usually occurs in starting a motor. As indicated in Fig. 8.7, the variable-speed work motor is supplied power by a dynamo which is driven by an ac or dc motor, which also drives an exciter. Normally the field current of the work motor is kept constant, although it might be reduced by a field regulator if required, the field coils, D, being supplied by the exciter. The speed of the work motor is controlled by variation of the current to the field coils, C, of the dynamo; this machine has also a series field winding, A, thus varying the voltage applied to the armature of the work motor. It is convenient to use a potentiometer regulator connected as shown so that the dynamo field current and voltage and the work motor speed can be adjusted from zero to maximum in either direction by sliding the moving contacts of the potentiometer in either direction from the middle position.

At the present time, the motive power for running the Ward-Leonard system is being provided by the silicon control rectifiers which are being increasingly employed for dc motor drives. Until recently dc motor drives have been powered by dc generator or mercury arc rectifiers, but the silicon control rectifier (Scr) has certain advantages over these older methods. Scr control provides increased efficiency, good power factor, lower maintenance cost, and smaller plant-space requirements. It thus appears that the large gap between drive method and modern technology has now been bridged with this solid-state device.

The Scr-controlled sectional drive has a much improved performance over the Ward-Leonard drive and has a comparable overall

3 AUTOMATIC CONTROL SYSTEM   521

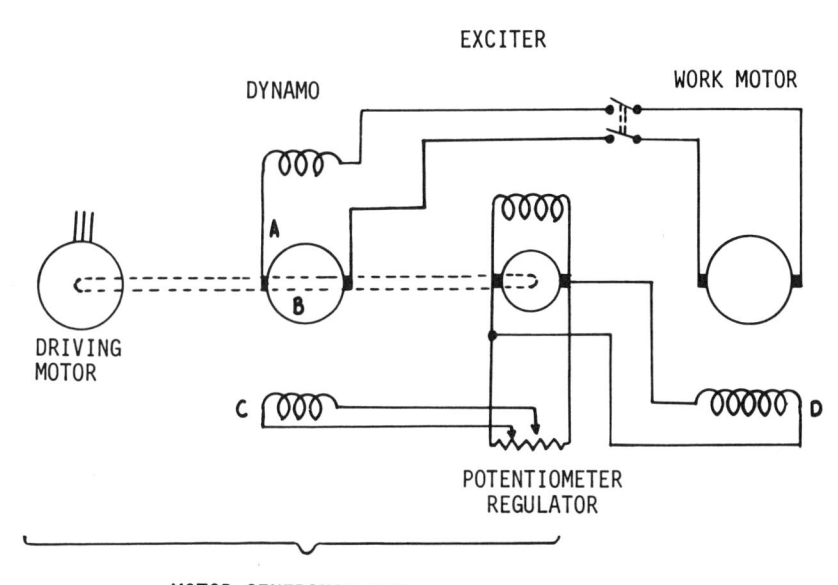

FIG. 8.7. Ward-Leonard control system.

efficiency of about 88%. Because the equipment is solid state, it needs less space, is lighter in weight, and requires less maintenance. In addition, response time to control signals is faster.

Other economical methods of controlling the speed of shunt or compound dc motors employ a variable voltage booster connected in series between the motor armature and supply mains. Similarly, a grid control rectifier can also be used to apply a variable voltage to the armature of a variable-speed dc motor, the fields of which are excited. These methods are not being described here and references are made to the literature [10-12] published on the subject, for further study.

Thyratrons have been used to effectively control the speed of the dc motor. Figures 8.8 and 8.9 show two basic thyratron circuits in which the thyratrons are operated by ac voltages applied to the plate and grid: the plate voltage is used to turn off the thyratrons while the grid voltage is used to turn them on. In Fig. 8.8, where armature control is obtained, the ac plate voltage is applied

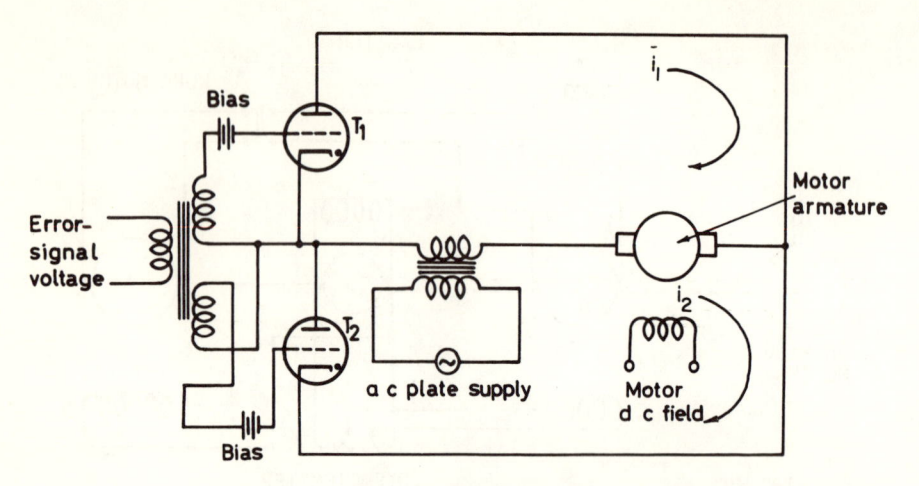

FIG. 8.8. Thyratron dc motor control circuits — armature control.

across the thyratrons in series with the motor armature in such a way that when thyratron T_1 has a positive cathode-to-plate potential, T_2 has a negative cathode-to-plate potential. Thus, T_1 can conduct on one half-cycle of the plate supply voltage and T_2 can conduct on the other half-cycle. The portion of the positive half-cycle during which either of the thyratrons conducts under zero-signal input

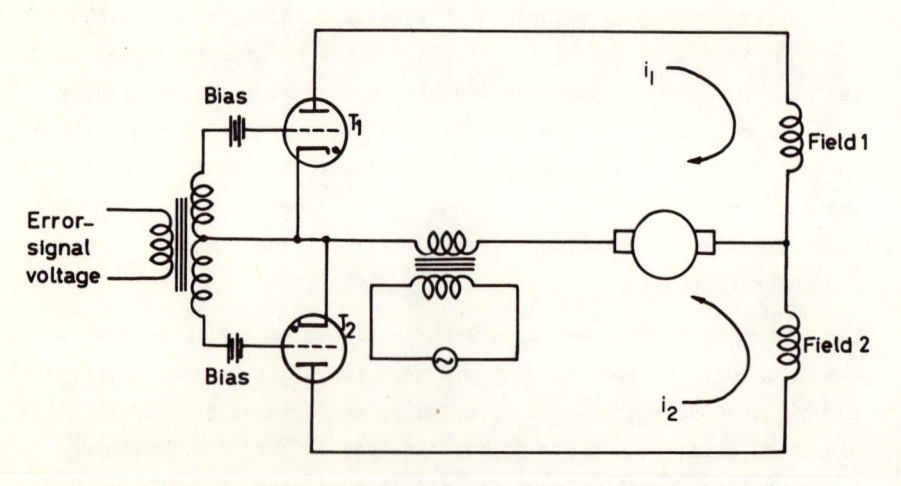

FIG. 8.9. Thyratron dc motor control circuits — field control.

3 AUTOMATIC CONTROL SYSTEM 523

conditions is determined by the bias voltage applied between its grid and cathode. In practice the bias voltages are adjusted so that each thyratron conducts for the same portion of its positive half-cycle. This means that current i_1 flowing when T_1 conducts is equal to current i_2 flowing when T_2 conducts and since the current flows in opposite directions through the motor armature, the dc component of armature current is zero and hence the motor torque is zero.

The phase relationship between the error voltage and the ac plate supply voltage is such that the error voltage supplied to plate potential of T_1 is in phase with the cathode-to-plate potential of T_2. Thus the error voltage tends to lengthen the period of conduction of the tube with whose cathode-to-plate voltage it is in phase and to shorten the period of conduction of the tube with whose cathode-to-plate potential it is out of phase. If the error signal is such as to lengthen the period of conduction of T_1 and shorten that of T_2, then i_1 flows for a longer time during each cycle than i_2, with a resultant dc component of armature current flowing in the direction of i_1. Since the difference between the lengths of the conducting periods for the two tubes is proportional to the amplitude of the error signal, proportional control is obtained. Also, if the error signal is of opposite phase, the polarity of the dc current reverses, so that directional control is obtained.

In Fig. 8.9, a circuit for obtaining proportional field control is shown. In this circuit, the thyratrons are arranged so that both can conduct during the same half-cycle of the ac plate supply voltage. With equal bias voltages and zero error-signal input, thyratrons T_1 and T_2 draw equal currents i_1 and i_2 over identical portions of the positive half of the plate supply cycle. These currents pass through field windings 1 and 2 in opposite directions, causing two equal but opposing fields, so that the net field is zero. Notice that they also pass through the motor armature in the same direction, supplying the necessary armature current. Thyratrons T_1 and T_2 receive error-signal inputs from opposite ends of the same input transformer.

524   VIII. AUTOMATIC CONTROL

These are phased with respect to the ac plate supply voltage so that one of the tubes receives an aiding signal during the conducting half-cycle, and the other tube receives an opposing signal. In the presence of an error signal, one thyratron conducts for a longer portion of the conducting half-cycle than the other thyratron. Thus, one of the motor fields becomes stronger than the other, and torque is produced. Notice that since one current decreases and the other current increases in response to the error signal the net current flowing through the motor armature remains relatively constant as required when field control of a dc motor is being exercised. The grid potential required to cause ionization in a thyratron for a particular cathode-to-plate potential is called the critical grid potential. Because of variations in critical grid potential between thyratrons or in the same thyratron over a period of time, accurate control of thyratrons requires steeper grid waveforms than can be obtained using the basic circuits of Figs. 8.8 and 8.9. For this reason, somewhat more complex arrangements are usually required. One very straightforward way of obtaining a steeper triggering waveform is to use ac bias as well as dc bias and to have the ac bias operating 90° out of phase with the ac plate voltage.

Since thyratron control is normally used in higher-power applications where dc motors are also advantageous, thyratrons are normally used to control dc motors. Another advantage of using thyratrons to control dc motors is that this control can be performed in response to ac error input signals to the thyratrons since the thyratrons perform a rectification function as well as a control function.

There are some basic advantages and disadvantages of dc control motors when compared with ac motors. The advantages are as follows:

    1. Direct-current motors can deliver a high output from a small frame size, since there are no slip losses as in an ac motor.

    2. Usually, a dc motor can be driven from a smaller control amplifier than an equal rating ac motor.

    3. Direct-current motor circuitry permits the use of a variety of stabilizing techniques.

3 AUTOMATIC CONTROL SYSTEM

4. Residual voltages are usually negligible in dc motor circuits.

5. Direct-current motors are more efficient than ac motors, especially in applications requiring variable speed.

6. Direct-current motors may require no power under no-signal conditions for certain designs. (In contrast, ac motors require main field power.) This makes them ideal for applications involving long periods of stand-by and intermittent, high output.

7. Direct-current motors can easily be controlled to give variable speed and special speed-torque characteristics at high efficiency.

8. Direct-current motors can be used as dc tachometers.

The disadvantages of the dc motor are as follows:

1. Direct-current vacuum servoamplifiers drift (gradually develop an output for zero input), and therefore require a zeroing adjustment or a relatively unreliable chopper-type drift-balancing circuit.

2. Direct-current motors have commutators that require periodic maintenance checks to ensure reliable brush performance. Such maintenance may not be feasible where many miniature control motors are used in a complex assembly. Probably the brushes represent the greatest single deterrent to the more widespread use of small dc motors.

3. A secondary objection is the radio interference generated by the brushes. Special filters and shielding are often required to reduce this interference to a satisfactory level.

4. Commutator and brushes occupy a large percentage of available motor volume in small sizes and add substantially to motor friction.

5. Isolation and impedance matching difficulties mitigate against the use of dc circuits (and motors).

6. The use of the induction-type electrical resolvers (for which there is no completely satisfactory dc equivalent) by the military has promoted the development of ac systems, in preference to dc systems (and therefore motors).

7. The high field strengths used in dc machines increase cogging and therefore decrease small signal sensitivity. This is further accentuated by brush friction.

8. In field control circuits, hysteresis, nonlinearity, and a highly inductive input circuit add to the stabilization problem.

9. Units with strong permanent magnet fields develop high drag due to rotor hysteresis losses.

These disadvantages constitute a relative rather than an absolute index of reliability. For many applications, dc motor life is completely satisfactory.

3.6.2 Speed Control of ac Motors. A large proportion of computers and servomechanisms in current use in industrial control applications are ac systems. Alternating-current servos have inherent advantages, of which the most important are the simplicity and freedom from drift of the associated amplifiers, the reliability and ruggedness of the ac servo induction motor, and the availability of certain inductive transducers such as synchros. On the other hand, ac servos have certain drawbacks, namely, greater susceptibility to spurious signals and increased complexity of servonetwork stabilization. The design of ac servos concerns itself primarily with the resolution of these difficulties. The basic theory of ac systems is the same as that of dc systems, though there are differences in details.

Generally the same considerations which are applicable to dc series-type motors apply to ac series-type motors. The choice between dc and ac types is mostly dictated by the type of power available. For a given motor size, ac series motors are less efficient and have a lower starting torque. On the other hand, the use of an alternating current greatly simplifies the arc-suppression problem.

Many types of servomotors not adaptable to continuous control systems are employed successfully in contactor systems. However, due to the high starting torque and frequent necessity of some form of friction damping, the output of a contactor servomechanism is apt to be quite jerky when a series type of motor is employed. For this reason systems employing such motors are most suitable when the command input tends to remain constant for extended periods. When the input varies continuously, a smoother output response may generally be obtained by employing a shunt-type motor.

The motor speed can be controlled below and above synchronous speed by simple movement of the brushes; these may be operated by means of a handwheel, remote mechanical control, or remote electrical

3 AUTOMATIC CONTROL SYSTEM

control by means of a pilot motor responding to push-button switches. The motor must be protected against overload by some form of overload device connected in the secondary circuit, since the full-load secondary current is practically constant. The safe-load horsepower is practically proportional to the speed, subject to possible reduction at low speeds. The motor is normally started with the brushes set for the lowest speed, and this gear is normally electrically interlocked with the switch to prevent starting with any other brush setting. Where pilot motor control is used the control gear is usually designed so the pilot motor automatically returns the brushes to the slow-speed position when the motor is switched off. The starting torque may be about twice full-load torque with about $1\frac{1}{2}$ times full-load current. Motors of 3 to 250 hp or more are available with a speed range of 3 to 1. Ranges of 15 to 1 can be obtained in the more expensive motors. These motors are suitable for driving textile plant and paper-making machines used for drying purposes.

Purely ac servos are usually only met within low powers due to the difficulty of controlling speed or torque in a high-efficiency polyphase induction motor. The speed of an induction-type motor can be continuously varied over a wide range by rotation of the poles; this is a potentially powerful method of high-power ac speed control. Low-power applications at the present time usually use two-phase squirrel cage machines in which a control winding is supplied with current proportional to error and leading or lagging by 90° on the reference phase winding, depending on the sign of error; motor torque is then roughly proportional to error signal over a limited range. For satisfactory operation the rotor must be designed to have a reactance-to-resistance ratio of about unity to ensure that the starting torque is high.

Thyratrons can also be used to obtain proportional directional control of two-phase ac motors. One arrangement of four thyratrons to obtain this type of control is shown in Fig. 8.10. Assume that T_3 and T_4 are prevented from firing. Then alternating current in

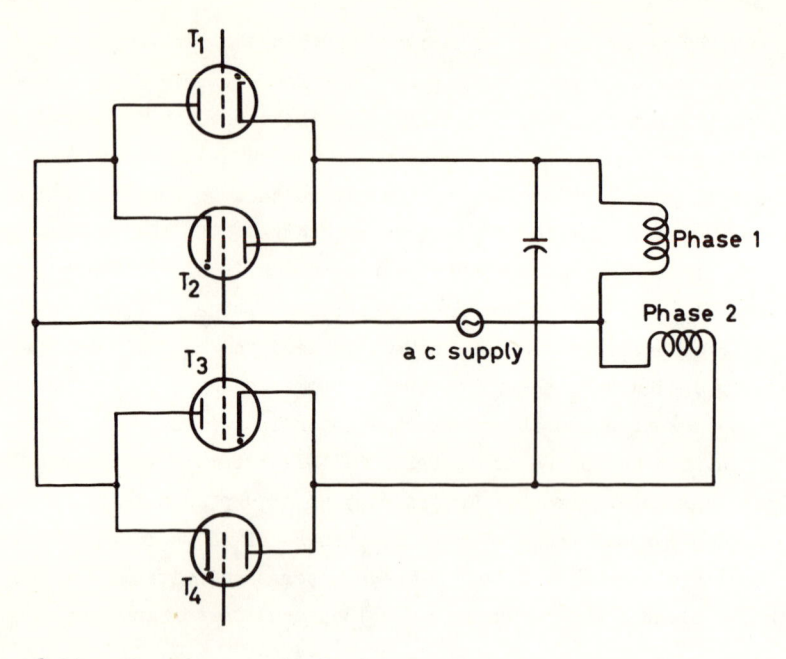

FIG. 8.10. Thyratron control of two-phase ac motor.

phase with the ac supply voltage can be driven through phase 1 of the motor by firing T_1 on one half-cycle and T_2 on the other half-cycle. At the same time, current in quadrature with the ac supply voltage is driven through phase 2 in series with phase-shifting capacitor. The value of the current during each half-cycle is controlled by variation of the grid voltages of T_1 and T_2. Thus proportional control is obtained. In order to reverse the direction of the motor, T_1 and T_2 are prevented from firing, and T_3 and T_4 are used instead. Under this condition in-phase current is drawn through phase 2 of the motor and quadrature current is drawn through phase 1. An advantage of this type of control, when compared to the fixed-phase type of control normally employed for two-phase motors, is that no current is supplied to the motor under zero-error conditions. Thus the motor dissipates power only when it is producing torque.

3 AUTOMATIC CONTROL SYSTEM 529

3.7 Electronic Controls

Conventional control systems have been firmly established for several decades, and it is only during the last 10 years that electronic systems have gained wide acceptance. The present trend in this direction stems largely from the recent phenomenal developments in semiconductor devices and techniques that promise to secure the advantages in size, performance, and reliability that any new system must offer. Some of the more important advantages and disadvantages of electronic systems are as follows:

1. Information already available on the reliability of semiconductor devices indicates that correctly designed equipments are as reliable as comparable pneumatic equipments and probably more so.

2. Less preventive maintenance is required and installation and fault location are easier. Wires are cheaper and easier to install than pipes and are less prone to leakage. Transmission lags are eliminated. In pneumatic and hydraulic circuits, there is a time lag due to friction, and inertia of the air and liquid, respectively. These lags can become objectionable and the control engineer must always consider this aspect of the problem. Moreover, controllers can readily be designed or adapted to give any desired form of control function, and a substantially linear controller scale can be obtained.

3. Electronic systems are extremely flexible. Units can readily be arranged in any desired layout and removed when required.

4. Many measuring devices generate electrical signals and these can be used to produce a control signal directly without intermediate conversion. This eliminates mechanical hysteresis and simplifies the control loop, thus increasing its performance and reliability.

5. Electrical signals are more acceptable to the data-handling equipment and computers which will be applied increasingly to the control of complex processes during the next few years.

6. On the debit side, the initial cost of electronic instruments is at present some 30% greater than that of comparable pneumatic equipment, and also electrical actuators are still inadequate for many purposes.

7. A great deal of work is being carried out by many instrument manufacturers to eliminate these drawbacks, and it seems clear that the swing toward electronic control will continue rapidly.

8. To make full use of the potentialities of electronic control, it is essential that the system be designed around the use of separable modular units, employing a common type of transmission signal and capable of being interconnected in any desired arrangement. The units must be small, and as far as possible each should perform a single standard function.

9. The system should be of the parallel type, so that the failure of any mechanical or electronic equipment, such as a recorder or indicator or integrator, does not affect the operation of the control loop.

10. Electronic equipments employed in the past have a more complex control loop containing more moving parts than necessary, and are therefore less desirable from the viewpoint of reliability.

There has been a steady but not revolutionary extension of the use of electronic controllers, selective rather than general. Actual prices, and relation to corresponding prices of pneumatic equipment, have not changed sufficiently to influence the rate of application either way. There are, however, a few instances where the superior accuracy of the electronic controller in significant respects has been turned to good account, despite the losses known to arise from control inaccuracies. This is not unrecognized, and there are examples of interest and importance where this is taken into account, e.g., in feed-forward systems which must be inherently accurate and not dependent on feedback corrections.

The commutator motor is becoming very popular for providing a variable-speed drive from two- or three-phase ac mains. It has the following advantages:

1. Infinite range of speed between maximum and minimum
2. High ratio of maximum to minimum speed
3. Simple means of control
4. The full-load torque is practically constant at all speeds
5. The machine is very efficient, with no external resistance
6. The speed variation on varying load is much less than that of a slip-ring motor run at reduced speed by rotor resistance

3 AUTOMATIC CONTROL SYSTEM   531

There are two types of ac commutator motor, the rotor fed and the stator fed. The rotor-fed type has a primary winding which is situated on the rotor and is fed from the main through slip rings. The rotor also carries an auxiliary or regulating winding, which is similar to the armature winding of a dc motor and is connected to a commutator. The secondary winding of this motor is fitted on the stator, each phase of these windings being connected to two brushes which rest on the commutator. The commutator brush gear consists of two movable rockers, each of which has three brush spindles per pair of poles, the two rockers being geared together. The two sets of brushes cover separate portions of the commutator so they can be placed in line or separated in either direction at will.

The modern trend is toward development of solid-state control devices using transistors, zener diodes, silicon rectifiers, and thermistors. The merits and demerits of semiconducting devices such as these have already been described in the section on electronic controllers. The solid-state servosystem is being developed [13] with a view to replacing the conventional ac servosystems which have been described earlier. The only difference between the solid-state servosystem and the conventional ac servosystem is that the servomotor and slide wire are replaced by a demodulator and two indirectly heated thermisotrs Th_1 and Th_2 (Fig. 8.11). These are so arranged that the presence of an ac error signal lowers the resistance of one of the thermistor beads and raises that of the other, thus moving their common point toward one end of the total resistance. The total resistance remains very approximately constant, though this is not of fundamental importance, and the action is phase sensitive, reversing when the phase of the error signal reverses. Thermal lag in the beads is sufficient to smooth the demodulated drive signal. The system drives itself toward a condition of balance in the usual way unless the amplifier has a high gain, which is given as:

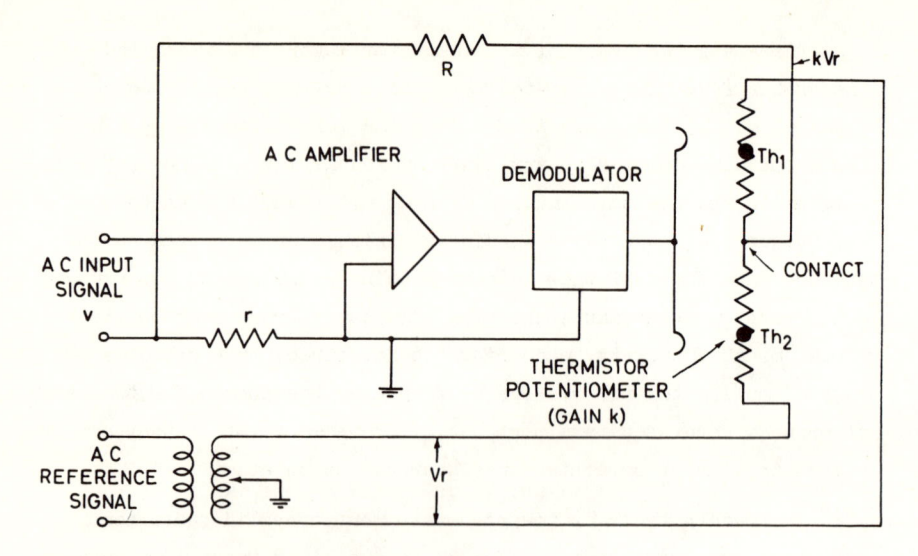

FIG. 8.11. Solid-state servosystem.

$$k = \frac{R + r}{r} = \frac{v}{V_r} \tag{8.1}$$

where k is the gain of the thermistor potentiometer, R and r are resistances, and v and V_r are the two ac signals (Fig. 8.11).

In this solid-state servosystem gain k of the thermistor potentiometer, defined as the ratio of its output to the voltage applied across it, is automatically adjusted in proportion to v/V_r, the ratio of the two ac signals.

4   APPLICATIONS OF AUTOMATIC CONTROL OF MOISTURE

4.1   Textile Processing

4.1.1   Introduction. In textile processing, drying forms perhaps the most important operation. At the end of the finishing process, the fabrics have to be dried. In order to produce and maintain specific properties, it is necessary that the fabric have residual moisture content, which differs with the type of the fabric, and needs to be kept constant. Drying is generally associated with shrinkage, and, therefore, the fabrics are carried in the drying room on stretching frames, which, with endless circular clamps, catch the edges of the fabric and keep it stretched to the desired width. During its passage in the drying room, the fabric is dried by warm air blown through nozzles.

Adjustment of the speed of the machine, according to the readings of the measuring apparatus, is done by hand or automatically. In the first case, the machinist is required to watch the measuring apparatus and then to adjust the speed of the machine in such a way that the reading coincides always with the desired point; some of the apparatus have an optical signaling device to indicate whether the fabric is normal, too moist, or too dry. In fully automatic plants the adjustment of the machine is done automatically. The aim of continuous control of moisture of textile dryers and their automatic regulation is twofold. First, one should ascertain that the controlled machine is operating with maximum efficiency, with possible low specific heat consumption, i.e., rationalization is brought out in the drying operation. Second, one should also be certain that the outgoing fabric has constant desired moisture content.

4.1.2 Operating Conditions for Moisture Control in Textile Processes.
In the case of a dryer, whether regulated by hand or by automatic control, it is necessary to know its constants, i.e., the actual operating conditions. It is very important to know the average passage time, that is, the average speed of the fabric divided by the length of the fabric in the drying zone. In all regulating processes, lag (inertia) as a function of passage time must always be taken into consideration. It is very important to consider this point because in practice we find conflicting views concerning other regulating devices, such as those for voltage regulation and so on, which cannot be transferred on the diverse conditions of drying. In the case of adjustment of speed, adjustment is followed by changes

in moisture content. A change of the speed of the machine becomes effective only after the full passage of time [14]. Figure 8.12 shows the relationship of the moisture content of a fabric that passes through a tentering frame. If the fabric travels through this tentering frame slowly, it is overdried, as shown by the lower portions of curves A and B. Even if the speed is raised promptly, there is no guarantee that the cloth does not turn out overdry. On the other hand, a fabric traveling with a high speed would still be too moist, as shown by the upper portions of curves A and B.

If the regulating system works in this way, then the faster regulating process would be followed by a slower regulating process, i.e., the regulation would be in cyclic variations. The regulator must be so adjusted that it advances as many steps as are necessary in the unit time, which corresponds to a normal passage, in order to produce the desired moisture content in the state of rest and not during the passage period. It means that with a nicely adjusted regulator, each correction becomes effective only after one passage. It is a common feature in all drying systems that in the range of low balancing, the moisture content of outgoing fabric changes very little by the change of speed, while from a definite

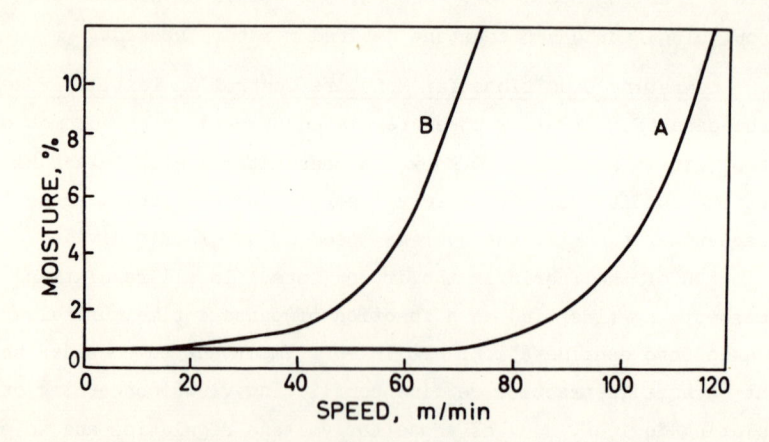

FIG. 8.12. Graph showing relationship between moisture content and speed of drying machine.

4 APPLICATIONS

point onward, small changes of speed produce large changes of moisture content.

4.1.3 Moisture Control by Controlling the Drying Speed. There is a definite relationship between the moisture content of the fabric and the operating speed of a dryer (Fig. 8.12). Air drying and cylindrical drying machines, tentering frames, and tension-free dryers behave similarly concerning this basic principle. With very slow machine speed, the fabric is dried to almost zero moisture content, and with increasing machine speed, the value increases at first very slowly, yielding an almost horizontal curve. With a certain speed, depending on the heaviness of the fabric, slight changes in the speed cause large changes in the moisture content. The efficiency of a dryer for a sheetlike fabric is calculated on the assumption that outside conditions remain constant, as drying efficiency is given in kilograms of water evaporated per hour. Taking the speed of the web of the cloth to be dried as V (meters per minute) and the breadth of the cloth as b (meters), the drying efficiency, E_d, is given as follows:

$$E_d = \frac{G(F_a - F_e) \cdot b \cdot V \cdot 60}{10^5} \quad \frac{kg}{hr} \qquad (8.2)$$

where G stands for the specific dry weight of the sheetlike moving fabric; F_a is the moisture content of the fabric on entering the drying chamber; and F_e is the moisture content of the dried fabric.

As to how far we can approach this theoretical value in practice depends on the goods to be dried, the climate in the dryer, the temperature, and the saturation degree of the outgoing air that carries out the evaporated water into the open air. In addition to this one has to take into consideration the quantity of heat required to increase the temperature of the material, the drying chamber, and cover the heat losses caused by continuous radiation. If the machine operative judges the drying effect from feel, his judgment is limited to the flat part of the curve. What he feels above all is excessive drying with its easily discovered results, e.g., warps sticking together or damp fabrics. Thus he will try to be on the safe side and will run his machine with the range indicated by the upper parts of curves A and B (Fig. 8.12). As can be seen from the diagram, the amount of residual moisture differs only slightly within a speed range of between 25 and 40 m/min, small fluctuations of drying conditions being practically of no importance. However, uniform drying within the above-mentioned range actually means excessive drying, resulting in high costs. In order to maintain a reasonable amount of residual moisture, the operator would have to increase the speed of the machine considerably. Besides the high-speed machine operation will result in low specific steam consumption. To have the dryer operated without danger under the most economical conditions, a moisture-indicating and -controlling set will prove to be indispensable. Even if small changes in moisture content are announced without delay, it is possible to counteract any deviation from the desired value. The aim of the control apparatus is to come out of the flat part of the curves A and B and approach the optimum point of moisture content, which almost always lies in its steep portion. In most of the industrial control machinery used for the control of moisture, the control is applied by changing the speed of a motor. Thus in the textile industry the cloth is allowed to pass and its moisture content is measured continuously; and the time of drying is suitably adjusted so that the cloth has uniform moisture content.

For general drying operations fabrics should be dried somewhat drier [15] than the normal regain value accepted for a 65% relative humidity and a 70°C temperature. The reason for this is that mill floor conditions of relative humidity and temperature are different from laboratory conditions. In general cotton should be dried to a moisture content of about 5%, wool to about 10%, acetate to $4\frac{1}{2}$%, and viscose rayon about 8%. However, these fabrics should not be overdried, as overdrying damages the textile materials considerably, resulting in the loss of tensile strength and proper handle or drape

4 APPLICATIONS

as well as tear strength. In the case of rayons and acetate overdrying results in the evaporation of expensive finishing materials. In wool the effects of overdrying are much greater; hence the operation of woolen dryers is carried out at a much lower temperature, with subsequent loss of production.

For all industrial control equipment requiring movement, either rotary or translatory, as its ultimate output, the electric motor, either ac or dc, is used. The dc motor has excellent variable-speed characteristics and is readily controllable at good efficiency with electronic circuits, but unlike the ac motor, it requires a separate field supply. A system of armature voltage control for a dc motor in which the speed of the motor is controlled by adjusting the voltage applied to its armature from a generator is shown in Fig. 8.13. The speed control in this case is possible even if the dc motor in question has a constant field excitation. The ac motor is frequently employed in the smaller sizes, particularly where controlled speed is not a necessity. In the larger sizes the unstable speed characteristics and low efficiency of the ac motor have caused the circuit designer to turn to the time-proven shunt-field dc motor in spite of the field excitation requirements. Electronic control is now usually coupled with such motors. Among other advantages, electronic control makes possible the operation of dc motors from the ac lines, thus avoiding the need for separate dc power generation.

The application of thyratrons for controlling the speed of a dryer in a textile processing was made by Chamberlain [16], who utilized a resistance detector in combination with thyratron tubes for controlling the moisture content in a drying process, and showed that such control can be compared favorably with pneumatic and hydraulic control employed in similar conditions.

Pande and Jain [17] have developed an automatic control device by using the SRI dielectric moisture meter as the measuring and sensing element. A block diagram of this control unit is shown in Fig. 8.14 and the circuit diagram is shown in Fig. 8.15. The error

538   VIII. AUTOMATIC CONTROL

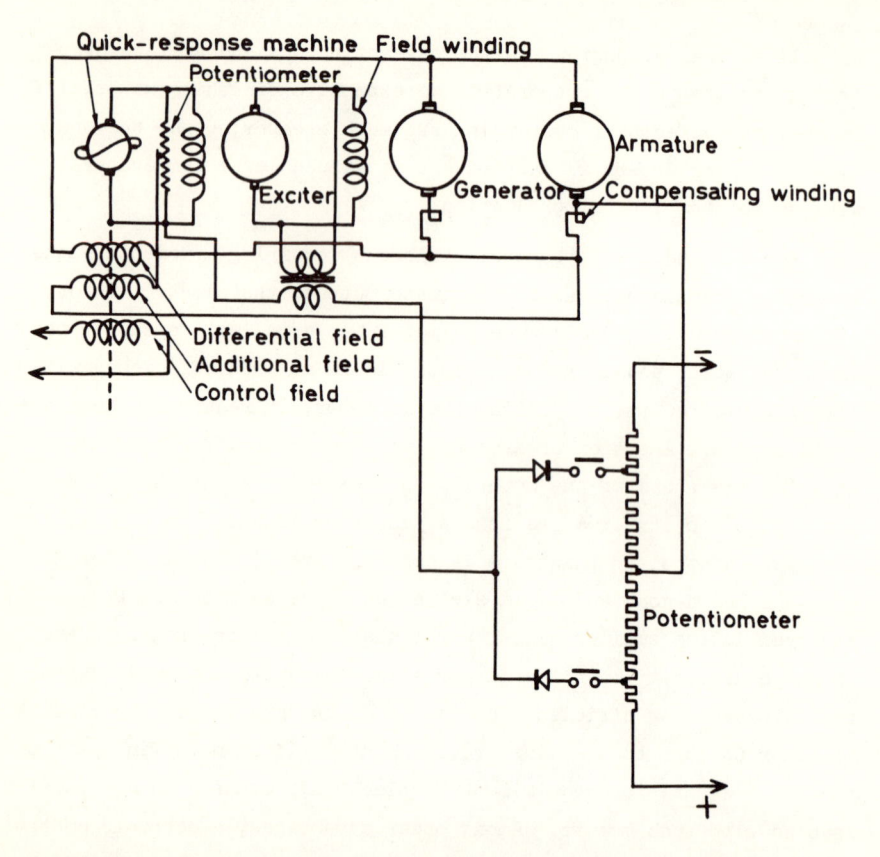

FIG. 8.13. Speed control of dc motor.

signal obtained from the moisture meter is amplified and fed to a pair of thyratron valves whose outputs are connected to time delay relays and contactors. The contactors are connected to a fractional horsepower pilot motor, which is connected to the main motor whose speed is to be varied. The pilot motor is coupled to the main motor through mechanical variable gears which reduce or increase the speed of the main motor in accordance with the signals received from the contactors. When the moisture content is below 6%, one of the two thyratron tubes is fired, energizing the relay 1, and connecting one of the contactors. This contactor changes the phase of the ac

4 APPLICATIONS

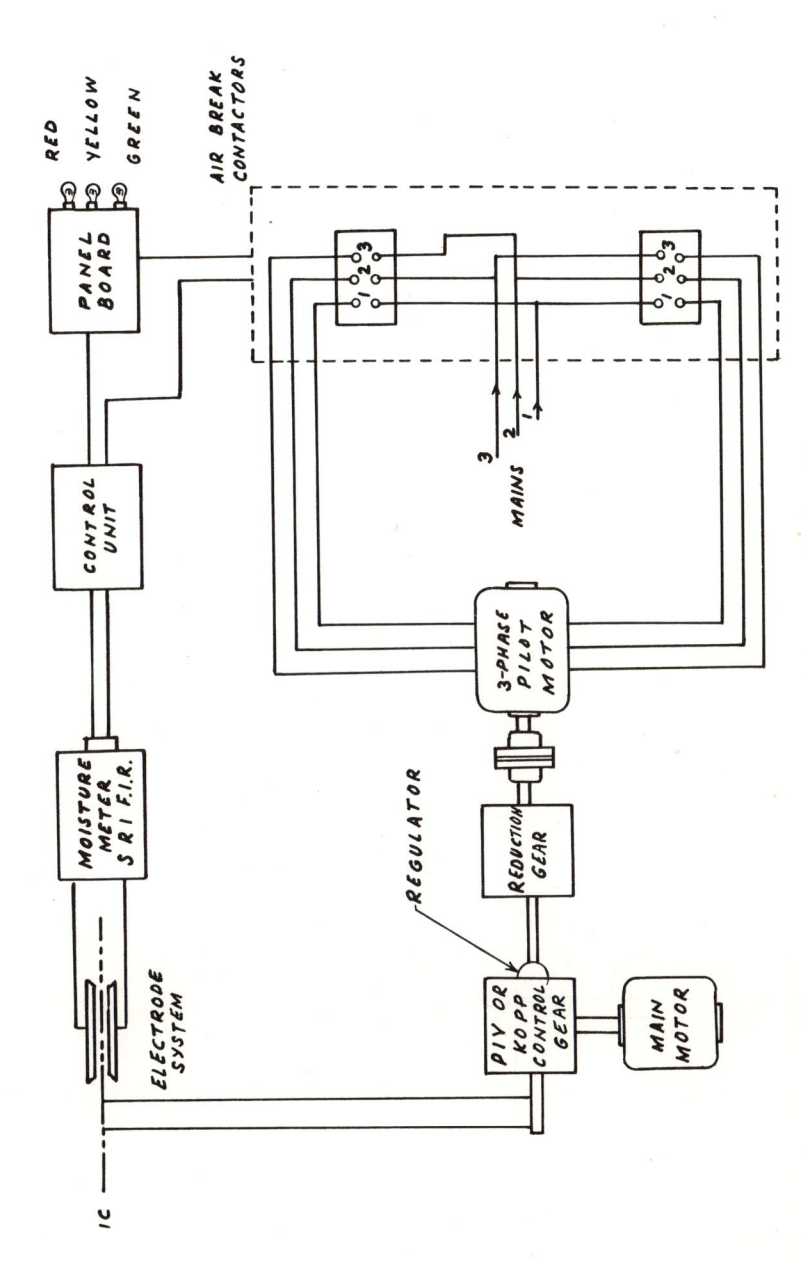

FIG. 8.14. Block diagram of SRI automatic moisture-control unit.

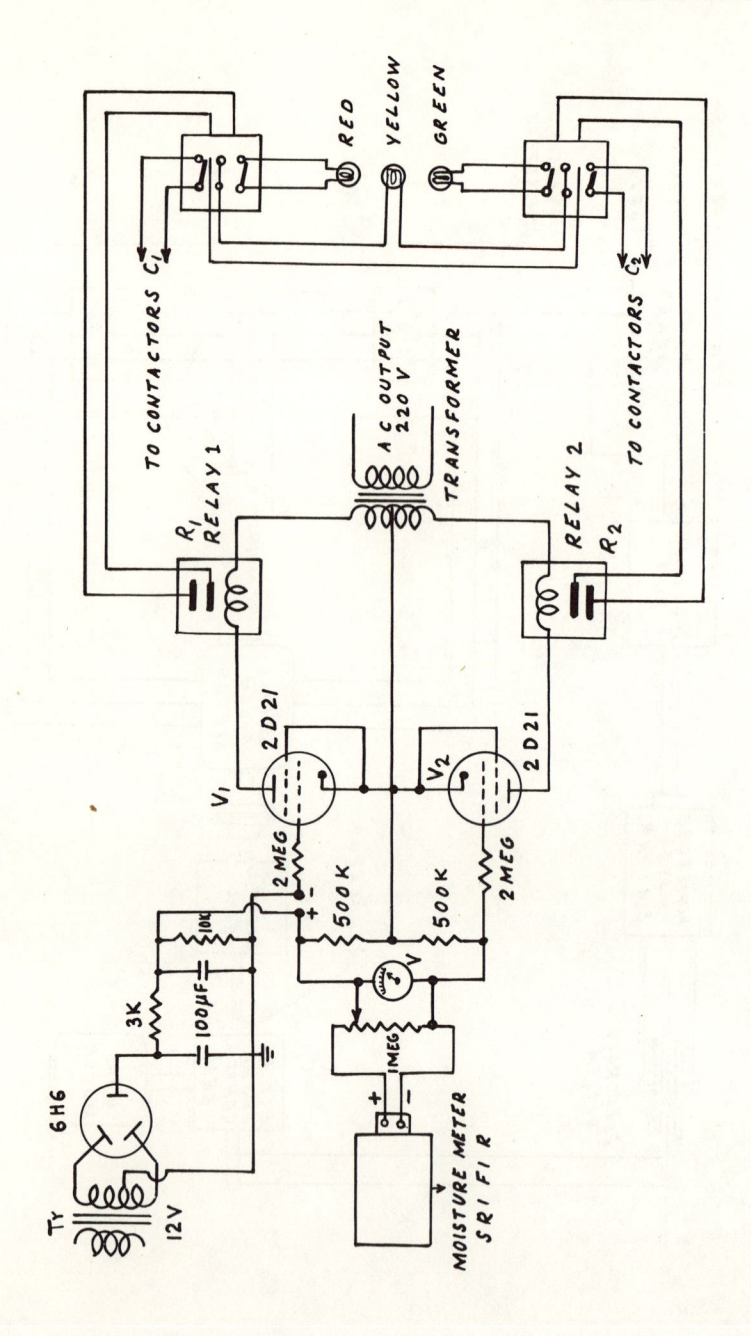

FIG. 8.15. Circuit diagram of SRI automatic moisture-control unit.

4 APPLICATIONS

supply going to the pilot motor whose direction of motion is in such a way as to increase the speed of the main motor, thus giving less time to the moving fabric or beam of yarns to dry which results in higher moisture content. Similarly, when the moisture content goes beyond 8%, the other thyratron tube is fired and the connected relay 2 and the contactor corresponding to this relay are energized, which changes to the direction of the pilot for the fabric or beam of yarns to dry, resulting in lower moisture content. As long as the moisture content remains within the desired limit of, say, 6 to 8% none of the thyratron tubes are fired and the fabric or web of yarn moves at the predetermined speed.

In order to eliminate "hunting effects" due to process time lag as well as control time lag, a proportional control unit in which the speed of the slasher is controlled in a proportional manner with change in moisture content of textile materials has also been developed. A similar moisture control device known as the Moisture Monitor [18] has been developed commercially. The working of these control devices is similar to that described earlier, hence no further details are given.

Another automatic control system using the capacitance method of moisture measurement has been developed by Fielden [19]. In this system the fabric or the beam of yarn is allowed to pass through the two plates of the Fielden moisture meter or Drimeter (fixed on the machine), and the error signal obtained in the output of the moisture meter after suitable amplification is utilized for actuating relays and contactor units for controlling the speed of synchronous motors employed for driving the slashers or tenters (Fig. 8.16). If the moisture content exceeds a desired limit, the speed of the motor is reduced, giving greater time to the fabric or yarn to dry; and in case the moisture content value is below the optimum value, the speed of the motors will be increased, giving a lesser time interval to the material to dry out. The period between corrections must be long if the machine is going slowly, and small

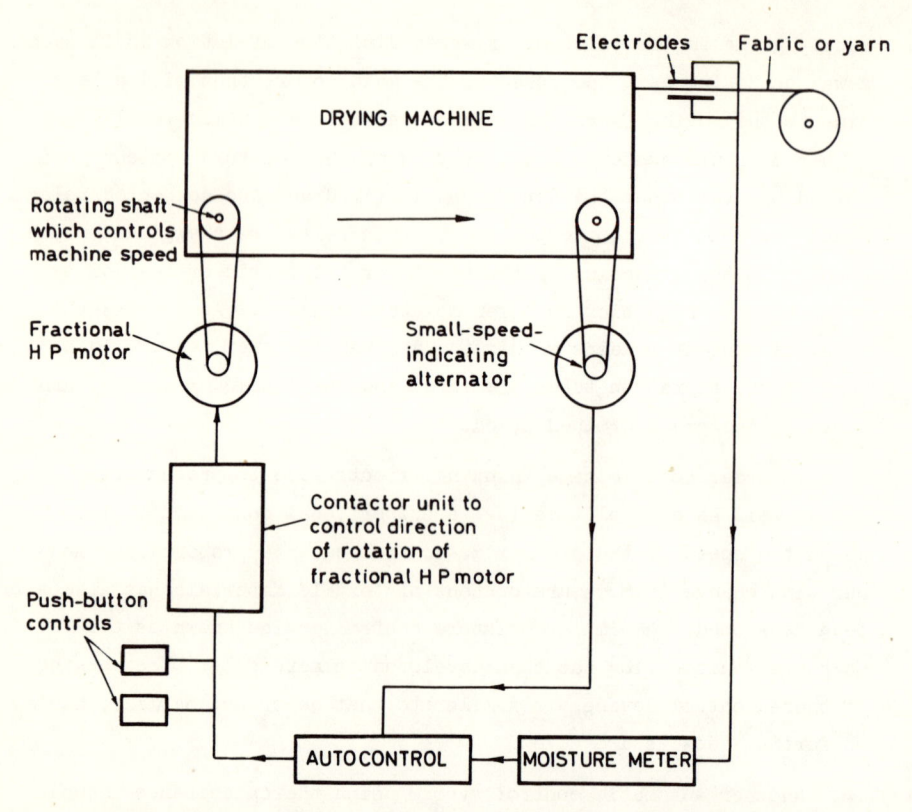

FIG. 8.16. Block diagram of Fielden automatic control unit.

when the machine is running quickly. If the corrections are too frequent, "hunting" results and if they are too infrequent, efficiency is affected. Therefore the mechanism which provides the correction must be initiated at the correct moment by the error signal available in the output of the moisture meter used to indicate the moisture content. The control must also become inoperative if the machine is stopped or runs out of the material. This control unit receives information from the following two sources:

   1. The moisture meter gives an output voltage proportional to the moisture content of the textile fabric or yarn.

   2. A small alternator driven by the machine provides a voltage proportional to the speed of the machine. The control unit thus

4 APPLICATIONS

equipped with the information supplied as above takes complete charge of the drying machine and maintains desired speed for optimum moisture content.

A schematic diagram of the electronic control circuit is shown in Fig. 8.17. The alternating voltage output from the moisture meter is fed to a stable power amplifier p, which provides one output at low impedance which is applied to a bolometer bridge, and another at relatively higher impedance which is used as a reference phase in a phase-discriminating gating circuit. When the material is being delivered at the correct moisture level, there is no out-of-balance voltage developed at the bridge terminals. However, any departure from the required moisture level produces an out-of-balance voltage proportional to the deviation from the desired value. This deviated voltage is amplified by another amplifier Q and used first to determine the direction of rotation of the correcting motor, and secondly to control the duration for which the motor should run, i.e., the amount of correction to the speed of the drying machine.

The phase gate circuit consists of two pentodes with their supressor grids driven in antiphase by a reference voltage derived from the preamplifier P, and their control grids driven by the amplified voltage output from the amplifier Q. Initially the tubes of amplifiers are biased to a nonconducting point and the two relays A and B (which are connected in their anode circuits) are deenergized. Any deviation in the bridge produces a voltage at their control grids, which makes one of the tubes conducting and energizes the corresponding relay, which determines only the direction of rotation of the correcting motor. This relay energizes an interlock circuit which prevents the reversal of the motor while it is running. This relay charges a condenser, which after a 3-sec time interval initiates the flip-flop circuit, which in turn energizes relay C which starts and stops the correcting motor, locks the circuit while the motor is running, and operates the corresponding signal lamp at the front panel. The flip period of this circuit is the time for which the correcting motor runs, and the flop period is the duration of correction. It is so designed that the flip period is proportional

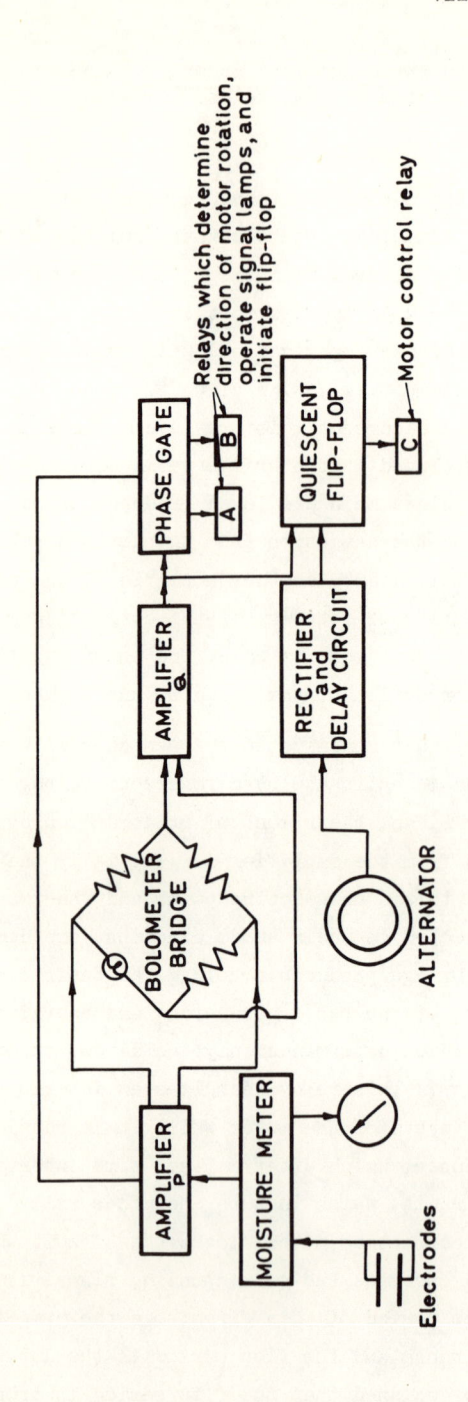

FIG. 8.17. Schematic diagram of Fielden electronic control unit.

4 APPLICATIONS 545

to a rectified voltage derived from the out-of-balance voltage amplifier P, and thus the resulting correction is proportional to the error in moisture content. The flop period is inversely proportional to a rectified ac voltage derived from a small alternator driven by the drying machine, and thus the intervals between the corrections vary inversely with machine speed. If the machine is stopped and there is no voltage present from this source, the circuit will not operate.

Based on the principle and technique described earlier Fielden Electronics (London) has marketed a proportionating recorder specifically designed for use with the Fielden Drimeter for the control of any type of drying machine. This unit gives a permanent record of the day's production and automatically controls the machine speed to maintain output always at the desired moisture content. The required level of operation is adjusted by setting the index pointer on the face of the recorder. The design is based on the following considerations:

In a drying machine, there is an inevitable time lag between a correction to speed and the effect of this correction on the moisture content of the output. This time is not constant but depends on the characteristics of the particular machine, and the speed at which it is running. If an alteration to speed is necessary to correct an error, the amount of correction required is determined by both the error and the machine characteristics. If smaller correction is required subsequently, a time interval must be allowed, dependent on machine speed. The equipment makes corrections in speed proportional to the moisture content error, at intervals which vary in length in inverse proportion to machine speed.

The two variables fed to the automatic recorder controller are:

1. A voltage derived from the Drimeter which varies in proportion to moisture content
2. A voltage proportional to machine speed and derived from a small alternator driven by belt from a moving shaft of the machine

546								VIII. AUTOMATIC CONTROL

    The controller is quiescent until an error in moisture content appears, when it instantaneously makes a correction proportional to error. The timing for further corrections is initiated by the first correction. The speed correction is made by a small electric motor which operates the control mechanism of the machine through a V-pulley (fitted in place of the handle), driving it through a reduction countershaft from the motor. The motor is remote-controlled from push buttons through a contactor unit. The push buttons for hand control may be duplicated or triplicated for positioning whenever convenient on the machine. The automatic control unit connects into the push-button circuit and when connected for automatic control takes complete charge of the machine. On certain modern drying tenters and similar machines the pony motor, relay unit, and push buttons are already in existence and the automatic control unit may be connected directly to the push button circuit, no further fitting being required. In some instances a small relay unit may be needed if the push-button circuit is unsuitable for direct connection to the control unit.

    Although the instrument can be adjusted to suit the characteristics of any drying machine, the efficiency of the automatic control on any drying machine depends on the quality of material being processed. If the control is used on a fabric drying machine, and the material is well woven and of constant thickness, it is possible to operate the control at a tolerance of ±1%. If the material has been woven on looms with faulty taking-up motions, or from weft of uneven counts, the material will dry unevenly and a wider tolerance must be allowed. On warp-sizing machines the yarn usually dries even and it is possible to operate at a very small tolerance. The damp "bars" produced by the seams in the usual twin-cylinder sizing machine are ignored by the controller.

    One of the first commercial instruments to be developed for automatic control of moisture in textiles is the Textometer, whose working is based on the electrical conductivity method of moisture measurement. Irrespective of the quality or the weight per unit

4 APPLICATIONS

area of the handled goods, the operating speed of the machine is controlled in such a way that the material leaving the dryer emerges with the desired amount of moisture. Changes in drying conditions due to fluctuations of steam pressure, for instance, or to other factors acting from outside, are automatically taken into consideration. The automatic control electronic unit of the Textometer (Fig. 8.18) works according to the following principle.

In case the moisture content of the textile material differs from the desired value, i.e., is too low or too high as compared to the adjusted value, control signals are sent out in order to change gradually the operating speed of the machine by means of a pilot motor. The frequency of the impulses is a function of the difference between the measured value and the desired value, i.e., is proportional to the error signal. Greater deviation from desired value implies a rapid series of impulses, while for lower deviations, low-frequency pulses are generated. This is known as proportional regulation. In order to avoid moist warps of fabrics, control is working faster in the direction of dry than in the direction of wet. Besides the actual measuring value, its derivative is effective. Thus regulation is accelerated when the measured value is leaving the adjusted value, but is slowed down when the measured value is approaching the adjusted value (derivative action). In other words, regulation on the desired value takes place most promptly excluding overcompensation resulting in irregular machine operation. This device minimizes hunting.

By this method moisture content is set on its true value, i.e., is not subjected to a tolerance. A measuring value which is proportional to the machine operating speed is returned to the control system by means of a tachodyanano (proportional feedback). Thus regulation is automatically adapted to the actual machine operating speed and, consequently, to the weight per unit area of the textile material, i.e., no manipulation is necessary when handling a light material after a heavy one, or vice versa. At the same time the derivative of the machine operating speed is returned to the control

548   VIII.   AUTOMATIC CONTROL

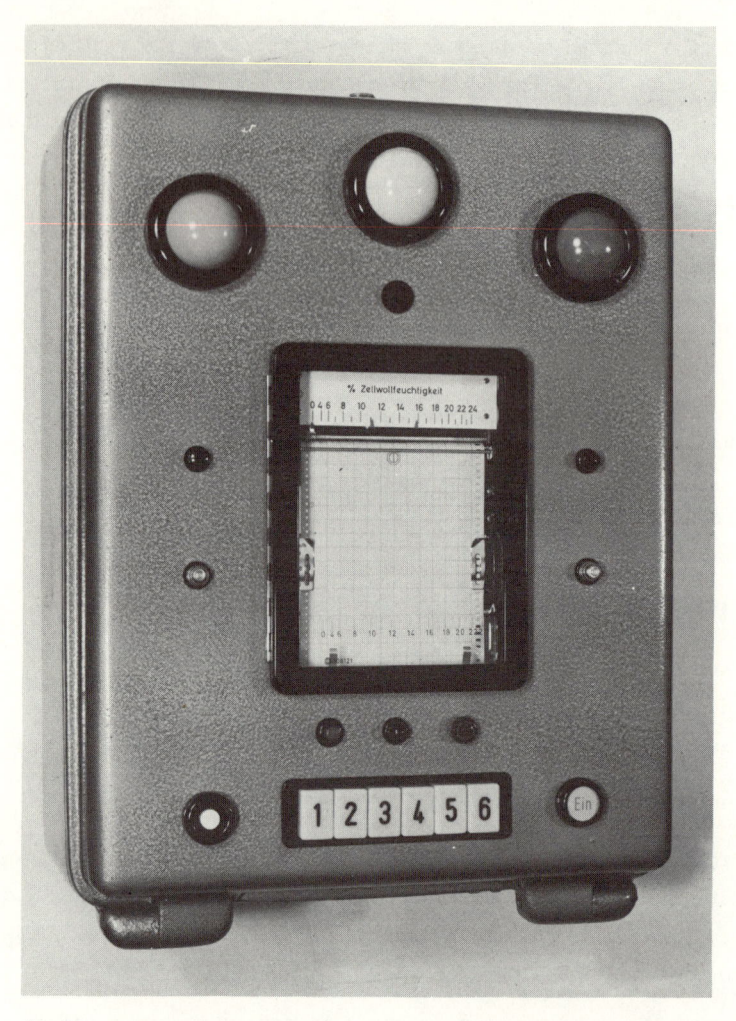

FIG. 8.18. Photograph of an automatic electronic control unit.

system (derivative feedback). Thus repercussions of a nonlinear
characteristic of the machine drive hindering accurate control work
are eliminated. Similarly, repercussions of play between pilot
motor and controlled element are avoided. The automatic control
unit is blocked during periods of standstill as well as during low-
speed operation, thus combining and computing all factors affecting
the operation of automatic control unit.

4 APPLICATIONS

The electrodes used as transducers to pick up the electrical value corresponding to the amount of moisture present in a textile fabric consist of two, three, or four rollers (Fig. 8.19) and are installed at the exit of the dryer. On the rocking shaft, one or, in case of broad material, several revolving feeler rolls are mounted. The feeler roll or rolls can be shifted across the breadth of the warp or of the fabric to permit the distribution of moisture to be determined and the uniformity of drying action to be ascertained. This variable arrangement of the electrode system causes the control action to become effective before the material leaves the drying chamber. The Textometer has a proportional integrally acting controller with derivative action, with the result that a progressively controlled action is possible, which is proportional to the error signal, i.e., the greater the difference between measured moisture content and preadjusted desired value, the more rapid the control action. The drying conditions corresponding to the desired moisture level are actually obtained and no deviation is allowed, so that the maximum efficiency is achieved.

Another commercial automatic moisture-controlling device based on the variation of electrical resistance of moist textile materials is known as the Moist-O-Graph system (manufactured by the Minneapolis-Honeywell Regulator Company, USA). It provides an automatic control system [20] for maintaining desired moisture content in sheets, webs, or granular materials. This control system (Fig. 8.20) consists of (1) a primary sensing element (detecting roll or probe), (2) transmitter, and (3) the indicating and recording instrument, which can be equipped with electronic or pneumatic controls.

The normal operating pressure (which is adjustable) of the roller is 15 lb. The ac supply is transformed to a suitable voltage and rectified to provide power for the measuring portion of the circuit. This power passes from the detector roll or probe, through the material whose moisture content is being measured, to a grounded roll or portion of the machine. From the ground it returns through two series resistors, to the power supply. The voltage drop across

550 VIII. AUTOMATIC CONTROL

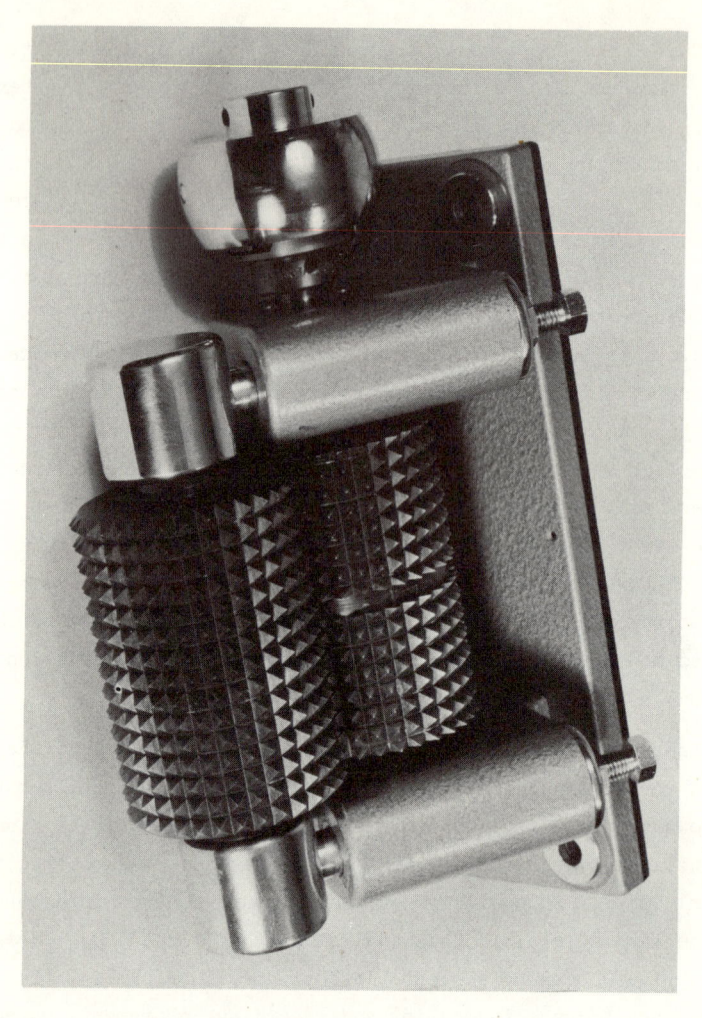

FIG. 8.19. Electrode system of a control unit.

one of these resistors, the measuring resistor, provides a signal inversely proportional to the unknown sample resistance being measured. This voltage signal is the input to the cathode-follower amplifier portion of the transmitter. The cathode-follower amplifier provides the 0 to 10 mV output signal from the transmitter which may be indicated or recorded by a standard instrument with a range of 0 to 10 mV.

4 APPLICATIONS   551

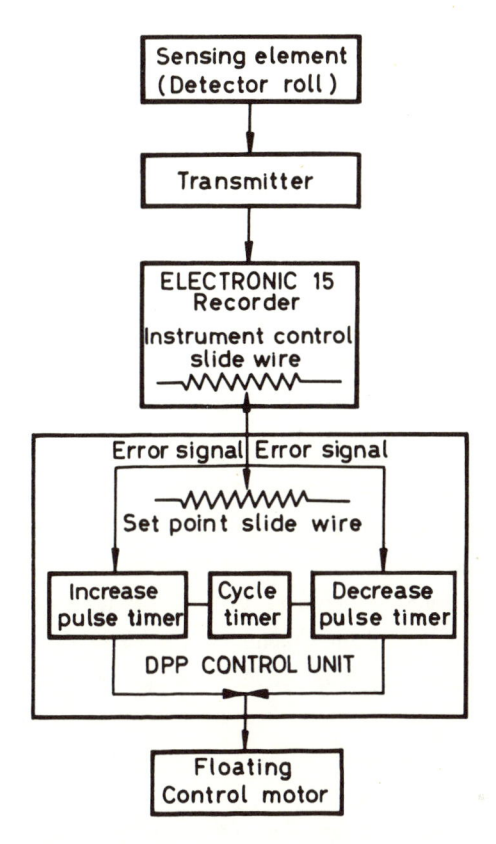

FIG. 8.20. Automatic Moist-O-Graph control unit.

    This system can be used effectively on high-speed processes, as it has faster response cutting to a minimum the amount of processed material containing an incorrect percentage of moisture. The detecting system measures relatively low electrical resistances, and consequently, relatively high moisture contents. Although the specific range of moisture content that can be measured differs somewhat for different materials, this feature makes possible accurate measurements of moisture content of many wet materials. The measuring circuit has been so designed as to minimize the effect of static electricity so that low moisture content can also be measured accurately. This system with deviation proportional pulse (DPP) control unit accurately measures and effectively controls the regain of yarn on high-speed slashers or the regain of fabrics on tenters. This DPP control unit compares the position of the control slide wires against the position of its set point slide wire, and if they do not match, sends to the slashers' speed control motor a correcting pulse of a duration directly proportional to the deviation of the measured regain from the desired regain. The duration of the correcting pulse sent to the control motor is directly proportional to the amount of deviation from the normal or desired regain. The control unit quickly adjusts the slasher speed before any appreciable amount of yarn or fabric passes through. The desired percentage regain is held constant for practically the entire range of production.

In the sizing of cotton yarns, the control of moisture is one of the important requirements. The control is carried out either manually, after observing the moisture content by a moisture meter, or automatically through a control device. Figure 8.21 shows a schematic diagram of a cotton slasher using automatic control. The yarn is fed through rolls, the speed of which is controlled by a variable-speed drive unit. Only one equipment is shown and this is labeled SC, a speed controller. It regulates the speed of the rolls in response to the moisture content of the yarn. After the yarn leaves the dryer or slasher and enters into the weaving room, it has been found that costs can be decreased by approximately 25% if the sizing operation in the slasher is performed correctly. The control of moisture in the yarn at the outlet of the slasher is the criterion of the sizing operation. If the moisture content is excessive, the speed controller will slow down the drying drums so that a longer period of time of contact with the rolls will be provided. This will bring the moisture content to the desired value. The moisture is detected by a detector roll, which contacts the yarn as it passes over it. Its principle of operation is based on the variation in electric conductivity due to variations in moisture content. The amount of current that will pass from the detector roll through the yarn to the grounded part of the press roll is dependent on the moisture content of the cotton warp. Thus the speed controller

4 APPLICATIONS

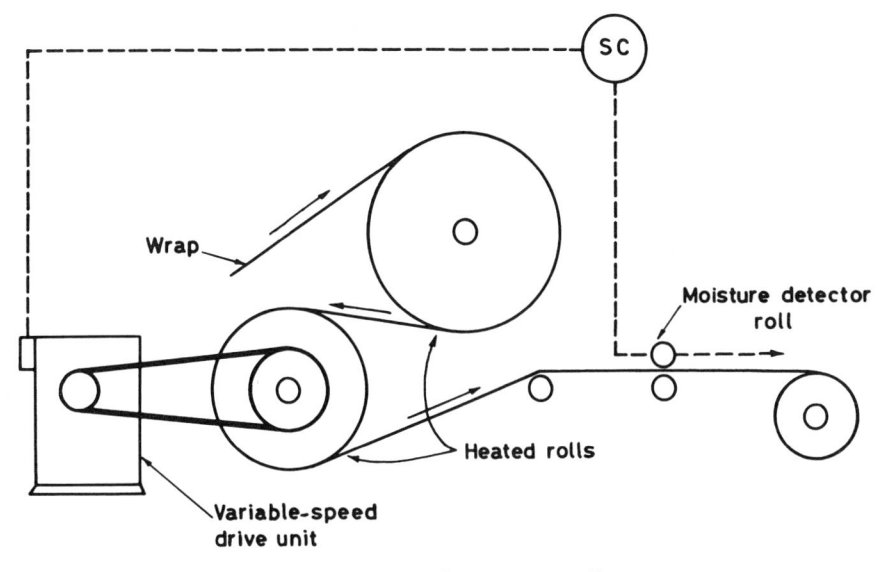

FIG. 8.21. Moisture control on a two-cylinder cotton slasher.

receives an input signal of electrical conductivity which is calibrated in terms of moisture content. The controller output actuates the variable-speed drive and maintains the beam of yarns at a constant moisture content.

A new automatic control device and moisture meter, known as the Electropsychrometer, manufactured by Electronova S.A. (Geneva, Switzerland) and based on the principle of counting the hydrogen anions in the free water in the material being dried, has been developed. By the use of this principle, it has been found that the relationship in the entire range from zero to 100% is quite linear in both the cases of increasing and decreasing moisture content (Fig. 8.22). Also the range of measurement is increased considerably; i.e., moisture content as high as 100% can be measured and controlled by this method. Measuring electrodes are normally constituted by two arrangements, one of which, consisting of rollers, is positioned at the exit of the drying machine. The other electrode, of special

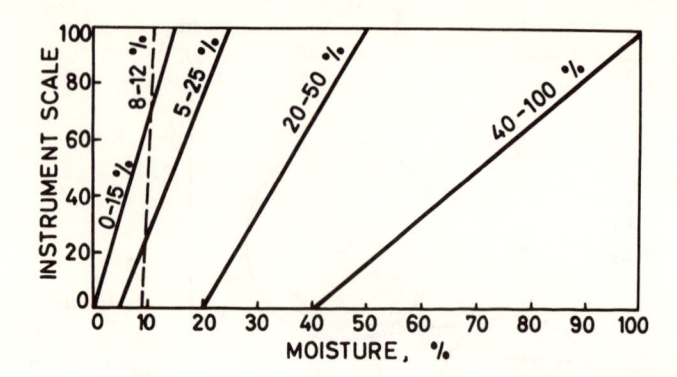

FIG. 8.22. Graphs showing linear variation of moisture content over a wide range.

design, is located in the interior of the machine. Its mechanical construction and its electrical arrangement are according to the machine and the type of material to be controlled. The indications of the moisture meter can be permanently recorded at a distance from the machine by a recorder coupled in series with the measuring instrument.

The important characteristic of the automatic control of the Electropsychrometer is claimed to be absolute freedom from hunting effects in speed variation of the drying or sizing machine when sudden changes in the weight of the material take place. Usually the automatic control devices oscillate until the correct speed adjustment is reached, with the result that with modern high-speed machines, considerable differences in moisture content occur for very long lengths of material. The Electropsychrometer regulates the machine smoothly and virtually instantaneously to the correct speed adjustment. Figure 8.23 shows the difference between both the old and new regulating principles at a speed of 110/min. Should the drying process, for mechanical or other processing reasons, require the machine to be stopped, an electronic device compensates precisely for subsequent overdrying and determines automatically the timing of the retakeover of the automatic control when the machine starts up again. This compensation is proportional to the weight of

4 APPLICATIONS   555

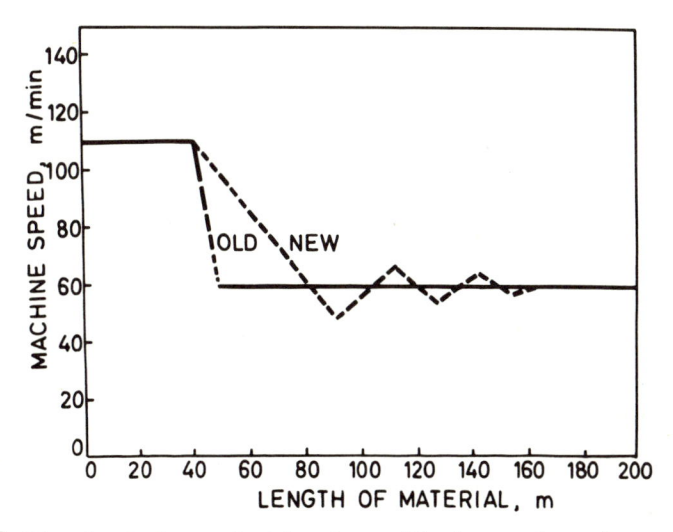

FIG. 8.23. Comparison of old and new Electropsychrometer speeds through a textile material.

the material and to its preset moisture content, and it thus guarantees a new hunting-free speed adjustment on restarting.

The main switch of the instrument allows switching off the automatic control and using the Electropsychrometer for measuring purposes only. For sizing machines, the Electropsychrometer has the added advantage of continuously checking the size mixing consistency while the machine is working, and of giving warning of any sensitive deterioration of the mixing by causing the machine to abruptly lose speed. It is claimed by the manufacturer that other industries having continuous drying processes can use the Electropsychrometer for automatic regulation and control of their production.

4.1.4 <u>Moisture Control by Control of Temperature</u>. The finish and feel of hosiery are important properties which depend to a large measure on the moisture content of the finished products. Before and after finishing, it is necessary to have an optimum moisture content. Therefore, for the production of quality hosiery, the need for automatic control of moisture is recognized in certain phases of the production process. The moisture content in this case can be controlled by controlling the temperature of the hosiery boarding machine, as the rates of drying and of residual moisture content are largely dependent on the ambient temperature. In this case the control is very simple and only one instrument, labeled TRC, a temperature recorder and controller, is used (Fig. 8.24). A thermometer bulb is located in the interior of the dryer. It transmits a signal of temperature to the controller. The signal from the controller is transmitted to a solenoid valve. The steam supply to the heater coils is regulated by a two-position controller in response to the temperature of the air in the dryer. A dryer fan operating continuously forces air through baffles onto the board. In actual operation a large number of boards are contained on a sliding rack, and the drying operation is carried on for a prescribed time period at the controlled temperature. This is a comparatively inexpensive control system.

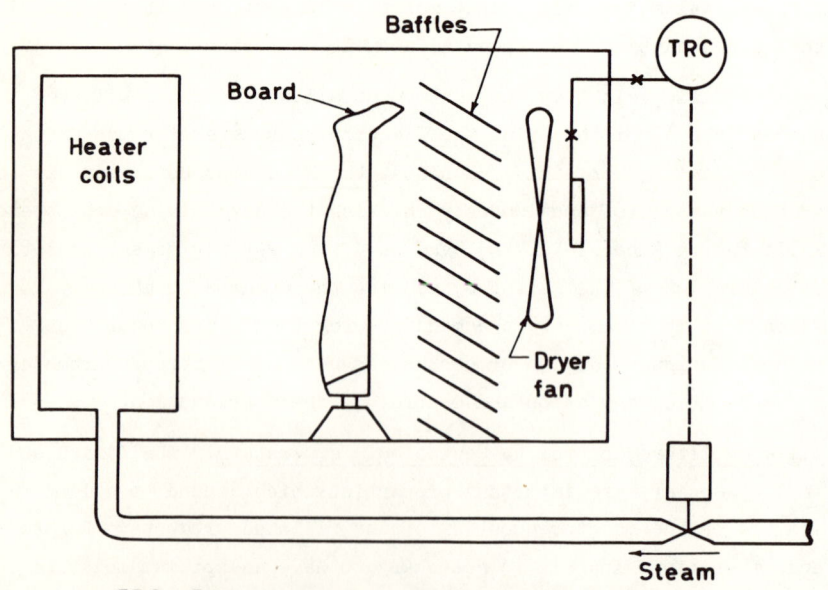

FIG. 8.24. Control of drying in a hosiery boarding machine.

4 APPLICATIONS

4.1.5 Moisture Control Based on Humidity Measurement. In practice it is often not important to measure the moisture content of a material in absolute terms, but it may be desired to control this moisture content so that the material will be in approximate moisture equilibrium with the atmosphere that will ultimately surround it. This may be done by measuring the relative humidity of air in moisture equilibrium with the material and adjusting the moisture content so that this relative humidity corresponds to that of the atmosphere in which the material will find itself. As there is a definite relationship between the ambient relative humidity and moisture content of a material, the measurement of the relative humidity of air in moisture equilibrium with the material is often a sufficient indication as to the moisture content of the material.

A method for continuous measurement and control of moisture content of textiles and similar hygroscopic materials has been developed by the Bradford Dyers Association (UK) [21]. In this method measurement is made of the moisture content of the air-permeable material in terms of the relative humidity of air in moisture equilibrium with it for the purpose of controlling its moisture content by means of a pair of electrical wet and dry thermometers which yield a single signal, and past which air in moisture equilibrium with the material is drawn, the single signal being modified by a second dry thermometer in accordance with variations in the temperature of the airstream. This modified single signal is then fed to a meter from which an operator may see the relative humidity and make appropriate manual adjustments to the apparatus affecting the moisture content of the material. Alternatively, where, for example, the material passes through a drying apparatus, the signal may be fed to an automatic control system, for example, controlling the speed of travel of the material through the apparatus or the temperature in the apparatus.

By an electrical thermometer is meant a device which responds to changes in temperature in a way that can directly be measured electrically; thermistors, electrical resistance thermometers, and thermocouples are used for this measurement. In this method use is made of a pair of thermistors, most suitably of the bead type, owing to their small bulk and high response to temperature changes, but other types of electric thermometer can be used if their lower response and greater bulk can be tolerated. Preferably the single signal from a pair of electrical wet and dry thermometers is fed to a nonlinear amplifier, and the gain of this amplifier is controlled as a function of the output of the second dry thermometer to yield a signal which is substantially independent of the temperature of the airstream. This method is particularly useful for controlling the moisture content of textile materials moving in continuous lengths through a drying apparatus, but may also be used for controlling the moisture content of other air-permeable materials such as bales of cotton, wool, tobacco, hay, and silage. Such materials may, for example, be stored in a container, and their moisture content may be controlled by suitable alterations in the temperature or humidity of air passed through the container, or in the speed at which air is passed through the container.

As stated above, the relative humidity of the atmosphere with which the material is in moisture equilibrium is a measure of the adequacy of drying, and is indicated by the meter, but if the percentage moisture content by weight is required, this can be obtained from published data giving a relationship between humidity and moisture content for a given material in moisture equilibrium with the surrounding atmosphere. An important advantage of the wet and dry bulb humidity method is that it very rapidly recovers from 100% humidity if wet material should come through, for example, on starting up a drying apparatus.

Figure 8.25 is a diagram of the apparatus for measuring the humidity of the air drawn from or through a textile material leaving a drying machine and shows a width of textile material in section as it leaves a drying chamber. Air is slowly drawn from or through the material by a suction pump into an air-intake hood and from there over a "dry" thermistor, that is a thermistor bead housed in a thin

4 APPLICATIONS

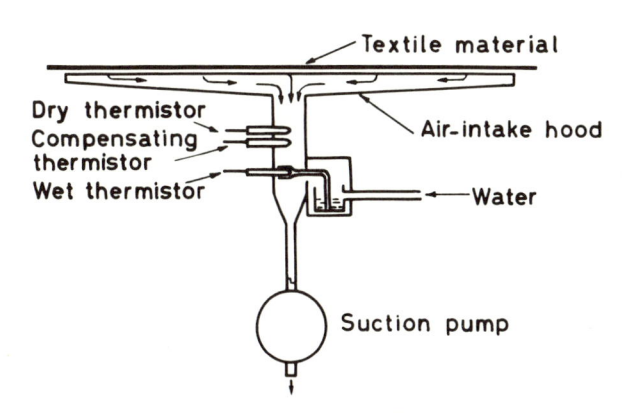

FIG. 8.25. Apparatus for measuring humidity of the air drawn through a textile material.

glass bulb, and over a "wet" thermistor, that is, an identical thermistor bead also housed in a thin glass bulb which is kept moist by means of a wick dipping into a reservoir containing water. Water is supplied through a pipe to make up for the loss by evaporation. When the water reaches the desired level in the tank, the supply is interrupted automatically by electrical means (not shown). A temperature compensating thermistor is located close to the dry thermistor so that these two thermistors remain at the same temperature. The speed of the air must be slow (preferably below 1 ft/min) as it is drawn from the material, since otherwise ambient air will be included and measured together with the air which has been carried along by the material and is in moisture equilibrium with it. The speed of the air as it passes the thermistors should conveniently be about 3 to 5 ft/sec.

In the electronic system oscillator provides a 1000-Hz voltage which is fed through an impedance-matching valve into a balanced transformer that gives two equal antiphase outputs which are fed, respectively, to the dry thermistor and the wet thermistor. The output from the thermistors, which is the vector sum of the antiphase inputs, is thus dependent on the difference in resistance between the dry and wet thermistors. For example, if both thermistors have equal resistance, the output is zero and the humidity is at its maximum. Since both thermistors alter resistance equally with change of temperature but only the wet thermistor changes resistance with humidity, the amplitude of the output is proportional to humidity.

The output from the thermistors is amplified by an amplifier and is then fed to a nonlinear amplifier. It is then rectified and passed to an amplifier which is shunted by a limiting circuit which includes a nonlinear resistor. The modified output of the amplifier is passed to the meter. The gain of the nonlinear amplifier is controlled by the negative bias applied to it through the thermistor. By these means the meter can be adjusted to give readings corresponding to the humidity of the air which would be in moisture equilibrium with the material at the standardized temperature. The dc output of the amplifier is fed to a control unit by which the moisture content of the material can be controlled, for example, by altering the speed and/or temperature of the drying apparatus. Both methods of control can also be exercised simultaneously.

Another electronic equipment has been developed recently by Sellers Electronics Ltd. (England), based on humidity measurement to be used in conjunction with otherwise conventional hot-air drying machines for controlling moisture content of loose wool. With this equipment, drying conditions are controlled by maintaining a continuous check and making corrections as necessary to keep constant the relative humidity of the hot air used for drying. The control apparatus consists of basically two measuring heads, one for relative humidity and the other for temperature. These are suitably placed in the drying chamber along with two independently mounted control units housing electronic equipment working in conjunction with the measuring heads. The two control units are interconnected electrically. The relative humidity and temperature of the hot air in the drying section are controlled through servomotor; in the case of relative humidity the motor adjusts the air damper, which allows moist air to be exhausted from the machine at a controlled rate, and

4 APPLICATIONS

in the case of temperature, the same motor controls the heater system, normally through a steam valve. At the start of processing selected conditions of relative humidity and temperature are set on dial on the control units to give the desired moisture content in the wool leaving the machine. Relative humidity is used for control and the control units are designed to maintain relative humidity constant under all conditions. Any change in conditions in the machine causes a change in the relative humidity of the air, and as these occur the control unit automatically adjusts the air damper to provide the necessary correction. Temperature is maintained at the preset figure until the damper reaches the limit of the adjustment in either direction when, through the interconnection of the two control units, the temperature is either raised or lowered as necessary to bring the conditions back within the range of control of the air damper. Precise control over drying conditions by this means is said to raise the efficiency of the drying machine and to result in an extremely uniform moisture content in the wool material delivered.

In addition to the above-mentioned methods, a series of other techniques are available in literature. In one of the methods, it has been proposed to put a definite length of a fiber on a balance, by which procedure greater weight would indicate high moisture content, and slight weight low moisture content. According to another proposal, the temperature of the fabric is measured at different spots by thermocouples and the differences of temperature measurements between two places is used as a measuring criterion. According to a third proposal, a radioactive preparation is placed under the fabric breadth, whereby the quantity of radiation passing through β rays is recorded by a measuring apparatus, a Geiger counter placed above the fabric breadth. In another method static charges developed in proportion to moisture content are utilized to control the moisture content. However, these methods have not been found to be industrially feasible and practical.

4.2 Paper Processing

4.2.1 Introduction.

The finish of the paper is largely dependent on control of the drying process and the efficiency of elimination of moisture. During the production process much of the free water is eliminated by drainage and press action through the initial rolls. These first stages of water elimination have little effect on the final characteristics of the paper finish. In the dryer section of the process, the paper is conducted through heated drums which remove the water of hydration of the fibers of the paper. Usually the dryer in a paper mill consists of a series of drums extending distances of up to 100 ft or more. The purpose of the large number of drums is to remove the moisture gradually and uniformly. At the beginning of the drying operation it is desirable that the temperature be comparatively low so that it will not cause too rapid a vaporization of the moisture at the surface. Too high a temperature has a damaging effect on the material and its finish. Therefore, in the efficient production of a paper product it is necessary to establish a definite temperature gradient from the wet to the dry end of the dryer.

Even the most modern machinery and continuous drying process can give rise to a considerable amount of defective production if they are not controlled and regulated with absolute accuracy. The present-day high operating speeds obtained as a result of other technical improvements preclude the use of the hand "feel" of even the most experienced operative, and require accurate and rapid-reacting measuring instruments. Only by employing an automatic moisture-measuring and -control instrument can a true picture of the possible production of a drying machine be obtained, excluding at the same time excessive overdrying of material and costly wastage of steam and power.

4.2.2 Moisture-Control Techniques.

On many paper machines control of moisture content of the paper is attempted by measuring and controlling something else, such as steam temperature or pressure, or

4 APPLICATIONS

perhaps cylinder surface temperature or condensate flow rate. The reason for this odd state of affairs is that really useful moisture meters have been available only recently and the paper maker finds it hard to believe that moisture control is better than his skill. Once the moisture content is known this knowledge is to be used to control the paper drying machine. Theoretical considerations suggest that a cascade system is best for such a purpose both for supply-side and load-side disturbances. The slave loop (in this case steam pressure, say) is normally proportional only, but some improvement can be expected by adding an integral term. The master loop should have P + L (proportional and integral) or three terms, depending on the dynamics of the loop. It is possible to control the main bank of cylinders in any of the following ways:

1. Simple moisture control
2. Simple steam pressure (manifold) control
3. Simple steam temperature (manifold) control
4. Simple cylinder surface temperature control
5. Moisture/steam pressure (cascade)
6. Moisture/steam temperature (cascade)
7. Moisture/cylinder temperature (cascade)

At the same time a moisture control loop after dryers should ensure that β-gauge records are not affected appreciably by changes due to presize press adjustments in moisture.

Methods of regulation used in the industry have been based on either the control of steam flow to the drums, the steam pressure, or the temperature of the cylinder. All these methods of approach, if designed carefully, provide a means of controlling the operation of the drying process. Figure 8.26 shows a diagram of only two of the paper rolls in the kiln, together with the location of the control instrument and the sensing element. This method of control is based on the temperature of the drying cylinder. There is only one instrument involved, labeled TRC, which signifies a temperature recorder and controller. The dashed line leading from the drum to the controller indicates that an electric signal is being transmitted

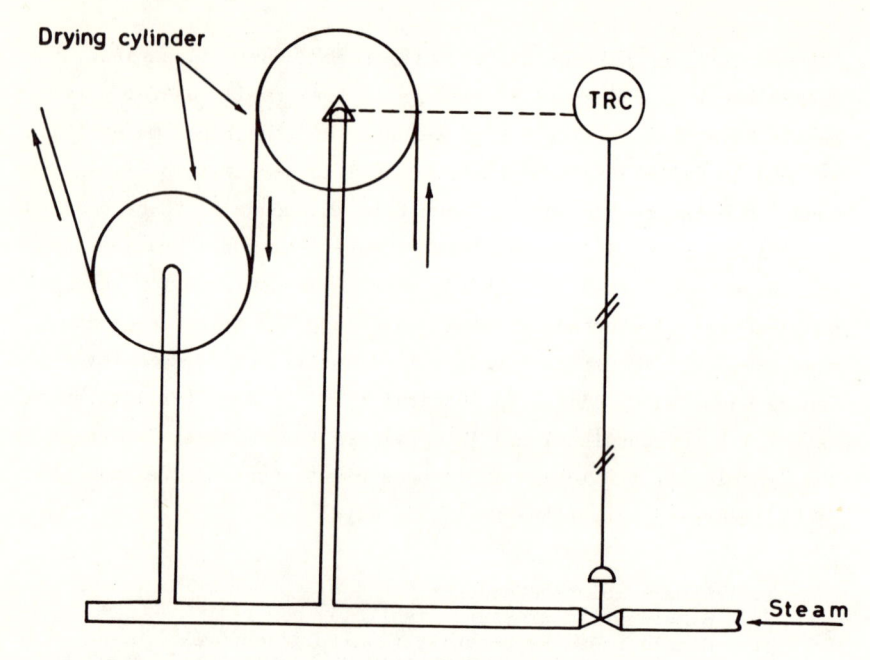

FIG. 8.26. Automatic control of a paper-drying machine.

from the sensing element to the instrument. The solid line leading from the instrument to the control valve is marked in accordance with the code to show that the controller sends a pneumatic output to the control valve. The TRC instrument is both electric and pneumatic in operation. The measuring portion is electric and the controlling portion is pneumatic.

Small variations in temperature of the cylinder surface are detected by the instrument, and the steam flow is corrected accordingly. In the event of sheet breakage, which occurs occasionally in the production of paper, the controller acts to prevent overheating of the rolls. This has resulted in a considerable saving in steam consumption compared with that in a manually operated unit.

A pneumatic and electrical combined control system known as the Moist-O-Graph has been commercially developed by the Honeywell Co.

4 APPLICATIONS   565

(US). Figure 8.27 shows the pneumatic and electrical schematics of a typical pneumatic system for controlling a paper machine. This is basically a cascade control system wherein the recorder-controller resets the set point of a pressure controller which controls the steam pressure to the last dryer section of the machine. But there are several added features which provide superior control and greater operating convenience. First, both recorder-controllers are provided with integral manual bypass panels which either permit straight pressure control of the dryer or allow to position manually the control valve when necessary. A paper break, or stop switch (identified as S-S in Fig. 8.27) located on the paper machine is another feature. When the control system is on automatic operation and a paper break occurs, the set point of the pressure controller is automatically lowered by a preset amount below the pressure that existed immediately prior to the break. The magnitude of this lowering is adjusted by the bias-loaded regulator. When the machine is restarted after a break, a lockout timer maintains this reduced pressure for a preset interval of time, and then automatically returns the system to automatic control at the original pressure.

With the machine operating normally, and the system on automatic control, the break switch S-S is open and R_1 is deenergized. The lockout timer will be timed out and its contact T-BD will be open so that solenoid valve S-V is deenergized. With the solenoid valve deenergized, airflow through the valve is from port C to A. Therefore, controlled air from the recorder-controller passes directly through the capacity chamber and the solenoid valve to the remote index setting unit of the pressure recorder-controller, and the system operates as a cascade control system. During this time, timer contact T-A is closed and the pen positioning relay P-P-R in the recorder-controller is energized. Its load contacts are connected so that the recorder pen follows the moisture being measured.

When a paper break occurs, switch S-S closes, energizing relay R_1. Its load contact opens, causing the timer to reset. The solenoid valve is then energized through contacts T-BD and R_2 causing air to

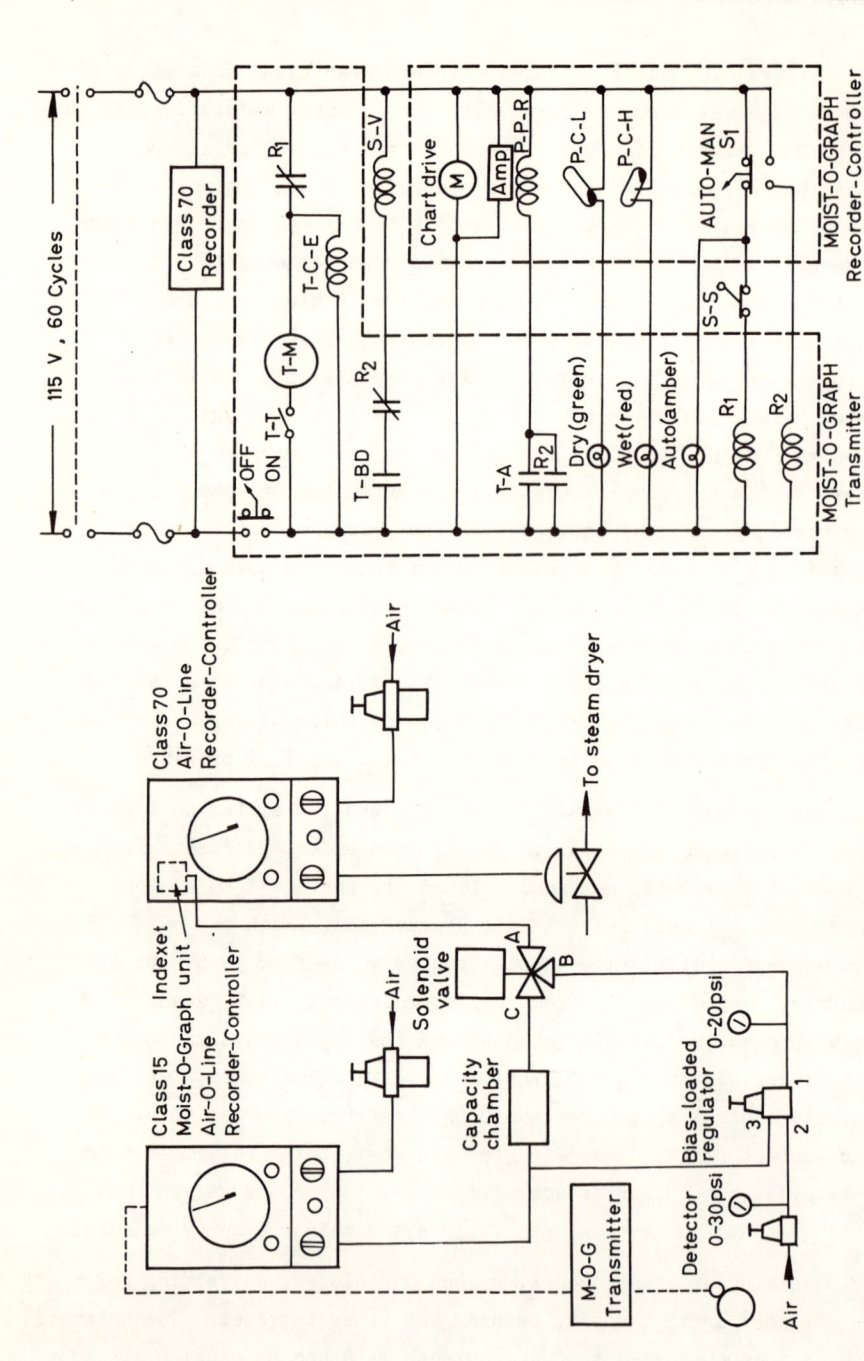

FIG. 8.27. Moist-O-Graph automatic control unit for paper dryer.

flow through the valve from port B to A. Simultaneously, timer contact T-A opens and the pen-positioning relay is deenergized, causing the recorder-controller pen to be positioned to its index. Controlled air from the recorder-controller now remains at the value which existed immediately prior to the paper break. This air-control signal goes to the bonnet chamber, port 3, of the bias-loaded regulator. Operation of this regulator is such that its output air signal from port 1 is the pressure signal into port 3 minus a manually set pressure. This output signal passes through the solenoid valve and positions the remote index setting unit of the pressure recorder-controller.

According to the manufacturer's claim, this control system can detect and control moisture variations as soon as they occur, and corrections are made automatically before an appreciable amount of off-quality paper is produced. It has a high speed of response so that even on high-speed machinery, this control system controls the moisture content effectively.

A scanning-type dielectric moisture-measuring and -controlling device has been developed by Church [22] for controlling the moisture content in the paper-making process. To achieve automatic control, the control valves of the spray-beam nozzles are supplied through a manifold, installed in the spray cabinet in the form of an arc. These needle valves are scanned and adjusted by a center-pivoted arm which traverses in synchronism with the moisture-measuring head on the machine. The error signal, which initiates the control system, is obtained by comparing the actual output voltage from the moisture meter with an internal reference voltage, the latter being produced by adjustment of the moisture control point to the desired moisture value required on the finished paper.

A high-gain, solid-state amplifier is used to feed the control windings of a magnetic amplifier. The balanced outputs of this magnetic amplifier are fed directly to the control windings of an electrohydraulic valve. With a balanced electrical input to this unit, the servopiston is held in the neutral position. Consequently, there is no torque on the output shaft of the hydraulic motor, which applies the necessary control action to the appropriate valve. The needle valve spindle is adjusted axially through a V-toothed rack. These teeth are engaged in sensitive contact fingers connected to a hydraulic motor and move the valve in the required direction. At the completion of each control action, the whole system is neutralized in readiness for the next valve position.

To ensure that each valve is accurately positioned, a feedback voltage is provided by a potentiometer, which is coupled to the shaft of a hydraulic motor through a magnetic clutch. Varying the voltage to this potentiometer gives a degree of control over the valve movement and hence introduces a proportional action to the control function. Control action on each valve is initiated, thus allowing sufficient time for the measuring head to detect the changes produced by the selective spray system and to ensure that the time constants on the control valves are all the same. Testing facilities are provided to enable manually introduced error signal to be fed into the equipment, and at the same time isolating the output voltage from the moisture meter. It is thus possible to simulate the actual variables on manual control without affecting the measured output of the moisture meter, and thus test the effectiveness of the selective spray control system without loss of production to the machine.

In order to ensure that the selective spraying system can operate both effectively and efficiently it was necessary to integrate the system with the steam pressure control of the drying cylinders. During trials with selective spraying, conditions arose where all the spray valves were open. This was entirely due to variations in the machine direction's moisture. Under these conditions, without the sprays working, the sheet would have been in an overdried state. Conversely, conditions arose where the peak moisture increased considerably due to the general moisture level although the sprays were shut on these peaks. Provided the dryer man was in constant attendance and controlled the drying cylinders' steam pressure as a function of the peak moistures, the system worked effectively [22].

4 APPLICATIONS   569

The two systems were integrated successfully by the use of a peak detector.

The peak detector operates by direct comparison of the moisture meter's output, the desired moisture value's reference voltage, and the position of the spray water control valve. When measuring a peak, the control valve in this position should be closed, and no output should exist to the selective spray equipment. Under these conditions an electrical relay is made, which indicates that the desired value has been achieved, and also ensures that the drying cylinder's steam pressure controller's control points are locked in. But when conditions are such that the peak moisture is above that of the desired moisture, the peak detector's output is cascaded to the steam-pressure controller's control point, and automatically a time function is built into this signal to prevent overshooting. Conversely, when the peak moisture is below the control point, the peak detector's output lowers the control point of the pressure controller, and thus brings the peak to the desired level. The system is entirely automatic, and requires no attention from the machine operator.

The results from the complete integration of the selective spray system, with the drying cylinders' steam-pressure control, are excellent. On most papers manufactured it is possible to control to within ±1% moisture content, but there are quite a number of papers where control has been established at ±0.5%. Controlling the transverse moisture profile results in considerable improvement in the paper's general qualities and that this quality can be maintained indefinitely. Also a substantial increase in output has been obtained, due to increased speed, more efficient drying and glazing, and an optimum moisture content in the reel.

Lippke [23] has developed a device for controlling overdrying of paper, pulp, or board. By this device an excessive consumption of steam and slowing down of the paper machine is avoided. The control system enables the moisture content of the paper to be rendered substantially uniform while still in the drying process, and furthermore allows a subsequent correction of the moisture content of the paper web, namely in the direction of travel of the web as well as across the web by a subsequent correction of irregularities which unavoidably remain after the forming and drying of the web. By means of this control system it is also possible to eliminate variations in the basis weight of the web of paper.

Investigations by Lippke [23] have shown that the irregularities along and across the paper web, which are a disadvantageous influence to an economical drying, result from variations in the basic weight, provided that the steam for the drying process is supplied constantly. The irregularities of the stuff in the web are eliminated by the following procedure. By a periodic movement of a measuring and sensing device of a moisture meter which is installed at or behind the dry end of the paper machine, the moisture content of every part of the web which corresponds to the breadth of the measuring sensing device is measured. In relation to these measured values, a plurality of portions of a stuff inlet slit are adjusted by means of a regulating arrangement. Similarly, a plurality of portions of a moisture apparatus are adjusted. Thereby, first the basic weight variations are substantially uniform basic weight, and then the moisture content is finally obtained. The device can be better understood by a number of illustrative drawings given in the patent specifications [23] to which the reader is referred for further study. The following advantages of automatic control of moisture in paper making are apparent:

1. Quality drying in the most favorable moisture content range
2. Optimum utilization of the machine drying capacity
3. Minimum steam and power consumption
4. Maximum simplicity for the operative

4.3 Processing of Wood Shavings

A continuous moisture-gauging and -regulating system known as Aqua control has been recently developed by K. F. Mundiger GMBH

4 APPLICATIONS

(West Germany). This device is applied to check and regulate the moisture content of moving continuous sheets of wood shavings, e.g., in conjunction with machines and drying plants for the production and processing of textiles, paper, etc. The working method of the measuring device depends on the principle of electric conductivity, which is proportional to the moisture content of the materials. The measuring dial of the apparatus indicates continuously moisture content directly in percentage, while a built-in-curve drawing recorder registers time for the supervision of manufacture. For the adjustment of the desired measuring range, there are one minimum and one maximum limiting value indications which can be adjusted manually. The best method of measuring the moisture of the shavings is that it should be done after the drying process. This measurement after drying is much more exact, because the moisture differences of shavings are of low order.

A built-in line recorder for the production control is made available for three optionally adjustable chart speeds of 30, 60, and 120 mm/hr. Minimal and maximal limit value transmitters for controlling signal lights and signs and the impulse transmitter for automatic control can be set up as required over the entire measuring range. Regulation is effected by the impedantly operating transmitters with infinitely variable adjustment of impulse frequencies between 1 and 6 sec. Impulse relays with a contact rating of about 600 VA for controlling regulating gears, steam valves, and air flaps are connected.

This apparatus is intended to be attached to the mains supply between 110 and 260 V ac and has a rated capacity of 30 VA. The power-supplying element is fully stabilized and renders ineffective fluctuations up to ±25% of the voltage system. The electrode used for wood shavings is made of two profile rollers. One of these rollers is driven by a motor and the other roller is placed tightly. The outer tips of profile rollers serve to pass through the surface of the shavings in order to have full moisture cross section. The speed of the driven roller is adapted to the traversing speed of shavings in order to avoid disturbances in the flow of shavings.

In order to avoid the loss of material the measured shavings are carried into the main flow. An electromotor with power consumption of 125 W is enough for the drive of the profile roller electrode. One of the many applications of this control device is its use in the moisture control in the manufacture of wood-shaving boards. Moisture control is possible in different stages of manufacture, while for supervision regulating equipment of this type is necessary.

4.4 Production of Lumber, Timber, and Veneer

In the production of dry lumber, manufacturers are taking advantage of the benefits realized when the drying process is equipped to operate automatically. Green lumber contains a considerable amount of free water plus a comparatively large portion of water absorbed by the fibers. The drying process must be carried out in a manner that will not only give production efficiency, but also give a good product which is free of warp. This requires careful control of both temperature and humidity. Figure 8.28 shows a cross-sectional view of a portion of the drying kiln and the conditioning equipment under automatic control. Two controlling instruments are also shown. Here TRC 1 is a temperature recorder and controller which maintains the temperature in the kiln under constant control. The second instrument, labeled MRC 2, is a moisture recorder and controller which maintains the proper amount of humidity in the air entering the dry kiln. In actual practice there would be several sensing elements of both dry bulb and wet bulb located at strategic points throughout the kiln. Lumber kilns are extremely large in size and a practical spacing of the measuring elements must be determined by experiments which will give the best overall average condition of the atmosphere in the kiln.

When green lumber enters the kiln there is usually sufficient moisture in the lumber so that no further addition of water to the conditioner is necessary. Not shown in the diagram is a provision for venting, which is usually necessary during the start of the

4 APPLICATIONS

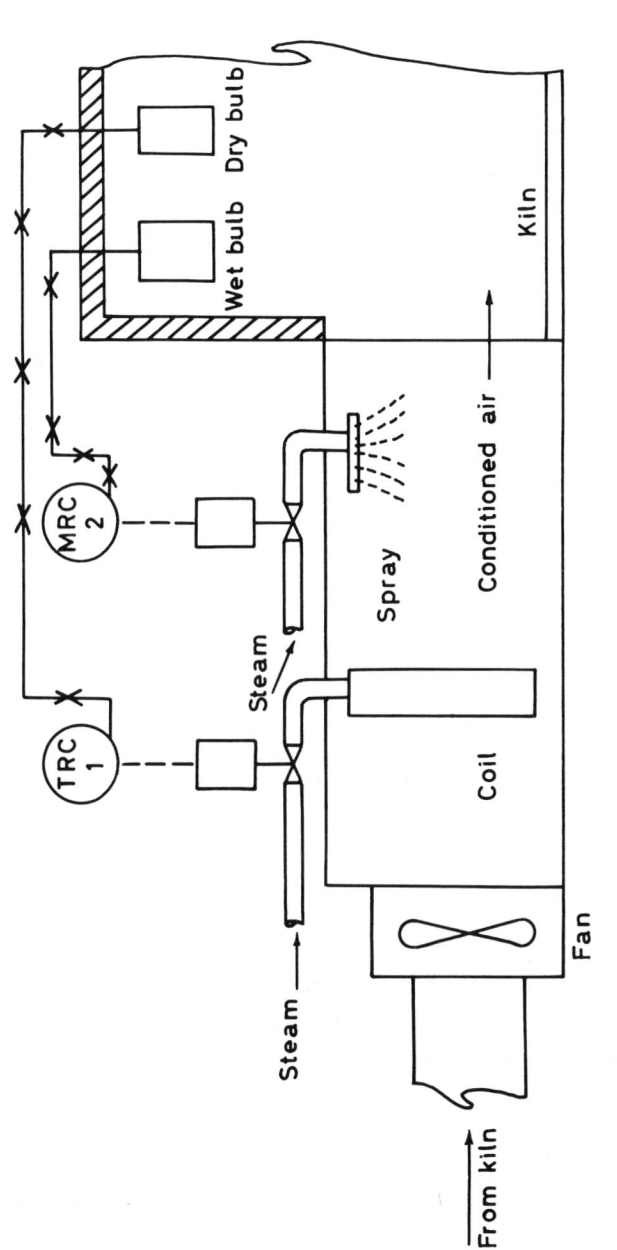

FIG. 8.28. Moisture control of a lumber-drying kiln.

TRC 1 = Temperature recorder and controller
MRC 2 = Moisture recorder and controller

drying operation where an overabundance of moisture is present. As the drying process continues and the lumber becomes drier, the moisture controller actuates a spray to introduce moisture and thus control the rate of drying. This is necessary to prevent warpage of the lumber. The control system described here has been used successfully in the production of a quality kiln-dried lumber. In this application the lumber dryness is not measured. Consequently, it would be classified as an open-loop control system.

A new machine (Fig. 8.29) has recently been developed by James [24] which is used for continuously measuring and controlling the moisture content of moving lumber, veneer, or paper. In particular, it is designed to mark or reject automatically the material with a moisture content improper for use. It is used for sorting lumber or veneer on the dry chain or for inspecting material approaching cutting tables or planers. This device is a combination of the resistance-type and capacitance-type meters.

4.5 Food Industry

The preparation of foods for distribution and storage involves many varied production operations. A few typical manufacturing procedures used in the preparation of foods are pasteurization, blanching, peeling, cleaning, drying, and neutralization. In this section an automatic grain dryer developed for the purpose of maintaining a constant moisture content in grains for storage purposes is described.

One of the common problems encountered by the producer of grain products is the preparation for storage. If the grain has not been properly dried, fermentation or germination is likely to occur. This will produce a temperature rise in the stored product, which causes a deterioration. Occasionally spontaneous combustion will occur and cause the complete loss of the product. A better-quality product and one which is less likely to be lost through the elements can be obtained if the grain is dried prior to storage. In the storage device usually employed a gasoline engine drives a

4   APPLICATIONS

FIG. 8.29. Automatic control of moisture content of timber on a conveyor belt.

fan that supplies heated air to the grain bin. The fuel used in the combustion chamber is oil. Two temperature controllers are used. These are thermocouple types incorporating a bimetallic element in them. Also there are two electrically operated valves provided in the device. One of the temperature controllers will shut off the main supply of oil to the furnace in the event that the temperature reaches an excessive limit. It would be called a high-limit control. The other temperature controller regulates the flow of oil to the combustion chamber in response to the temperature of the heated air entering the dryer bin. The valves are solenoid operated, and therefore the automatic control embodied in this system is a two-position type. A conventional oil burner control much like those used in the home, which provide for a return of ignition in case of flame failure, is also used. Also a means is provided to shut off the main oil supply in the event of failure to ignite. Once the flame is established, a supply of oil somewhat less than that required to bring the air up to the desired temperature is always being supplied to the combustion chamber. Thus the temperature control instruments only add or cancel an additional flow of oil in response to the temperature of the heated air.

4.6 Cottonseed Processing

Accurate and automatic control of moisture in cottonseed meats has long been recognized as the way to more efficient processing. The problem is to find an instrument that can continuously and automatically measure the moisture content of the cottonseed meats before they are processed and then regulate the addition of moisture. An automatic control device for continuously measuring and automatically controlling the moisture content of cottonseed in the processing has been developed recently by the Minneapolis-Honeywell Regulator Company (US) and is described briefly. The automatic control device is shown in Fig. 8.30 wherein a probe-type electrode sensing element installed in a duct sends electric signals to a controller. The instrument converts this signal into a moisture content measurement and then signals a corresponding control action to a valve fitted on a water line of a spray unit. The duct is grounded to complete an electric signal.

As the cottonseed meats pass this probe, current tries to flow. But dry cottonseed is a nonconductor. Since water is a good conductor, the amount of resistance to current flow will depend on how much moisture is in the meats. The measuring circuit in the instrument is a Wheatstone bridge. The unknown resistance of the cottonseed meats passing by the sensing element forms one leg of this bridge. Any change across this leg of the bridge causes a momentary electrical unbalance. This starts the balancing motor which moves a contactor across a slide-wire resistor until the bridge is again balanced. The indicator pen and pointer are also connected to the balancing motor, so they indicate and record the variations. The slightest movement of the pen causes the control element to operate

4 APPLICATIONS   577

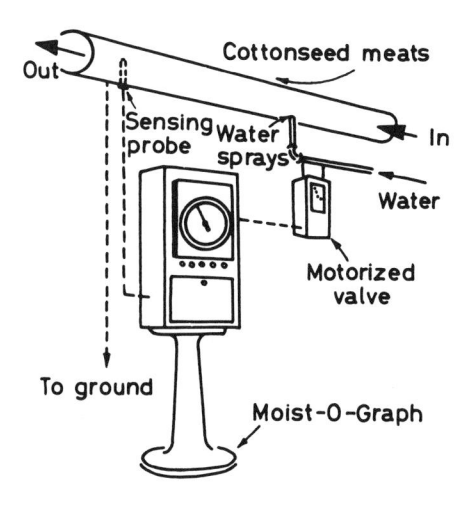

FIG. 8.30. Moist-O-Graph automatic control of cottonseed meats.

a valve controlling a water spray in the humidifier. This control
action can be either electric floating control or proportional pneumatic control, depending on the requirements of the plant. For the
system to be effective the cottonseed meats must be uniformly compact and be moving at a constant speed when they pass the sensing
probe and through the humidifer. Any variation in compactness when
the meats pass the sensing probe will lead to erroneous measurements.
If the cottonseed meats pass the humidifier more rapidly or at
greater concentration from time to time, those meats will not have
the proper amount of moisture added. On the other hand, if they
move too slowly or are relatively unconcentrated, they will receive
too much moisture.

4.7 Conclusion

In the foregoing sections only a few drying processes in which
techniques of automatic control are used have been described. As
will be observed from these descriptions, the broad principles are
the same in every case: hence, quite a number of other applications
are being omitted. The reader interested in a particular field is
referred to these descriptions for detailed study. From these

descriptions, it should be observed that automation is a tool of such immense possibilities that no one can yet see the full extent of what it can achieve for better productivity and quality control. Automation in the true sense can, however, be brought to full fruition only through a thorough exploitation of its three major elements, i.e., communication, computation, and control, "the three C's."

5 ECONOMICS OF AUTOMATIC CONTROL OF MOISTURE

Automatic control devices are used because their application results in economical behavior of the system under control or because they are required for humanitarian purposes. There are many advantages to the widespread use of automatic control. Some of these advantages are as follows:

1. Increase in quantity or number of products
2. Improvement in quality of products
3. Improvement in uniformity of products
4. Savings in processing materials
5. Savings in energy or power requirement
6. Savings in plant equipment
7. Decrease in human drudgery

These factors generally lead to an increase in productivity. It is not always easy to assess the cost of installing additional process instruments or that of automatic controllers replacing measurement. Often several alternative schemes will have to be put forward for discussion, and exact figures will have to be produced to justify the capital outlay.

To work out the economics of the idea of instrumentation, usually several of the above points have to be considered together. In one instance, automatic temperature and humidity control might allow to increase conveyor speed of a continuous dryer and at the same time to achieve a better dried product quality. Efficient automatic process control depends on two main factors, namely on the design and function of automatic control instruments applied, and on

5 ECONOMICS

what is called controllability of the controlled process. It is generally realized that automatic controllers must be suitable for the controlled process and have certain characteristics to enable them to perform their duty efficiently. Less known, however, is the fact that process characteristics play a very great part in the achievement of close control results. One process, being simple from the manufacturing angle, might prove to be less easy to control by means of instruments than another more elaborate process having better controllability.

The plant engineer, irrespective of the branch of industry in which he works, should be familiar with process controllability before attempting to apply automatic process control. The outstanding problems of engineering economy studies related specifically to automatic process control are those of establishing: (1) adequacy of data on process operation, and (2) an acceptable measure or index of control system performance. Progress in getting process and system operating data will not of itself yield a sufficient basis for studies of process control economics or even technical comparisons. It is, however, unlikely that any progress will be made which will commend itself to technically critical people without this effort to assemble the data completely on every facet of system operation and design, quantitatively and numerically.

In general, the relations between process variables have been studied as part of a process study for ultimate use in development projects. The concept of design springs from a more basic concept of answering the questions "What does a control installation do, in quantitative as well as qualitative terms?" The practical goal of the most economical control system design would be achieved if the values selected for the system parameters were such as to minimize this expression of cost. At the present stage of development of automatic process control and of the application of engineering economy studies in this field, it cannot be said that any actual system has been analyzed in such a way that statements of this sort could be made about costs. Some systems may in practice approach such achievements, but this could hardly be regarded as really demonstrable. The statement is as yet only formal, but it does effectively describe certain criteria to be aimed at, and indicates the contribution of important plant and process parameters to the control economic statement.

Gillings [25] has made systematic studies in cost and profitability of the automatic process control and according to statistics provided by him, the total installation cost of instrumentation and automatic controlling devices varies from 5 to 15%, the plant cost depending on the type and size of the plant. This estimate is slightly lower than that given a few years back. Similarly, the effectiveness of maintenance in terms of the assessment used has also been improved greatly over recent years. As it is not possible to give a quantitative estimate of the profits accruing due to automation, a few typical examples will be given which will give an idea of the order of benefits involved in automatic control of various drying processes in different industries.

In the case of the paper industry, mills utilize a large quantity of steam in their drying operations. Some mills use up to one million pounds of steam daily. Thus only a small percentage of savings results in a large economy in the manufacturing operation. There are countless examples of applications where the costs of the automatic controls have been realized completely in less than 1 year. This is based on the savings that result in both production costs and product quality.

Similar observations have been reported by Pande [26] in the case of drying cylinders installed in a textile mill, wherein a provision was made to measure and control the moisture content of dried fabrics. It was observed that there is a very close relationship between the change in the moisture content and the steam consumed during a predetermined period of time. These results are shown in Table 8.1. However, greater saving is achieved in the specific steam consumption rather than in the total steam consumption.

5 ECONOMICS

TABLE 8.1

Results of Operational Studies of SRI Moisture Meter of Drying Cylinders in a Textile Mill

Speed (yd/min)	Regain of moisture content values (%)	Quality of fabric	Steam pressure (lb)	Total steam consumed as indicated by mill meter installed for the purpose
19	3.5	Towel	20-18	
19	4.5	Towel	20-18	
19	4.5-5.0	Towel	20-22	Steam consumed in 15 min, 280 lb
19	5.0-5.5	Towel	20-22	
19	5.0-4.5	Towel	20-22	
19	5.5-6.0	Towel	20-18	Steam consumed in 15 min, 210 lb
19	5.5-6.0	Towel	20-18	
19	6.0-6.5	Towel	20-18	

Mahlo [27] has also estimated the saving in the steam consumption while using the automatic moisture control device developed by him. He has calculated roughly the difference in steam consumption when in this dryer the same fabric is dried once 4% lower and at another time 6% lower. With drying to 6%, we get the specific consumption of 1.6 g/kg evaporated water quantity; with a drying to 4%, we get 2.1 g/kg. If we fix the price of 1 kg normal steam at 0.9 penny, then for a single working hour, it indicates a difference of 1.2 to 1.4 DM, which means about 25 DM/month. These figures are applicable in the case when higher moisture contents are produced by throttling the steam feed. More advantage is gained if the speed can be increased. The costs for a tentering frame hour, including steam and power, range between DM 20 and 30; these are independent of the machine speed. Only a 20% increase of speed, taking into consideration the stoppage time and other factors, saves about 100 DM.

These values, however, do not indicate that we get the above-mentioned advantages by using a regulating device for a dryer, immediately and in all cases. In all cases, it is necessary to collect all the operational experience and then to evaluate it systematically. A foreman gets good results when he thinks deeply about the operational data and continues to correlate them to get good results. Failure in the process indicates lack of imagination in a foreman.

A continuous process possesses a number of degrees of freedom given by the number of variables and defining relations for the system. These variables are generally the temperature, pressure, flow rate, moisture content, and composition of each of the entering and leaving materials. Usually the purpose of the process is to produce one or more products at (1) given composition and moisture content, (2) a given or maximum flow rate, and (3) best economy (employing least materials, energy, personnel time, and equipment). Production composition is best ensured by measuring product composition and controlling it by manipulating one of the degrees of freedom of the process. Optimum moisture content is obtained by automatically controlling the ambient temperature, humidity, and speed of the process in industrial processings, as described earlier. Fixed-product flow rate usually requires flow controllers at several points of the entering and leaving materials. If the product flow rate is to be a maximum, the flow controllers should not be employed, or else they should be manipulated to achieve one of the purposes of the process.

Best economy is accomplished by maintaining all process variables in a predetermined relation such that the highest efficiency and maximum productivity and least wastage are achieved. This can be achieved by employing a computing machine and relating all variables, even in a transient state, so that the desired criteria are met.

REFERENCES

1. J. G. Truxal, *Control Engineers Handbook*, McGraw-Hill, New York, 1958.

2. P. E. Donald, *Automatic Process Control*, Wiley, New York, 1958.

3. E. R. Johnson, *Servomechanisms*, Prentice-Hall, Englewood Cliffs, N. J., 1963.

4. M. H. Lajoy, *Industrial Automatic Control*, Prentice-Hall, Englewood Cliffs, N. J., 1961.

5. W. G. Holzbock, *Automatic Control*, Reinhold, New York, 1958.

6. G. H. Farrington, *Fundamentals of Automatic Control*, Chapman and Hall, London, 1951.

7. J. D. Ryder, *Engineering Electronics*, Wiley, New York, 1961.

8. P. H. Hammond, *Feedback Theory and Its Applications*, The English Universities Press, London, 1958.

9. M. C. Doughlas, *Process Instruments and Controls Handbook*, McGraw-Hill, New York, 1958.

10. G. B. Marson and I. C. Hutcheon, *Electronics in Industrial Process Control*, Publication No. TP 5054, George Kent, Ltd., England, 1961; *Control*, 4, 33 (1961).

11. P. R. Wyman, *Trans. Soc. Instrum. Technol.*, 14, 23-24 (1962).

12. R. Brewer, Proceedings of the International Conference on Semi-conductor Devices, Paris, 1961.

13. I. C. Hutcheon and G. B. Marson, Publication No. TP 5053, George Kent, Ltd., England, 1961.

14. H. Mahlo, *Melliand Textilber.*, 34, 741-742 (1953).

15. D. Bunch, Jr., *Amer. Dyest. Rept.*, 39, 369-370 (1950).

16. N. H. Chamberlain, *Text. Mfr.*, 163-173 (1945).

17. A. Pande and M. C. Jain, Unpublished results on Automatic Control of Moisture, 1963.

18. Monitor Model No. M-600, Strandberg Engineering Laboratories, published literature on Moisture Control.

19. J. E. Fielden, British Patent 619,534 (1954); Electron. Eng., 9, 10-12 (1949).

20. F. H. Slade, Text. Mfr., 88, 99 (1962).

21. Bradford Dyers Association, British Patent 951,942 (1964).

22. F. Church, Instrum. Pract., 437-840 (1963).

23. P. Lippke, British Patent 844,386 (1960).

24. W. L. James, Forest Products Laboratory, Rep. No. 1660, U.S. Department of Agriculture, Madison, Wisconsin, 1958.

25. D. M. Gillings, Instrum. Pract., 18, Parts 1-6, 483, 597, 715, 951, 1155, 1245 (1964).

26. A. Pande, Unpublished results, 1964.

27. H. Mahlo, Melliand Textilber., 34, 846-847 (1953).